HURRICANE

BOOKS BY MARJORY STONEMAN DOUGLAS

THE EVERGLADES-RIVER OF GRASS

ROAD TO THE SUN

FREEDOM RIVER

HURRICANE

"HURRICANE"

by Marjory Stoneman Douglas

RINEHART & COMPANY, INC.

NEW YORK
TORONTO

Grateful acknowledgment is made to the University of North Carolina Press, Chapel Hill, N.C., for permission to reprint a selection from pages 44 and 45 of *Graveyard of the Atlantic*, by David Stick.

Published simultaneously in Canada by
Clarke, Irwin & Company, Ltd., Toronto

Library of Congress Catalog Card Number: 58-5205

ACKNOWLEDGMENTS

The people whose knowledge, patience and willingness to help are taxed by the importunate author of a book such as this can hardly be thanked enough. Without their assistance, and that of many more who are perhaps almost nameless but whose generosity in time and attention cannot be replaced, this book could never have been written.

It could never have been begun or carried through to any sort of conclusion without the hearty co-operation of the men of the U.S. Weather Bureau, especially of the Miami office. First helper and invaluable friend, whose wide background of reading and scientific knowledge has never failed, has been Leonard Pardue. Gordon Dunn, eminent forecaster and hurricane expert, now head of the Miami office, has been untiring in his encouragement, and Walter Davis and Frances Warren and all the others. R. C. Gentry of the West Palm Beach Hurricane Research Center and R. W. Schloemer, assistant to the Director, the U.S. Weather Bureau in Washington, have been most helpful. Weather Bureau directors in all sorts of places have given freely of their time and attention, such as Mr. Reuben L. Frost of Wilmington, North Carolina, who with Mrs. Frost showed me much of the Carolina coast and the Cape Fear River, Mr. John A. Cummings, director of the Charleston, South Carolina, Bureau and Mr. R. C. Commander, a leader in the Amateur Radio Association. Dear Mrs. S. Ed Taylor of Southport, North Carolina, was kind far beyond her duties as weather observer. Other

v

Weather Bureau heads who have patiently answered innumerable queries have been Mr. Ernest Carson of Galveston, Texas, Mr. Stephen Lichtblau of New Orleans, Mr. Glenn V. Sachse of Norfolk, Virginia, Mr. Oscar Tenenbaum of Boston. Mr. Ivan Ray Tannehill, now retired from the Weather Bureau, who wrote the book that is an invaluable textbook on hurricanes and the late Dr. Charles F. Brooks of the Blue Hill Observatory in Massachusetts gave me most valuable information.

Archeologists and anthropologists have patiently explained things and tirelessly answered letters. The list begins always with Dr. John M. Goggin, professor of Anthropology at the University of Florida and goes on to Dr. Mathew S. Sterling, Dr. William Sturtevant, and Dr. J. Eric Thompson of the Smithsonian Institution, Dr. Irving Rouse of Yale, Dr. Robert Eliot Smith and Dr. Ralph L. Roys of the Carnegie Institution, Mr. Louis Capron, of West Palm Beach, Florida, and Sr. Emile de Boyrie-Moya, of Santo Domingo.

Other specialists to whom I am indebted are, Dr. F. G. Walton Smith of the Department of Marine Biology, and Dr. J. Riis Owre of the Graduate School of the University of Miami, Dr. Archie Carr, zoologist, of the University of Florida, Dr. Paul B. Sears, Chairman of the Conservation Program, Yale University, Captain William Gray of the Miami Seaquarium, Mr. Charles L. Brookfield and Mr. Alexander Sprunt, Jr., for the National Audubon Society, Captain J. Kent Loomis, assistant to the Director of Naval History, the Department of the Navy, Mr. Ralston E. Lattimore of the Fort Pulaski National Monument, Savannah Beach, Georgia, and especially Mr. Hazen Brooks of the National Park Service, who was so kind to me at Ocracoke, North Carolina.

Help of all kinds has come from generous people in all sorts of places; from Mr. and Mrs. Frank Stick of Kitty Hawk, and Mr. David Stick, of Kill Devil Hills, Mrs. Bessie W. Howard of Ocracoke, all of North Carolina, Miss Else Loeber, then in Toronto, Canada, Miss Nancy Hay in Newport, Rhode Island, Miss Elaine Sanceau and Admiral Gogo Cantinho of Portugal, the late Father Gutierrez-Lanza years ago in Havana, and Mr. and Mrs. García Carratalá and Dr. Fernando Ortiz only a year or two ago in Havana, Mr. and Mrs. Thomas Murray of Petersburg, Virginia, the late Doc Lowe of Tavernier and Jane Wood of the Miami Daily

News, Mr. Willard Hubbell of Miami, Mr. Leo Brownson who by way of my helpful friend Mr. Leonard Ormerod sent me, a total stranger, a most useful book from New Orleans; Margaret Davis Cate of Sea Island, Georgia, and Mr. Windom J. Robertson of St. Georges, Grenada, B. W. I., Dr. and Mrs. Julian S. Carrington of the University of Miami, Miss Joel Babylon of New Orleans and Miss Gretchen Wagner, of Fort Walton Beach, Florida, and Mrs. R. S. Manley of Orange, Texas. My especial thanks to Mrs. John T. Wainwright for the letters by her father, the late Colonel R. M. Cutts, to Mrs. Henry Chapin, for her lively narrative of Friends' Service Relief Work in Mexico, and to innumerable people in Jamaica for their hurricane experiences.

When it comes to Florida history and his own scholarly work with wrecks and treasures and maps, no one could have been more constantly kind than my friend Mr. David O. True of Miami; but my thanks go also to Dr. Mark F. Boyd of Tallahassee, Mrs. Edwin Link of Binghamton, New York, Mr. Alan Cass, Mrs. Roy Dickie all of Miami, Mr. Francisco Campos of Merida, Yucatan, and my own cousins, who have given help far beyond the duties of cousinship, Miss Pauline Hopson of Hartford, Connecticut, and Mrs. Irvin E. Warner of Wallingford, Connecticut.

From Pan-American Airways people I had all sorts of assistance, from Mr. Robert Brush, Mr. Roger Wollin, Mr. Rollin Rogers, Mr. E. V. W. Jones and others.

But in the last analysis it is to libraries and librarians one must turn for the solid background of material necessary to this sort of book. Some people take it for granted that library people give unstintingly of their time and knowledge, their interest and enthusiasm. I am always and increasingly stirred by it. Library loans throughout the country now make all but a study of primary source material possible anywhere in the country within phone call of a public or university library, but the combination of eager personal interest and countrywide book service creates a kind of magic for which one cannot be grateful enough.

Such librarians are Dr. Archie McNeal, Mrs. Isabel Klingler, Mr. George Rosner, Mrs. de Bettis and Mrs. Larry Donavan of the University of Miami Library, and Dr. Frank Sessa, director, who does not scorn to deliver his own books. Mr. Norman Graham,

Mrs. Edna Murphy and many others of the Miami Public Library; Mr. Julian C. Yonge, librarian emeritus and history expert of the Florida Library at the University of Florida, and Mrs. Edna Forsyth, curator of the Fairfield, Connecticut, Historical Society.

                                        Marjory Stoneman Douglas

Coconut Grove, Florida
May, 1958

FOR CAROLYN

TABLE OF CONTENTS

BOOK ONE

THE NATURE OF HURRICANES

1 *HURRICANE*

The hurricane had shut down completely on the ship and the men on it. Drunkenly buffeted, half-drowned, hardly able to see, unable to hear, each, in the strangeness and the terror, was alone.

The increasing sea had been a nightmare of waves since before the wind had built up to this screaming steel. The dark green, wind-carved, rain-pitted swells had turned black, had swollen, fretted and tumbling with white, swills of white, sheets of white that made the speed of the wind visible in lightning blasts of foam.

Men clung as they could to something in some lee, gasping to breathe within the hammering air, holding as the decks lifted and dropped and yawed and came bucking up to meet tons and smashing tons of water. When a man could free his scalded eyes, there was nothing to see but dizzying, streaming grayness out of which, as the ship rose desperate to throw off its burden, the jagged wrecks of rails, deck houses, boats, hatch covers emerged like broken rocks. Or saw a shadowy thing growing solid, coming over, a wall, a hill high as the skeletal bridge, with the ship falling away under its falling, like the man, shuddering.

Once there had been a clamor of separate sounds, crests hissing and roaring, wires screaming, metal racketing, crashings and boomings far inside the distraught vessel, the wind in a man's very ears. Now there was nothing to hear but the single uproar, as if each person were enclosed in the tossed hollow of pandemonium.

What work there was to be done, in hope of keeping some puny order in irresistible chaos, came as a fragment of an order screamed in a man's ear, an insect sound from far away, from out an obscured face. The order was carried out painfully, by a man crawling and clinging under the wrench of exploding water, slow as a cripple in the agonized shocks of the ship. Within his stupefied body a man's thoughts crawled, also, grasping the habit of duty, the single idea of

3

what must be done as if it were a lifeline not so much away from death as toward reality.

If later in a brilliant day the ship found itself in a wide, wind-flattened green and boiling sea, under sky dazzle from far up, then men could stand on shaking legs and stare at what was left of the ship and one another, the aged and half-remembered faces. They were not distinguished now as captain or oiler, but as living men.

Behind them they saw rising up an enormous seething white wall, a parapet of cloud, far away there the rest went around. They were imprisoned in light and peace like the free birds that soared and dipped ahead of them.

There would be a little time to grope for food and fresh water or to cut loose some hampering debris or nail futilely at the yawn of a hatchway. The far white walls were drawing nearer. Soon the light would be shadowed by the first blown veils of fog. Their dread was now not so much the old fear of death but of what, as living men, they must still endure.

To the women shut up in the house there was at least some solidity underfoot. The walls were already shaking a little under the growing attacks of wind that was the whole world beyond. The room was dark and breathless except for the candle flames pointing steadily in their bright halos except when some knifing draft flattened them and made darkness solider. The women could watch other women's faces grow unfamiliar with strain as black ripples of water ran down the shuttered windows or a rug near the door bellied up suddenly as if an animal had run under it. They turned their heads halfway, as if deafened, to the blows that made the room as hollow as a drum and to that deeper booming coming up out there. But they looked most searchingly at the faces of the children they held or who stood by their knees, or got up quickly to put questioning hands on the baby's crib they had lifted to the table, with a mattress roofing it against the seeping mist of water blowing in their faces from the whistling cracks.

The tumult outside was one enormous sound of horror under which the house shook steadily. They saw in the others' eyes the image of the sea as they had last seen it when the dim light went, a sea like a disorderly broken yellow meadow racing and foaming dirty white, seeming not so much to move as to be there, higher, more enormous, where it had never been before. They had not looked again, hurrying with shutters, hurrying to lock doors and pull the heaviest furniture against them, buckling flimsily under their desperate hands, hurrying to gather in the children and the old man and food and water, snatching at candles and matches and warm coats. And then to sit, or stand, and listen.

The high screaming outside shook the house with a deep, increasing hoarse vibration, like the high roar and shaking of a freight train, racing very near, never drawing away. The voice of the sea grew louder. Within the room and the small house on the sand, they were encased in sound that was solid, that could crush them.

A long arm, the branch of a tree, burst into the room silently, through splintering glass in released uproar and instant blackness, in icy wet, in icy terror. Salt streamed into their gasping mouths. Their hair, their faces, their clothing dripped wet. Or the roof lifted away like a leaf, silently, and water came in one cataract. Or the sea spread a dark skin of water under the door and bucked up and crashed the floor planks and caught them by the throats. Or a wall went down and they were out there, thrashing in blackness, a knot of them, holding the children, holding up the baby, holding the old man, their cold thin hands locked like wires, clutching at bushes, clutching at timbers, at a wall. . . .

They lived or they died.

What more is there to know about hurricanes?

There is only one story, that of the survivor. Million-fold, endless, there is not another one like it. There is no hurricane but the hurricane one had lived through.

Yet in the five recorded centuries in the vast area of the Caribbean and the North Atlantic, the coasts and islands of the great region of hurricanes, there has never been a year without one somewhere, always enormous, always significant. Yet the last one is the one remembered. The rest fall away into history clouded by man's amazing hopefulness that there will never be another.

Already this year, in June, or perhaps in some freak of May or January, there may have been hurricanes, on crowded or empty coasts or far out to sea, with nothing but the birds to know them. In the late summer and fall, the warnings will be sounding for another that will bring to people who have never experienced one the strangeness and the terror of this extraordinary rage of nature. Devastation such as will be known has been repeated again and again and again, endlessly. Yet every hurricane will bring a new experience, like life itself.

It is only since 1900, and the great Galveston hurricane, that the American people have been shocked into a recognition that these vast crises in our coastal weather, over incredible years, have been constant, unending and, so far, inevitable. The Texas coast learned it many times. The people of Florida, along whose coast the wrecks of centuries have gathered, never seemed to be aware what fate August and September and even early October could bring them until 1926, followed by the catastrophes of 1928 and 1935 and lesser ones so repeated that even the newcomers could not ignore what the North called "Florida hurricanes."

But in the North, it was not until 1938 that a hurricane forced New England people to recognize that hurricanes were not only possible for them in any autumn, but highly probable. They had assured themselves that in fifty years they had had only two violent hurricanes and these were accidents. But the disastrous years of 1954 and 1955 gave them to understand that New England had always lain square in the path of such tropical cyclones as the thirty-eight, from 1886 to 1955, that were only prevented from being great disasters by the failure of weather forces such as no one yet understands.

As the hurricane coasts have been filled up and crowded with people, the ruin of a single storm has mounted. People have been forced to face the facts of them by loss and suffering and death. It is not enough to count averages and argue about cycles. It is time to realize what part these astonishing storms have played in all our history, by their presence, or even by their absence, in discoveries, in settlements, in war and peace, in the thoughts and habits and fortunes of all the people whose lives, in the five centuries, have made records of them. The dramas are all different. But it is as if the causes were the same hurricane.

2 *BIRTH*

No human eye has ever seen the beginning of a hurricane. Perhaps that moment when the enormous winds stir to their rise can never be seen by anyone, or never be entirely understood. There is no living scientist who knows all the forces which combine to bring into being and motion this tropical climax of all the world's weather.

As tropical cyclones they may begin in all but a few places in the perturbed seas on each side of the heated equator. North of it, they whirl counterclockwise; south, with the clock. In the western Pacific, the Philippines dread them as "baguios" and Japan as "reppus." From the Timor Sea to northwestern Australia they are feared as "willy-willies." The Indian Ocean all the way to Mauritius is ravaged by typhoons that terrify the Arabian coasts as "asifa-t."

In the American hemisphere only these tropical disturbances are known by the ancient and truly American name of hurricanes. They have been at work here in the Caribbean and the western Atlantic as long as the sea winds have blown, and longer than any man, white or Indian, has lived here. Lives beyond memory have been changed by them.

The hurricane, like all tropical cyclones, is a creation of the amazing resilient substance, the air, a gas or complex of gases which lifts far above us and the outermost clouds, to about twelve miles. It gives us life.

At sea level, the air is crushed down upon us and becomes denser by its own weight, a mass of more than fourteen pounds on each square inch of surface or our own skins, a weight of one ton of every square foot. This is the varying pressure a barometer measures. All this nearer atmosphere is called the troposphere, with its rising or falling limit, the tropopause, under the vast thinning quiet realm of the stratosphere.

In our human layer of the troposphere float the clouds, all the varieties of condensation of water vapor, from the low rainy haze of nimbus, the great convoluted glistening domes of cumulus that lift on their invisible rising column of air as high as 55,000 feet, in cold of 80 degrees below zero. Far above all this the cirrus blows over in fine hairs and plumes of icy particles that we can see in haze about the moon.

The winds blow in their paths around the world, as they have blown since the earth began, regular belts of winds, urged on or altered by the vast turning of the globe. Around the frozen poles, from the east, surge the circumpolar winds, occasionally dipping southward. The rising air slants and blows the other way in the prevailing westerlies that makes the streaming succession of North American weather variable and electric with cold and warm fronts, blizzards, tornadoes, rains and beautiful fair days.

South of the westerlies reaches the narrow belt of calm and change called by sailors "the horse latitudes" because there horses had to be thrown overboard to save drinking water on board a becalmed and thirsty ship.

But south of that blow the steady, wonderful westward-roaring trade winds. They lift high up, perhaps 13,000 feet, in the heat rising over the African Sahara, and smash down across the Atlantic, picking up force across the blue-purple Caribbean until the Central American mountains foil them for a while. Beyond that they flow north and south of the equator across the Pacific, across the islands, across the Indian Ocean and so to Africa again.

Around the middle bulge of the world, below the great current of the trades, in heat and steamy airs, over jungles and deserts, the equator goes, not an imaginary line but a varying band of heat. Over its watery places even the trade winds fail. The shining waters breathe sluggishly. A little rain pocks them. Bits of matted yellow sargasso weed from the central mass in the middle of the Atlantic currents drift there. The strong-winged oceanic birds dive in it for surfacing fish or on its smoothness preen and sputter like ducks in a pond. The heat that shimmers up from all this rises high to mingle northward with the great tongues of polar air thrust south, in the eternal mingling of heat and cold.

On each side of this equatorial calm there are narrow bands of frayed and uncertain airs. There are gray skies and rain. Or the sun flashes out. Small storms pass, churning the waves. These are the doldrums that sailors hated and feared more than the horse latitudes, where the sails of a becalmed ship might slat and hang and rot for weeks. This band of sticky weather is not fixed. It crawls north with the sun in summer to 25 degrees. In the winter it regresses to ten or fifteen. In the changing days of late summer and fall in the north Atlantic, queer things begin to happen in the doldrums.

Tropical cyclones are of course creatures of the winds. But they are also created by the sea, the surging liquid that lies about all the lands and under the air and its winds, by which it is forever crinkled and pushed and beaten into waves. Without the winds—an impossible thought—all the oceans would be as stagnant as mirrors. The winds drive the great ocean currents curving and crawling about all the shapes of earth, in changing and branching bands of warm or chill rivers flowing as the earth turns. All the motions of the waters are the products of the winds except the tides pulled about the world by the inscrutable magnetism of the moon and sun together. No winds change the sure progress of the tides or can affect their flow and volume, except the tropical cyclone.

No tropical cyclones, like temperate zone tornadoes, rise over land. The seas which give them birth must be warmed to at least 82 degrees. The heated air moves invisibly upward in wisps and puffs and quivering columns. High overhead as the heat from a teakettle's spout becomes visible as steam, the hot air, cooled by a kind of dilution, is condensed in foaming masses of cumulus clouds. Lightning flashes and thunder grumbles among their glistening hollows as the cooled water vapor drops in heavy tropic rain to the uneasily swelling sea. The waves are pushed to slow ridges by the variable and heavy airs. This is the place where tropical cyclones may be born.

The doldrums alone could never produce them without the trade winds. These do not flow in solid unchanging masses but in long currents and strands of winds that separate and flow together again. Sometimes they move in waves or travel with up-and-down kinks or ridges called "troughs" or "easterly waves." Such a wave may curl in on itself in a deep eddy that is embedded and carried in the wind stream all the way across an ocean. In August, September and

October, north of the equatorial trough, such an eddy may invade the doldrums and draw strength and spin from the rising heat.

Still, that is not enough to set off a fully developed tropical cyclone. There are forces far aloft in the troposphere or even in the calm stratosphere that men have begun to be aware of, without understanding. There is a strange high flow they have only just discovered which they call the planetary wind. It is a river of air which circles the world very high up in the north temperate zone. It flows generally from west to east but sometimes it dips down in enormous horizontal waves 4,000 miles across. It helps to mix the polar air with the warm air to the southward.

It makes vast undulating streamers or ribbons of wind that begin in slow waves and flap faster and faster to a climax. Then it slows down and idles until the wave begins again. Its middle line is called the jet stream. The whole thing may dip far southward bringing disturbed weather all along its curve down through the temperate zone. The jet stream or other upper winds may affect in some way that moving eddy, or loop, that hernialike protuberance in the trade winds.

No one is sure what is the effect of the jet stream here any more than anyone knows what the effect can be on our weather conditions of the great whirling storms of fire or spots of calm that move across the face of the sun.

With all these possibilities the strange thing is not that tropical cyclones begin to rise but that under apparently similar conditions so few of them do. There have rarely been more in a single year than twenty. Some years have known very few. No one can say why, except to believe that there must be some other cause or force or complex relation of internal and external forces which no man has yet measured or imagined, which must occur before such a cyclone can be brought successfully to life.

Supposing all the causes are present and the unusual thing happens that a tropic cyclone is born. The formative stage begins slowly. Perhaps a developing eddy dies out. Or it lives. Winds are diffused over a wide area of trouble. The surface pressure drops. There may be twelve hours yet before the eddy picks up force and its winds begin to circle in a vortex about a central calm perhaps miles across, the eye of the cyclone.

Its whirl persists and grows stronger, revolving counterclockwise. It is a spiral of air blowing up in a great boiling chimney of altocumulus cloud from 100 to a 1000 feet and lifting higher. It has become a vapory steam engine that, as the heated air from the sea rises and fuels it, extends long arms in which the rain is released. Its winds increase to eighty miles an hour. Its own energy moves it forward.

This is the way, in all the tropical oceans except the South Atlantic, tropic cyclones are thought to be born. They are exactly the same kind everywhere. They spring into life in disturbed airs over heated and troubled waters by the same complex of known and unknown forces.

But because the oceans where they occur differ so widely by the nature of the land masses around them, which affect profoundly their maturity and their dying, all these tropical cyclones differ in ways we might call their secondary characteristics. The North Atlantic, walled in by teeming continents, the enormous watery emptiness of the Pacific until it breaks westward among a bewilderment of islands, the Indian, hot, and empty from Australia to Arabia, except for the downthrust of India, seem to shape their cyclones with a difference.

Certainly our North Atlantic and Caribbean hurricanes, not only by the constant effects of land masses upon them, but by the density, the nature, the histories, the very reaction to catastrophe of the increasing populations they override, may be seen to be, like our name for them, unique.

3 GROWTH AND DEATH

The shapes of the land masses about the Atlantic and the Caribbean are the chief reasons why there are at least three, perhaps five, definite areas of warmed seas where hurricanes begin and from which they take their courses.

The continents of Africa and South America leave so much sea space between them that the South Atlantic is a cold ocean and no hurricanes rise in it. The currents from the Antarctic, which make their great circle here, extend across the equator on the African side and mingle their waters with the long uninterrupted stream of the equatorial current that flows west.

Off the bulk of Cape Verde, in Africa, among troubled waters and conflicts of winds from the north and the beginning great push of the trades, lie a little group of weathered rocks, the Cape Verde Islands. South of them, in late August and September, is the breeding ground for the most vicious hurricanes of the Atlantic known to North America. When one of those eddies in the trade winds knots and whirls and rises to life and begins to move, there is nothing to stop it all the way across the Atlantic.

Embedded in the steering current of the increasing trade winds and with the fuel for its upward and forward motion constantly sucked up from the warm equatorial current, their swirling winds may gain enormous velocity long before they have crossed half the ocean.

Their forward movement may be comparatively slow, from eight or ten to an unusual twenty miles, but their winds have been known to increase from 80 miles on to 120 and more with incredible gusts faster than 160.

It was always extremely difficult to record and follow the course and nature of an Atlantic hurricane unless an unfortunate ship lay so close that its radio could send warnings. Sailing ships fled the approach of such storms, if possible, or were wrecked by them. They might not arrive back at a port with the news until long after the hurricane had struck and gone on. It has often seemed that hurricanes start up, fully matured, only twenty-four hours away from the islands that guard the entrance to the Caribbean. Sometimes they curve away north and northeastward in the Atlantic without ever touching American land. Sometimes they make themselves felt after they have recrossed the ocean and surge southward along the coast of Ireland, or even farther, as the last of the Gulf Stream goes.

These most terrible of all hurricanes are known as Cape Verde storms. In their maturing, great funnels may have reached higher toward the tropopause than anyone has ever measured. What upper winds have acted as steering currents no one yet knows. But the first force that seems to affect them is an area in the Atlantic, like an airy mountain of high pressure, that centers south or east of the Bermuda Islands. It is called "the Bermuda high" and its position farther south, the scientists feel, contributes to the fact that many hurricanes follow courses straight into the Caribbean. If the Bermuda high is north, or east, it may permit the hurricane to sweep north-ward curving, as all tend to curve sooner or later, northeast, sliding off the great round surface of the turning world.

The Caribbean Sea, even more than the equatorial North Atlantic, is eternally haunted by hurricanes. It is also shaped more definitely by the land masses around it. It has often been called "the American Mediterranean" but except that each lies east and west at right angles to the axis of the Atlantic, both slightly north of the equator and between continents, they are not alike. The almost tideless Mediter-ranean has its troubling winds chiefly from the lands about it. It is almost completely landlocked, well-named, in the middle of earth. It has no hurricanes at all.

The Caribbean, rough with conflicting currents, stirred by con-stant tides, is not so much contained by the American continents as thrust between them. It has been carved and scraped by the deep inflow of the Atlantic equatorial current, pushed by the never-fail-ing whooping accelerating force of the trade winds.

The islands raised by volcanoes on the long curving fault that runs from South America toward the Bahama reefs and the Floridian plateau stand more like landmarks than barriers among the turbulent incoming tides. For their entire geologic history these volcanic islands have felt the fury of Cape Verde hurricanes. Their mountain jungles rise over the interlaced branches and roots of trees blown down by hurricane winds. The highest peaks of this chain, including the barren heights of Pelée, have never offered enough friction to the lower winds to have changed the course of any hurricane by a degree. The histories of their people, like their wild rocky wind-ward coasts, have been worked over and changed by hurricanes always. More than any others in this hemisphere these are hurricane islands.

There is an area in the Atlantic, northeast of the curve of the Lesser Antilles, where hurricanes have been thought to breed. The branch of the equatorial current, split off from the larger flow which penetrates the Caribbean from the south, flows up the Atlantic outside the islands to join the Florida current and make the Gulf Stream. The warm waters of that split-off stream on the edge of the doldrums, with the vagary of the trade winds called "an easterly wave," may combine here to make a hurricane. It is always possible that a hurricane thought to be from this area may have moved in from the Atlantic, without having been observed before.

Toward South America where the equatorial current pours in between the islands, a last filament of water from the Antarctic current has slid along the South American coast beyond the equator, which warms it less than the rest. It streams in between Trinidad and its parent continent.

Beyond Trinidad the coast of South America thrusts the bold range of the Venezuelan Cordilleras high over a narrow strip of sea coast. The wet winds from the Amazon and the Orinoco drop their moisture south of the mountains and then, as cold dry winds, sweep high over the Venezuelan waters. Here the earth's round shape pulls the moving stream of surface water away from the coast so that the bottom water rises in a cold upwelling.

Here no hurricanes ever breed. Few have ever intruded across the lower arc of the Lesser Antilles to touch the Margaritas or Curaçao and its neighbors, except some great Cape Verde blow.

The Caribbean is really two seas separated by reefs and deeps and ancient faulting. Southmost lies the great oval of the true Caribbean, empty between the Windward and Leeward Islands, the rampart of the South American coast and the bow of the Isthmus. Deep westward, embayed between rocks and jungles and strange currents lies the troubled Sea of Colombia. The full force of the trade winds harry its deep blue tumbling waters. The currents scour it. Cold winds may invade it straight north from the Pacific, across the Isthmus. Its tides burst and roar forever along barrier islands.

This is the desperate corner of the Caribbean where early in the season, or late, short vicious hurricanes sometimes start up. They blow north for a while. They have even been known to move northwest across Central America and up the Pacific coast. More commonly they move north by a little west past the jutting mass of Honduras and up into the second division of the Caribbean, the Sea of Yucatán.

The hurricanes may curve northeastward and attack the long

dragon shape of Cuba across its western end. Or blow north up the Yucatán Channel between Yucatán and Cuba's Cape Antonio, as the current boils over the rocky threshold into the Gulf of Mexico.

The great skull shape of the Gulf encloses a body of water very different from the double seas of the Caribbean, to which it is like an inner chamber. Its underwater surface is no longer ridged and troughed with ancient rock risings and faultings. It has an almost smooth basin floor rising gently from inner deeps to the coasts that almost surround it. But it is ravaged terribly by the same hurricanes.

Very early in the season, June perhaps, hurricanes have been known to start up just north of the northern mangrove coasts of Yucatán. Perhaps they really came unannounced from across the pathless jungles of the peninsula where nobody saw them. But they have been observed off the Alacrán Reefs, a bar of smudge on the horizon off Progreso or marching suddenly on Veracruz or Tampico. At this season they may stab across the narrow coastal plain of Mexico and die against the majestic slopes of the Sierras. Or farther inland into the rising plains of Texas or north still, to deluge the bayous of the great crowfoot delta of the Mississippi. Sometimes they carry across the mainland of north Florida from west to east, attacking the Atlantic by the back door anywhere from south of St. Augustine to Jacksonville and Fernandina.

Some 80 percent of the hurricanes that plow the Gulf form outside. Fifteen percent are thought to form somewhere in the northern Gulf and the rest in the southwest in the deep bay of Mexico and Yucatán. And all this, after the possible freaks of June and July, chiefly in August, September and October.

The equatorial current that flows over the threshold of the Yucatán Channel allows only a minor stream to branch and circle in the Gulf of Mexico. Its greatest flow curves around the western tip of Cuba sharply northeastward, as its own weight and force and the vaster turning of the world carry it to dredge a deep ditch between Cuba and the Florida Keys and up the straits west of the Bahamas. This is the strong Florida current that is soon joined by the other branch from the equatorial current that flows up outside the Bahamas. Off Hatteras it swings wide across the Atlantic in the vast system of the Gulf Stream. All this coast is vulnerable to the hurricanes that move up from below Puerto Rico or Haiti, or in from the Atlantic across the southern Bahamas. It used to be thought that

the warm waters of the Gulf Stream attracted them. Certainly it has
supplied them with heat and power.

The hurricanes that loom up in these tropical waters, then, may
have been hesitating a few days, picking up intensity from inside
and outside their system. When they begin to move, at about ten
miles an hour, west or west-northwest or northwest, they are gaining their maturity. Their central funnels of cloud lift higher, as on
a huge scale their complicated intake and outgo of heated air increases. And high before them the icy particles of pale cirrus clouds
reach out steadily. Rain bands extend in long squall lines all about
them. The winds of the upper right sector increase most viciously,
adding the forward speed of the hurricane to their own speeds. The
winds of the lower left hand sector are milder. Here are the heaviest
rains.

The most vicious winds are those that flow in and make the cloud
vortex around the central the extraordinary phenomenon of all
tropical cyclones, the eye.

It is a region of complete calm. It may be four or forty miles across.
Around it spin and boil the walls and pillars and balconies of the
clouds. Below, the sea is tossed in strange conflicting upthrust shapes.
It seems to swell and churn in deep blue marbled with upwelling
streaks of foam. Beyond the topmost vapors of the encircling clouds
and winds there may be brilliant blue sky with sun striking down
to make the whiteness dazzling. It is a place of mysteries not all yet
plumbed. Men who have penetrated there, in ships half-wrecked but
still afloat, in airplanes of which most, but not all, have survived,
speak of this place with awe.

The eye, the center about which the winds circulate, is not necessarily the only center. Instruments have found another center of
lowest pressure and another around which great spiral arms of
rains and highest winds are thrust out and move. For the hurricane
is not, as it was once described, a symmetrical doughnut of swirling
air. It is a vast sprawling shape with long arms like an octopus or
legs like a cloudy spider, and still a towering mass.

As the hurricane matures and moves forward, its spinning winds
and clouds tower higher and higher. Up to 10,000 feet their spread
is unchanged. Beyond that, to 30,000 or 50,000 feet the winds
decrease. And high up there where the last velocity is spent, some
speeding greater current of the upper air may catch the whole

structure and drag it along, almost toppling sidewise as the surface friction slows it.

Even its course before then is not a regular line or curve, as the charts used to mark it, but a series of curves or waves with the rain bands or the winds thrust out more strongly this side or that. Only a portion of the energy supplied in the release of latent heat by the condensation of all that water vapor drives the hurricane forward. Some is used to re-evaporate more water. Some of it affects certain kinds of chemical recombinations. The rest is felt somewhere as plain thermometer heat. But no one yet knows the exact nature of the whole process.

As to direction, the time of year seems to produce certain general tendencies. June and early July storms tend to form chiefly in the western Caribbean and move normally somewhat to the west of northward. They usually move into the Gulf of Mexico and miss Florida.

In midseason the great Cape Verde hurricanes flow across the Atlantic and move usually west-northwest about 14 miles an hour. If they recurve, they are likely to miss Florida. If they do not recurve, or not enough, they often hit the state or the coast northward. Late season hurricanes, late September, but chiefly October, or even early November, tend to form in the Caribbean as the early ones did, but they move differently, a little to the east of north or even to the northeast. It can be said that any western Caribbean hurricane late in the season is a threat to Florida. Almost every October storm that has hit Florida has come from there.

In the life of a hurricane over the sea, especially going north along the Atlantic Coast, there often comes a time when the original force of the storm seems to be spent, or it hesitates and hangs about, apparently lacking fuel. This seems to take place in the band of cooler air and water in the North Atlantic called the horse latitudes, a band about as wide as the distance from north Florida to Hatteras.

The weakening hurricane is often turned out to sea. The winds slow up around the vortex and the central calm is filled. The hurricane is dead.

On the other hand, sometimes, out of the weather streaming from the west of the United States, something happens to bring the flagging storm a new energy. Its winds pick up speed again. It may change direction and move fast. Its further direction may depend on other conditions. If an area of high pressure has moved east over the United States and stands near the coast, while the Bermuda high moves westward in the Atlantic, so that a trough or path of low pressure is left between them, it is inevitable that the revitalized hurricane should follow it.

If the Bermuda high is moving eastward, and the high at the coast comes pushing out to sea then the hurricane is likely to move eastward also. But if the landward high is still over the middle states, then it is highly likely that the hurricane will turn and invade the land behind the coast, anywhere from Georgia to New England.

That is the time when the exact path it will follow is the most difficult of all to foresee. The islands of the Caribbean, with the exception of the heights of Haiti and possibly some of the mountains of Cuba, have not been high or wide enough to slow up a hurricane. But the land mass of Mexico or Texas or the states offers to the lowest part of the great wind machine the drag of its endless friction. Sea water offers no resistance to the power of this air. But on land, every pebble, every particle of earth, trees, hills, slopes, mountains add something to hold it back. Sometimes, therefore, after only a short adventure over earth, the hurricane forces are worn out.

Sometimes a current of cold dry air meets a hurricane. Its power, without heat, is lessened. Or its shape is distorted against rising mountain slopes. Or in its progress over colder seas its force is diminished. For any of these reasons, and probably others, the hurricane lags. Its winds slow. Its hollow center fills up with gentler air. The hurricane dies.

Sometimes, on the other hand, the weather moving from the west brings new energy. Hurricanes have gone howling and blundering their way over astonished inland cities, curving variously in a general tendency northeast. The most energetic may even blow out over cold seas. But since a hurricane feeds upon heat and moisture, when either or both does not exist beyond the tropics, its hollow center fills and its winds die as gales and rainy breezes.

The whole process, from birth to death, may take a few days, a week, two weeks. But in that time no human chronicler could set down its total story.

4 *WINDS AND WAVES*

The hurricanes that have swept over the islands and shores of this continental region we may truly call hurricane country have blown here as long as the poles have been cold and the equator hot. They passed as the trade winds marched on their ceaseless progress and had their share in all the high mysterious mingling of air currents. Hurricanes moved here long before the shapes of these American continents were fixed and they have left their ineradicable marks on all sorts of forms of this natural world.

When there was no central land bridge between the upheaved stumps of North and South America and currents flowed and sharks swam uninterrupted in the salt ocean that reached around this hemisphere, nothing much would have prevented the progress westward of these airy cataclysms except the loss of their own energy and the shape of the world that bends their courses north-eastward. At a time when the icecap had shrunk back to the North Pole and the water from that enormous melting had raised the level of the warmer world ocean, hurricanes, less opposed by polar air masses may have ranged much farther north over the land than they have been known to. Over the expanse of the warmed water their velocity may have been phenomenal.

On the other hand, when the icecap froze again, taking up more sea water, and the thick ice under snowstorms crept in glaciers over New England and below the Great Lakes, tropical cyclones must have died young, against the advancing barrier of the cold.

In either case, there were always hurricanes.

In time the land bridge between the Americas was thrust up and joined at Darien, and the seas and the Gulf took something of their present shape. The lower peninsula of Florida, with the Everglades the latest of the lands, was dried by the sun after the retreat of the sea water. Along the great crescent of islands south to South America, over the broken vestiges of the continental ridge, the volcanoes of that beautiful chain blew up to make the Caribbean.

At once the winds and rains, Atlantic tides and inward surging currents went to work on them, and hurricanes brought their own violent changes. Their marks are visible over the whole area of low and high islands after hundreds of years or the last of last year's hurricane season.

The streaming winds with their even more terrible gusts came hurling out of their own darkness from the Atlantic and scoured the low sand islands such as Bermuda or Aves, lonely in the Caribbean, Swan Island set hazardously full in the course of cyclones from the Sea of Colombia, islands south of Santo Domingo, and Cuba, the Grand Caymans and reefs everywhere. A generation of seaside trees might grow up only to be swept away, their places taken by mangroves, which in turn might be killed off and nothing left to grow but tough seaside vines.

What the savage winds of hurricanes did to those beautiful volcanic islands, whose first eruptions of heavy, fiery ash some hurricane may have cooled and blown away, was much more complex. Hurricane rains not only gullied and washed down the ash-crusted slopes and stimulated great outbursts of steam from living craters, but, in unusual volume, seeped down the volcanoes' interior chimneys and in time caused new eruptions from deep below sea level.

The rocks of these piled islands, for all the volcanic sands and flung boulders, are tumbled masses of marine limestone and conglomerate. Seeping rains, and the tumultuous hurricane rains especially, have worn and eaten into these rock masses below volcanic ash and humus, especially on the exposed windward slopes, so that they are nothing more than limestone honeycombs. Seeds sprouted in their myriad holes and pits. Tree roots groped for holds in the porous rock or seized them in a tight rooty network.

Some trees are allowed to grow taller here but they have that harried, leaning look that gives them the name of "drunken forests." Sometimes they cling only sparsely to the rocks, dwarfed and distorted like the cedars of Bermuda. When some hurricane blew over a forest on the windward slope of a Caribbee island, the winds might snatch and topple over a tree taller than the others. Held tight in its roots, the rock itself gave way and tumbled over with the tree. The rains scoured away the humus from the pit and left deeper cracks. The thrown-down tree was promptly eaten by termites so even its rotting would leave no soil for other tree seeds, in the altered substratum, but only smaller shrubs. Into that opening, however, sprang the vines, the hooked and woody lianas of the tropics which scramble to the tops of trees and link them in a kind of aerial forest, an enormous dead weight. Air plants as big as bushel baskets also grow along the branches. In the next hurricane blast the forest was ready to crash down, roots and rocks and all, changing the whole character of the mountain growth.

Where hurricanes are frequent, few great trees ever grow. Good timber is not normal. The soil on the eastern side of these islands, except in a few sheltered places, will grow no gardens, only the tangles of manchineel and scrubby woods from which the people make their charcoal.

The white man's towns and villages and plantations were set therefore on the leeward western slopes of all these islands. Yet they did not escape. Hurricane rains sluicing and scouring down from the heights, washing out new stream beds, often marked the western mountainsides with ever deepening gullies or "ghauts," as they call them in Montserrat, or "guts" in Jamaica. They end at sea level in deep coves, "blue holes," where the waves bellow deep below green ferny hill-high banks.

No men settled or tried to make a living among such hurricane-stunted forests, in the leg-breaking tumble of the rocks. In the dim matted jungles at the tops of such windward slopes, in the wet cloud forests, among deep ravines and caves in the cruelly jagged forest floors, only outlaws found a refuge and set their huts, the hunted remnants of Carib Indians or slaves escaped from the plantations. Only hurricanes tore up their shelters here and destroyed their rocky garden patches.

The wild cockpit country of Jamaica is like that, high in the mountains, still inaccessible to any but the descendants of the maroons who found their freedom from the Spaniards there and in many other mountain fastnesses like those of Cuba.

On the continent of Central America, in Honduras and Yucatán, hurricane winds cut great swaths in flat land jungles, opening them up to lesser growths and so increasing the tough areas of scrub.

No trees grow tall along the Florida Keys, because of hurricanes, or for that matter, anywhere, east or west, along the pineland rim of the Everglades. Where the trees were blown down, along the Keys and outer beaches, the tough vines hurried to make tangles of stunted growths and others crawled on spiny elbows along the exposed sands. The live oaks and banyans of the once greatest tropical jungle on the mainland of the United States grew old and broad, but never high in that dark matted Miami Hammock that man has destroyed more thoroughly than any hurricane. Many a ficus, blown over by a hurricane blast here, sent up new branches at right angles to its prostrate trunk, which only a later hurricane threw down and conquered in its advanced and rotted age.

What other things hurricanes did to trees in the tropics depended on the speed of the wind. From fifty to sixty miles an hour small branches break and the leaves are stripped away. The heavier branches break off, often leaving the trunk standing, not dead. Over 100 or 125 miles an hour, if the trees are so well rooted that they are not overthrown, the bark blows off. Many branchless trees with the bark off die where they stand, acres and acres of stripped and silvery poles.

This overwhelming result was once thought to be the work of sheet lightning. Flammarion the scientist once wrote about an entire forest up the island peak of St. Vincent killed during a hurricane, in which not one tree was thrown down. The thousands of acres of open pine woods on the slopes of the Piñar del Rio region of Cuba, dead but still standing, and so many others are now considered the result entirely of wind blasts.

For all that, in the tropics many trees survived and continued to grow because there is no frost and winter to kill them. The tragedy worked by hurricane winds in northern forests is that few, still alive, can survive the northern winter. Everywhere, north or south, the blasting effects of sand and salt linger in blight miles inland from the ocean.

The effects of hurricane winds on the vast forests that covered the northern coastal states before the coming of the white man were perhaps not so easy to read but their marks are enduring. They have been recorded in many early writings by men able to make their way through the impenetrable American wildernesses, chiefly along the rivers.

A French soldier, in 1754, traveling among a company to the forks of the Ohio to build Fort Duquesne, wrote about French Creek, "We were obliged to navigate by short stages on this river because it was obstructed by many trees that had fallen in, either through decay or by hurricanes."

In 1770, on his trip down the Ohio, George Washington noted hurricane damage to the trees between Steubenville, Ohio, and Wheeling, West Virginia.

The effects of hurricane winds on these northern states, Pennsylvania, New York and New England, have been read by foresters from the forest surfaces.

In those regions ordinarily fifty to one hundred years are required for a tree to grow from seed to maturity. Forty-nine years was the longest time noted between severe hurricanes in eastern Massachusetts, Rhode Island and the eastern and central part of Connecticut, and there were many more frequent ones. So that few trees, especially on exposed hillsides, have ever come to maturity without danger from at least one hurricane.

Long before the coming of the white man trees were uprooted by hurricane winds tearing through these forests. Slowly the whole character of the forests and the forest surfaces were changed by them. Trees were torn out of the ground in swaths a mile or more in width, upending a mass of roots and soil often ten feet high. Where the roots had been was a deep pit. As the tree slowly decayed the earth and pebbles about the roots made a mound of bare mineral soil. Under the empty place in the forest canopy the rain leached the good soil down hill. The succession of mounds and pits made a blow-down landscape where only shallow-rooted plants could grow. The forest was dwarfed. Lesser kinds of trees that took root on these mounds where great forests had stood were more likely to be wind-thrown in storms not even so severe as the next hurricane.

The primeval forest that once covered the northern states is thought to have been largely hardwood and hemlock. But the great areas of white pine among the more ancient forests were thought to have grown up in throw-down landscapes on mounds older than the trees they supported where forest fires or the long-searching winds of hurricanes had laid them low.

Yet the winds of hurricanes and their torrential rains that leached bared soils and flooded rivers had no greater effect on the landscapes and geography of this country than the savage work of hurricane waves and surges that always precede and accompany them.

When a maturing hurricane begins its forward movement and its winds lash out like serpents in swift long coils about that central calm, they push the heavier and denser seawater away before the storm on all sides in straight swelling lines of waves. Ahead of its movement, of course, the greatest surge is pushed up, an advancing mounting crest of water. If the hurricane has a long expanse of sea over which it is free to move, the power of the marching waves increases as the distance lengthens. A long "fetch," as it is called, over half an ocean produces waves in walls fifteen or twenty feet in height.

When these cresting and foaming masses of hurricane water ride ashore on an incoming tide, the total hurricane surge is something that will overwhelm almost anything on our low shore lines. If the tide is going out, sometimes the tidewater is subtracted from the hurricane water and makes it less dangerous. But if the tidewater is moving out of a river against the force of hurricane winds and their surge, the ebb can be impounded and backed up. If the hurricane winds blow in that place until the next high tide, then that watery mass spreads backwards over bays and lowlands, up rivers and river plains, burning the growing things with bitter salt and leaving marks of silt and debris and soil wash for years on the rising ground.

It is this surge and thrash and pile up of hurricane water, under the wind's power, which have carved and scoured the changing shapes of our sea coasts.

From the Caribbean all the way to Cape Cod these coasts are curiously similar, regular, slow shelving, almost monotonous. North of the Isthmus, not quite continuously until Tampico in Mexico and the Rio Grande's San Pedro, all around the Gulf, around Florida, up the Atlantic Coast to Montauk on the eastern tip of Long Island, they are characterized by an interminable string of long narrow sand islands. In spots they are peninsulas. They guard the spreading mouths of mainland rivers the rising sea level has drowned. Their outer beaches take the tides of sea and gulf and ocean and the white breaking of endless wave action, in rain and fog and sun mist. The islands have been piled up on sunken reefs and bars. Within them lie calm lagoons and sounds and bays and inland waterways and peaceful swamps. Such islands take the full force of the trades and the thunder of the breaking waves along the Isthmus, whose quiet salt lagoons offer the only shelter from those constantly savage and destructive seas. Often the sounds they mark off from the full force of the Atlantic are themselves like shallower seas, much subject to storms, like Albemarle and Pamlico and Long Island Sound itself.

If these islands were built up by wave action from the sea side they glisten with white sand and are often crested with blown up dunes such as those of Kill Devil and Kitty Hawk on the Outer Banks of Hatteras, the Fire Island dunes of Long Island and the great dunes of the clenched fist and arm of Cape Cod. Where such islands have been built up from river silt they are bordered with dark mud and the bays and river mouths they guard have dark muddy silted shallows. The bayous and delta swamps of the Mississippi are like that and the wide branching river bottoms of the eastern shore.

Like the Sea Islands of Georgia, wherever the rivers have left silt, dense woods have sprung up of pines and oaks and magnolias and sweet gums, through whose leafy silences sounds the thunder of the outer surf. Some of these long islands are like the Florida Keys, built up marine limestones with coral shelves, their dangerous shallows bristling with coral heads.

Many islands built up on reefs beyond the coast like the rock and sand Bahamas and the myriad rock islands of Maine do not have the character of the long sandy coastal islands. Yet hurricanes have left their marks on these rocks and thinned and stunted and changed their tree growths, also. But it is on the sand islands of the long coasts that hurricanes eternally work their greatest change.

Along all the shores the tides and currents keep up a constant shifting of sands, gouging it out here and building it up there. But no changes are so marked and sudden as those made by hurricanes. The surges, in a few hours, may carve out a new channel through which the imprisoned tides roar. They may carry hundreds of tons of sand from a scooped-out backwater, and with it fill up completely an old passage between islands which generations of fishermen have used, and make one joined land out of many. They have swept away old reefs and dredged new river channels. They have filled a deep basin with a submerged bar and piled up the sand on it in a single

night so that a new island emerges under the sun, gleaming with
new shells and the first tracks of adventuring sandpipers.

The dunes of the coastal islands whose fine sand is kept crawling
by the usual sea winds are dissolved like sugar by hurricane waters,
or by wind action are picked up and hurled along to another place.

The roaring salt surges of hurricanes break new channels in
muddy river deltas and swamps, leaving new mud flats gleaming
where there were the islands. Among the great mangroves of
Florida's Ten Thousand Islands, hurricanes cut wide swaths, tearing
out the sand and mud under their arching roots, and piling up their
tangles around some new salt water lake, for the white heron and
the whiter egret to nest on.

It would be impossible to describe all the damage that hurricanes
have worked and will work along this north continent.

The spread of new kinds of trees and plants is more apparent about
the Caribbean as the warm tropics make possible the continuing
life of seeds.

The swing of the accustomed currents about this sea has carried
a constant drift of plants and seeds down rivers but chiefly from
along the beaches and near estuaries. Hurricane winds have broken
them off in windrows. Hurricane tides have hurried them along
faster. Much of this vegetable drift has reached the Gulf Stream,
and hastened by other hurricanes has been moved by the regular
currents far away to the Hebrides and the Orkney Islands, the
western coasts of Scotland, Ireland and Wales, to the Faroes and
even to Scandinavia. People have hoarded seeds picked up along
their beaches as so strange and unknown as to have magical and
healing properties, but none have survived the long voyage in sea
water as living seeds.

In the tropics, however, the more bouyant and viable seeds have
sprouted and grown green on other beaches and river mouths, as
they have in Florida or in the interior of such higher cays as Turk
Island in the Bahamas, where the highest hurricane swells have
tossed and stranded them, in more fertile inland soil.

The mangroves of the lower west coast of Florida, the greatest
mangrove forest in this hemisphere, are perhaps the most significant
product of this combination of natural drift and hurricane action.
There are actually three different kinds of mangrove here, the white,
the red and the black, and a related one, tropical buttonwood, found

in constant association. Severally these trees grow on the sandy edges of salt water, in mucky salt mud or striding out into clear salt water shallows, all on a bewilderment of arched and entwined roots. In the Pacific, as in the Caribbean, they grow about islands and at the salt mouths of rivers. They lodge on sand banks and stand like bouquets of deep green leaves among the water glitter and stride out again into new mud they have made.

The mangroves of Florida's Ten Thousand Islands grew up since the sea uncovered this land. Besides the advance of their interlocked arches, they produce seed, six or eight inches long, very hard and tough, that is actually germinated before it drops. It floats, right side up, in sea water which cannot kill it for a long time. When a tide or a hurricane surge drops it on any sort of soil, its roots catch and hold. Among the debris of a hurricane drying in a swamp beyond a beach, its leaves prick out, already green.

No one knows, of course, where the mangroves of the world began. It may be that the long equatorial currents, helped by hurricanes, brought the first mangroves westward from Africa to some sheltered Caribbean mud. But it is safe to believe that their spread about the coasts of Central America and Yucatán, the Colorado reefs along northwest Cuba and all the other places, was the work of hurricanes. Hurricanes, more even than the slower currents, must have brought them to Florida. And from Florida again, the long seagoing seeds may have been carried out.

There seems to be great mystery, if not argument, about the history of the amazing and beautiful coco palm, the coconut, in these American tropics.

Historians insist that early Spanish writers like Oviedo, who wrote about so many plants of the New World, never mentioned the coconut. They insist also that the first coconuts were brought to Mexico by the Manila galleons from the Philippines and grew first at Panama.

On the other hand, botanists argue that all the other "cocoid" palms are native to the American world, so why not the coconut, and who said Oviedo knew everything anyway?

At all events the lovely curve of the coco palm, balancing its fronds that rustle in the trade wind, strong enough to bend and endure all but the most powerful hurricane blasts, is the only "cocoid" palm which has particularly adapted its great nut, with tough outer fibers within a hard watertight skin, so that it can float in salt water and keep alive for long periods of time. The currents of the Caribbean swing them about. But the great surges of hurricanes carry them quickly, even float whole palm tops with their burdens of nuts, so that, after they have been left among debris on dry land under a hot sun, perhaps even months after a storm, they germinate. The first green leaves pierce the eye of the nut and crack it as the rooty foot thrusts downward. And a new coco palm grows somewhere, as it surely did along the coasts of Florida before the first white man saw it and planted more. On the shores of Honduras a great grove of coconuts is said to have grown up where their nuts were washed ashore many miles from a loaded ship wrecked in a hurricane.

A diversity of seeds that live longest have been carried, perhaps as freshly broken-off fruits, to root everywhere about the American tropics. Such as these are the manchineel with its poisonous sap but its usefulness as charcoal wood, the sapote known as "mammee apple," beach plums, the hog plum that still lives after two or three months in sea water and so was carried from Africa to Brazil by equatorial currents and then to the West Indies, where hurricane tides have carried it inland, where it is more at home; the sabal palms and the silver palms of the Florida Keys, the beautiful yellow cassia fistula called "Shower of Gold," the stout thespesias with their pink and yellow tulips and the purple tropical morning glories, the ipomea, that elbow their green strong way above barren sea sands.

Of course the sea beans that the people of the far North hold in reverence are everywhere in the South, the hard stony gray or brown sea nuts, the nicker beans and the mucuna, that people pick up to carry in their pockets and polish. They live long enough here to be deposited in good soil by hurricane waters and build dense viny jungles, all curving claws and thatch of golden blossoms. Undoubtedly the most common growth of all, the charming lavender blooming water hyacinth, whose dark green crisp leaves madden men by choking riverways and lakes, however it was introduced in this hemisphere, has been constantly spread and respread and carried by wind action and wave action in hurricanes.

So many of the jungle trees endure because they have learned how to live in hurricanes by sending down strong cables of roots like the ficus-banyans, or building up great roots like the ceibas and silk cottons that stand enormous and shaggy and alone on wind-swept hillsides, the buttressed cypresses of Gulf of Mexico swamps, the saw palmetto that, once blown over, fastens itself to the ground and writhes along like a great snake, and especially the wonderful royal palm of Cuba that gives up all its swishing fronds to the hurricane, one by one, and stands firm, under the bare pole of its tall cementlike trunk. There is the mahoe, no higher than twenty-five feet that walks and makes great thickets of its writhing coiling limbs. These and many others are trees that live because they have adapted to the hurricanes.

There are many kinds of brittle small trees and woody vines and shrubs that seem as if they have no chance for existence until after a hurricane has swept over and opened a jungle. On the jungle floor seeds have grown that ordinarily barely keep alive, pale, puny and weak, just strong enough to reproduce another sickly generation. With the large trees overthrown and sun reaching the forest floor, these seedlings of such as the paradise tree seem to spring into feverish life.

The poisonwood, metopium, may spring up everywhere in opened Florida country. It is very brittle. It withers when the large trees come back. The balsam apple hurries to cover everything, after a hurricane, with its mats of vines. The sea grape grows tall. Sea beans and the round hard nicker beans that float with hurricane waves and are tossed above high water marks on newer sands, send out the grasping coils of their tendrils, covered with spikes that keep off animals, haul themselves over dying bushes, up standing trees to burst over everything in umbrellas of green leaves, triumphant with blossoms as yellow as the sun. The weed called pokeroot, the wild papayas, the trema like a half bamboo come up after a hurricane like an invading army.

Of them all, the feathery tough casuarina called "Australian pine," introduced at almost the same time on the lower east and west coasts of Florida, has been the tree of them all most quickly spread about the Caribbean by the hurricanes. Its tiny carved nuts are carried far to sea still alive. It grows at once on sandbanks, reefs, old eroded shores. It comes hurrying in behind the jungles of mangroves that no hurricanes ever entirely kill. The casuarina may break and die in hurricane winds, but its seeds sprout again. More than any other it is the tree of hurricanes. It is increasing now everywhere in this tropic region which the hurricanes are always shaping and changing to their own designs.

5 *CREATURES OF THE STORM*

The wide calm eye of a hurricane, in which it differs so radically from waterspouts by sea and tornadoes by land, must exist as soon as the winds begin to swing in a vortex and the clouds rise up boiling and twisting about it. As it moves it is like a vast amphitheater often filled with entrapped birds.

Men on ships and airplanes have seen them there, who have been so lucky as to penetrate the dreadful winds, and ride safely within and get out again alive. They have reported with amazement the birds circling easily about the walls, rising and dipping to scoop up their food from the roughened wavetops, totally unafraid. If a bird flew too straightly across that open space, it was turned back by the solid clouds and the wind's velocity, like bars to the enormous airy cage. They were caught there as the hurricane grew and were carried by it unnoticingly in its advance across the Atlantic.

These are the far-flying pelagic birds whose narrow long wings beat and soar and are tireless, that feed and sleep and preen themselves in these equatorial waters. Some of them fly amazing distances, never seeing land. They are the shearwaters, Cory's shearwater, that breeds in the Azores and glides easily along to North America in the current of the trades, the greater shearwater which ranges swiftly from Greenland to the Cape of Good Hope, crossing the paths of hurricanes. There is the low-flying Audubon's shearwater from the Antilles and the Bahamas.

The petrels know the hurricanes, too, the black-capped, and the stormy that flies all the coasts of the Atlantic, the Madeira petrel from the Azores and Wilson's petrel that builds its nests in remote islands of the South Atlantic and courses northward in summer to ride the wakes of ships, "Mother Carey's Chickens" that all sailors love.

The hurricanes catch within their moving funnel greater birds whose home is the Atlantic, wonderful and strong in flight, the yellow-billed tropic bird, white as foam, with its snowy long tail feathers. And the most graceful, buoyant, strong and beautiful flyer of them all, the frigate or man-o'-war birds that swim and tumble in the gales, without rest. These were often called "hurricane birds" by early writers.

All these ocean birds within the hurricane are not aware of change until the forward winds move over a shore. It is the shores that frighten them. They beat their way back across the eye and try to penetrate the howling rampart of the rearward winds, to get home to ocean. But now their strong wings are helpless. Some powerful updraft tosses them like bits of paper in a chimney into higher and higher altitudes. Some die of the buffeting. The strongest may be caught by an upper current whose spin tumbles them out at last far northward, feeble bunches of feathers, inland, over hills and plowed fields where no one has ever seen their like before.

Man-o'-war birds have dropped down in northern Maine and Nova Scotia, tropic birds in New York state, shearwaters in Vermont and terns and petrels anywhere from Rhode Island to Kentucky, Ohio and Canada.

Many a ship, laboring in the winds outside a hurricane, has reported how her decks and rigging were covered with exhausted smaller birds, shore birds that flew before the storm or were caught up by it and took refuge where they could. These are petrels and terns for the most part, but often one of those sea-going migrations of little wood warblers that winter in the Bahamas or Cuba, the Cape May warbler that winters in Haiti, are cut off by winds and driven before them or killed by the thousands.

Perhaps it is amazing that any of these seagoing land birds are left, since they migrate in hurricane season like the prairie warbler that every fall flies south to Florida, to Cuba, to the Grand Caymans and to that lonely sand speck of Swan Island, lost in the Sea of Colombia. So often, in hurricanes, many must regularly be killed on their southward flight and on the islands.

One bird has made itself a legend everywhere in the West Indies as the mysterious and the true hurricane bird. Late in an afternoon in the blue and lovely weather of the day before, as the sunset began to redden, all the trees and roofs and ledges of one of those little island towns were covered with thousands of small sharptailed black birds. They struggled for place on the spars of ships in the open roadstead and darkened the slow sheltered waves that they rode like little boats. All night long their plaintive voices sounded mournfully, "twa-oo, twa-oo," as they rose and circled restlessly in the dark. By morning when the hurricane winds were beginning to rouse the sea, they vanished.

These are the sooty terns that fish in great flocks, hovering low over the water, and breed by the thousand on such lonely islands as the Dry Tortugas beyond Florida. They are known as hurricane birds only in the Caribbean but many a hurricane has blown sooty and bridled terns to Staten Island. Lighthousekeepers at Canaveral in Florida have reported clouds of sooty terns hovering in a storm before the brilliant lenses of the light.

In September along Long Island terns have been found blown from the south and black-skimmers caught by a hurricane on its long wandering north to the Bay of Fundy and back. More strangely, after the winds have passed, bird watchers have seen about a Long Island pond avocets from the west and golden plovers that, in their extraordinary long flight from their Arctic breeding grounds to Patagonia, stop no farther west than Cape Cod.

There was once reported from the island of Dominica a single humming bird of a kind found no where else but Brazil, that must somehow have ventured northward to be caught and dropped by a hurricane blast.

Long before the plants found a foothold on many a low limestone island just emerged from the sea, such as the Bahamas, it is the belief of ornithologists that the ancestors of the more than one hundred kinds of birds that nest here, terns, white-crowned pigeons, ground doves, honey creepers, Bahama mockingbirds and many more, were blown here by tropical cyclones. Other storms that have stirred up the sand from the shallows east of the Bahama Banks have made deserts of such islands as once-green Cay Verde to which for a while no bird can return.

The destruction of land birds is one of the greatest tragedies of hurricanes, great white heron drowned in the white muck waters of the Bay of Florida after a Key hurricane, heron speared on broken tree branches, birds killed by being blown against high walls and towers and buildings like the Empire State, clapper rails flooded out of Long Island salt meadows by hurricane waves, smashed along highways by car wheels.

The hurricane of 1944, over the west coast of Florida blew down eighteen trees with eagle nests, and damaged many others so that eggs were lost from forty-five nests out of 115. Other birds have died or been driven away by the ravage of their jungles and forests and the loss of their food.

However, it is amazing how the small land birds have survived some of the most savage of hurricanes, blue jays, mockingbirds, cardinals, palm warblers, woodpeckers, shrikes and the rest. They take shelter where they can, low down, where the winds cannot reach them, under eaves and perches, among the high roots of trees, in the lee of sheds. A blue-gray gnatcatcher was seen to sit for hours as a hurricane was passing, on a root just behind a tree trunk. In the moments when the gusts slackened, it nipped neatly at an insect to right or left, cowering down without a feather ruffled as its tree trunk creaked again and branches went dimly crashing through the aroused air.

And if some birds are starved out by the loss of their forest feeding places, the open swaths and rotting wood draw crowds of fly-catchers, white-throated sparrows, woodpeckers, winter wrens and others with food enough to double their numbers.

The story of the rare Cape Sable seaside sparrow, a bird so shy and secretive that it was never discovered until 1918, is a hurricane story. It may have been blown in the first place to this half-submerged, sun-bleached area of tall salt marshes, not more than six miles long and half a mile wide, long enough ago for it to develop its own unique if faint markings, setting it apart from any other seaside sparrow.

The killing hurricane of 1935 that swept bare the Florida Keys distressed the ornithologists because in its area, muddied and crushed by the winds' steam rollers, not a single Cape Sable sparrow was left. It had a stronger hold on life than anyone imagined. Some years later seven thriving colonies were found hidden among the swamps at the headwaters of some West Coast rivers, south of the Tamiami

Trail. The sparrows had flown low out of some vagrant wind current.

Many birds from the West Indies, in fact, have been blown into South Florida by recent hurricanes. They have become native where they found refuge, and are increasing. There are the black anis from Haiti called "tobacco pouches," two grassquits, the Bahama honeycreeper, the Bahama swallow, the Cuban cliff swallow and several West Indian doves and pigeons. The latest newcomer, blown to Florida within the last few hurricanes, is the slender white cattle egret from everywhere in the Antilles. A few appeared among the great herds of cattle feeding south of the Everglades. Now the cattle egret are everywhere with the herds, perching and looking for ticks on rumps of unconcerned beasts, or striding and quarreling, egret-fashion, among the stamping hooves.

Fish in hurricanes meet other fates, each after its own kind. The great ocean-going, the pelagic fish, swordfish, sharks, marlin, dolphin and fast swimming blues, merely swim deep below the troubled waters and flash away to other feeding grounds. The hurricanes may push along great clumps of Sargasso weed, torn from its slow moving clotted, undulating yellow meadows within the North Atlantic currents, under the high-pressure area that extends down from the Bermudas and keeps the hurricanes on their east-west directions. The tiny crabs and fish that live among the weed never know the difference until they are blown ashore by a hurricane tide. It is only to shallow water fish that hurricane waves and tides can be disastrous.

They are not reached by ordinary storms that cannot disturb the deep sediment like that that rivers bring down to bays and sounds, that cloaks the bottom with thick layers of silt. Shallow water fish are not affected where the water is clear or deeper than forty or fifty fathoms. In any case, the crabs and crustaceans bury themselves cozily in ooze and are safe.

But the hurricane ground swells out of the deeps reach down to the old deposits of sediment, stirring it violently so that all the water is clouded and heavy with it. The delicate gill membranes of bay fish, sheepsheads and porgies, cowfish and trunk fish are clogged up with it so that they cannot breathe oxygen enough. They are not agile nor strong swimmers enough to swim away. So with the fish of the Florida and other tropical reefs, angelfish, parrot fish, butterfly fish. So with the fine food and game fish, the snook, the bass, the pompano. Without oxygen they are weakened. The silt-clouded waves toss up tons of gasping fish along the storm-harried beaches, to flop and die in windrows of decay. Only the mullet can survive in the muddied waters.

There is no end to the destruction of such fish in waters roiled by the accumulation of years of slime and sediment. Even the plankton, the masses of tiny fish on which the larger fish depend, are killed by it. So that one hurricane may destroy the fishing grounds for a long time.

The greatest destruction of such fish has occurred in the frequent hurricanes that have ruined the lower East Coast of Florida. Biscayne Bay at Miami, where the fish always fed on the grassy flats, since the dynamiting of the rapids in the Miami River, has been allowed to be silted up by overflow waters from the mucky Everglades, to which years of sewage have been added. The hurricanes stirred up that accumulation of silt that extends to the Beaches and the Keys, so that hardly any fish were left alive.

North of Jupiter the fish were hurled in straight from the ocean, worn out by the Gulf Stream and the hurricane swells. Whole families of fish were killed, drumheads, croakers, trout and bass. Five years ago along this coast there were butterfly fish enough for everyone, the fishermen say. Now you hardly find any. The hurricanes killed them off, and many more.

The same conditions of disturbed silt kill fish in places along the shallow lagoons of the Texas coast. Oyster beds in the Gulf, that must have clear water, both salt and fresh, have been wiped out by hurricanes. Even shelves and reefs of corals, that must have clean sea water to raise their strange stony colonies, have been known to die by being muffled in silt in hurricane waves.

Silt is deposited chiefly where the tides are slow and shallow. From North Florida northward up past Georgia and the Carolinas, the greater range of tides keeps the sediment scoured out and moving. Fish there live in deeper water and are not killed in storms except by the bruising ground swells along the shelving Atlantic beaches. Florida suffers most.

The curious thing is that many fish, much more than birds, seem to be aware of the approach of a hurricane. Before the beginning of a bad storm, even as the barometer is going down, the fish will bite greedily. The bluefish deliberately swim to the bottom and gobble small stones and gravel and everything else they can eat, as if they were taking on ballast that would keep them in deep clear water, unaffected by ground swells.

Down the Keys, fishermen say they can tell when a bad storm, or a hurricane, is coming, because the bonefish are feeding greedily over the reefs. The water will be alive with their flipping tails. The great deep sea fish of the Florida coast, the sail fish, come to the surface in hundreds, if the seas are rough with north or northwest winds. They travel south with the wind against the Gulf Stream rolling northward. They swim high on the surface where the current is more slack. They escape out through the Straits beyond the Bahamas to the Atlantic Ocean, in whose great dim only softly stirring depths they and their kind live safe below the hurricane's reach.

It would be impossible to know, or to record, all the effects of hurricanes on these varying life forms of the seas and of these airs and landscapes.

None is more lowly nor more strange than the snail called "liguus" which lives in a shell like the most delightful peaked bubble of clear yellow banded with vermilion, or cream color marked with orange or gray and pinkish with soft lavendar and white. Perhaps they developed first in the remote high forests of Cuba, out of the most ancient Caribbean rocks. Hurricane winds and rains cannot affect their slow lifetimes, in which they develop the most charming varieties of colors and kinds. If their trees are blown down, and they are not crushed, there would be old fallen wood to crawl over and feed from.

If branches on which tree snails lived are broken off and carried to sea before hurricane winds the imperturbable life of the snails continues. After many days, on another shore, the snails slowly leave the old branch for a living tree. After slow years of breeding among dark trees they show some new delicacy of marking, pink or petal colored or brown or spotted, to indicate that they were aware of change.

So the tree snails must first have been carried to the new land of Florida, thousands of years ago, or last year, and found their place in the mysterious cycles of living, of which the hurricane's supreme rage had its little part.

6 THE MEANING OF THE NAME

There is no way of proving that the word "hurricane" is not one of
the oldest words ever spoken by the early people of America that is
still in use.

We have no idea how many centuries men have lived on these
American continents. They are thought to have pushed across the
Bering Strait from Asia and down to the regions haunted by hurricanes in a time of melting between one ice age and the next. They
crossed and recrossed the land bridge of Central America and the
Isthmus of Panama in slow confused wandering streams of people
so long ago that about the Caribbean was developed a bewilderment
of types and tribes and unlike speech. There is no way of knowing
when the first of them penetrated the Andean foothills and the
Caribbean coast of South America and its rivers, to the sea and the
ocean.

They were all Indians but already they looked different, they
differed in everything they did and in everything they thought and
in the words they spoke. But among the earliest people who shoved
their canoes out among that north-springing arc of islands from the
southern continent, a word that sounded like "hurricane" must have
been spoken and taught and handed down for generations.

One of the most widespread languages of that South American
coast was spoken by the Arawaks, a light-brown, cheerful, shapely
people, far advanced from primitive hunting and fishing to peaceful
agriculture on the slopes away from the sea. Their skulls were
flattened in childhood. They raised tobacco and smoked it and lived
on ground manioc root and vegetables. Their gods were the uncon-
trollable forces of nature on which their lives were wholly dependent, the sun, the stars, the rains, the storms.

When the most adventurous among them paddled out to those

islands they found a simple people there before them, who may have lived there a long, long time. They were very primitive hunters and fishers. They had no tools but shells with which they built mounds in the swamps and by the beaches. These people ran away before the Arawaks, although some of them were kept as servants. They found shelter in caves in remote mountains, especially in Cuba. The Arawaks called them "Rock Men" but today scientists have used for them the name of "Ciboneys."

Among the crude carved stones the Ciboneys left behind them in caves are some crude shafts topped by round heads with holes for eyes and mouths. About where the stomach would be in these armless figures another round head was cut, holes for eyes and shouting mouth. Two arms curve away from the head, one up, one down. Sometimes there are smaller stones carved with just this head and arm alone. It is rough, but it suggests horror and excited, whirling action. Dr. Fernando Ortiz of Havana thinks these are the symbols of the most frightening force the early people knew, the hurricane.

It is curious that the U.S. Weather Bureau, following an international conference of meteorological directors held in Copenhagen, adopted in 1939 a set of international weather symbols to designate all the different kinds of winds and rains and weathers. Before that they used the International Meteorological Organization Code of words. The official symbol for hurricane, therefore, now the special insignia of the Weather Bureau Research Project, is a circle from which two lines curve off in opposite directions. It is, of course, exactly made and very different from the crude carvings, but if you mark the circle with dots for eyes and open mouth you will have a drawing of the ancient Ciboney symbol to the life, after all those centuries.

It has even been thought by modern ethnologists that there may have been an even older people in the West Indies before the Ciboneys, for whom the hurricanes had the same awful meaning. And from whose ancient and unimaginable language stock the word was derived which has become our "hurricane."

The Arawaks evidently learned it in the Antilles where they made themselves at home and comfortable on the rich plains and among the higher valleys, with gardens about their sprawling villages of open thatched houses, with ball courts and temples. Life was easy on the cool slopes, with a little gold dust from the rivers to make into ornaments for their honored chiefs and their handsome youths. In every man's house was a table or shelf of small pottery figures of their gods, called "zemis," who kept the sun shining and brought the rain in season to the growing vegetable patches.

There was a powerful female zemi of the Arawaks of Puerto Rico, whose name was Guabancex. When she was angry she sent out her herald Guataba to order all the other zemis to lend her their winds, like the witches in Macbeth, and their rains to be gathered up in the high valleys between the mountains and so to smash them down upon the villages. When the hurricane was upon them the people shut themselves up in their leaky huts and shouted and banged drums and blew shell trumpets to keep the evil from destroying them.

The peaceful Arawaks increased throughout the islands when the Spaniards found them. These Indians of Puerto Rico and Hispaniola are often called now by their own name of "Tainos." The Lucayos, who were sub-Tainos of the Bahamas, believed that all their islands were once part of the mainland but had been cut off by the howling winds and waves of the hurricanes. The sub-Tainos, called "Igneri," of the Lesser Antilles, the most warlike people of them all, knew the hurricanes that came surging in from the Atlantic. Later, the European people of those islands believed that the Indians always knew long before anyone else when a hurricane was coming, and indeed, probably no one in the world knew the signs and portents better than they did. It was the Igneri, some scientists think, who kept alive and passed on the original word that became "hurricane."

The Arawaks, that the Spaniards would kill off in the Greater Antilles, were before them killed in the Lesser Antilles by a stronger and more ruthless stream of Indians from the river deltas of South America, the darker, taller, more fierce Caribs. Only the Igneri were able to fight them off and preserved their own language and customs in their remote villages in the mountains, while the Caribs were driving their great war canoes to conquer island after island beyond. In their sudden raids by moonlight they killed off all the men but took the comely Arawak women as wives and mothers of their children, who spoke among themselves the softer Arawak language. So the word like "hurricane" passed into Carib speech and the fierce people learned the terror of the savage storms.

Indeed, it is possible that the name was spread backward among the more enduring Arawak tribes of the mainland. There to this day, names similar to "hurricane" are spoken by the half-Arawak, half-Carib tribes, to mean "evil spirit." The Galibi called it "Yuracan," the Giuana Indians, "Yarukka." Other similar names were "Hyrorokan," "Yurakon," "Yuruk" or "Yoroko."

The bold Caribs of the islands, whose name was given to this sea, and to the word, "cannibal," because they ate symbolic parts of their war victims as a way of adding the strength and courage of their enemies to their own, were for all that both fearful and superstitious about evil, and about hurricanes. They had no small stone gods but believed in good and powerful bad spirits called "maboya," that caused all the misfortunes of their lives. They wore carved amulets and employed medicine men to drive the evil maboya away. They were terrified of spilling fresh water into the sea because that aroused the anger of hurricanes. They believed that beyond the maboya were great spirits, the male sun, the female moon. The spirits of the stars controlled the weather. A bird named Savacou was sent out by the angry maboya to call up the hurricane, and then became a star.

When the great storm began to rise out of the sea the Caribs blew frantically into the air to drive it away and chewed manioc bread and spat it, for the same purpose, into the air. When that was no use they gave way to panic and crouched in their great communal houses moaning, with their arms over their heads. They were reasonably safe there because they had made their houses very strong, with corner posts dug deep into the ground.

When the hurricane approached the Florida coasts, the medicine men of the North American Indians worked frantic incantations to drive the evil thing away.

But long before the Caribs had invaded the Antilles and learned in terror and suffering what the word "hurricane" meant, a similar word was in use in a different way back in Central America, where in other centuries had developed an astonishing civilization.

Out of the forested slopes of Guatemala and the thorny scrub of Yucatán, men who spoke the Quiche language, and would themselves be known to us as Mayas, had built marvelous stone ceremonial places, palaces, temple monasteries in vast carved and sculptured pyramid shapes. Villages, gardens, corn fields reached out around them in clearings in the jungle and in the scrub. These people, and the bloodier Aztecs who conquered them and built a more elaborate empire, were so far advanced over the island people that it hardly seems possible that they came from the same stock. Their language, habits, and beliefs seem to have had almost nothing in common. But in the foothills of Guatemala, the coasts of Honduras, the flat bulk of Yucatán, they all knew the force and fear of hurricanes.

The Maya gods of the wind and the rain were the Chacs. The people had a word "Jurakan" which did not mean hurricane so much as the name of a powerful god, like the Honduran "Kukulkan" who controlled the supreme forces of nature and was indeed one of the gods of creation. "Jurakan" means "one-legged god" who under other names, in the intricate stone carvings of the great places like Chichen-Itza, has one leg ending in a foot in a sandal and the other not with a foot, but with a plumed serpent. He is decked out in a profusion of carved spiral designs, S-curves and coils, like the coiling of the great storms. It was to appease such gods that the Aztecs made their terrible sacrifices of fresh blood and pulsing human hearts.

There is no way yet of knowing if there was ever any relation between the name of the great god, who had other names beside "Jurakan" and the old island word that became "Hurricane." Ethnologists say not, but we know that the spread of language is a very strange and unexpected thing.

The name "Jurakan" has been found in a fragment of a majestic book that alone of all the records of those amazing peoples has come down to us. It was written in the languages of the southern highlands of Guatemala and was translated into Spanish. It is called "The Popul Vuh" and it tells of the beginning of the world.

It begins, "At first, all was suspense, calm, tranquillity, silence. This was all there was in the sky. . . . There was only the sky.

"Nothing had any foundation; there existed only the quietness of the waters and the silence of the sea. . . .

"The gods alone . . . were in dazzling light . . . only the light showed what was yet uncreated; and they asked themselves, how will life be sustained by those forced to live in the shades of the night, by him who is the Heart of the Sky, whose name is Jurakan."

Under whatever name, and greater than the power of any god to avert, the people huddling in their houses and huts beyond the unaffected vast stone places, knew the destruction of the supreme winds. Tales of damage and suffering long before the white man have come down to us from the last days of the Mayan empire. The great stone city of Mayapan, already in bad repair after wars and depressions, too carelessly rebuilt, was deeply damaged by a hurricane in 1464. The ruthless Bishop Landa, who burned the great Mayan records and documents, at least set down the story of this hurricane, the first written record we have.

"During a winter's night," he wrote, long afterward, "about six o'clock in the evening, there arose a wind which kept increasing and soon changed into a hurricane of four winds. This hurricane overthrew all the large trees causing a great destruction of every kind of game; and it destroyed also all the tall houses which covered with straw and containing fire on account of the cold, were set on fire and they burned up a large part of the people. If any escaped, they were crippled by the blows which they received from the [flying] wood. This hurricane lasted till the next day at noon and it was found that those had escaped who dwelt in small houses."

After that, the people were exhorted not to cast their lots in houses of straw, because death would come of it. It was the literal casting of lots, they believed, that brought "the hurricane of the four winds."

Whatever they called it then, in all those diverse languages, under whatever gods, all the people of that world knew it for what it was, the most terrible force in nature.

BOOK TWO

THE SPANISH NEW WORLD

1 *WHITE MAN'S FIRST*

The three caravels had come a long way in that unknown ocean. It was a journey into fear, beyond all knowledge. It was to be the most marvelous voyage in the history of the civilized world.

The waters over which the caravels had drawn the line of their westing were blue as flowers. They breathed and glittered under the warming sun where the superstition of Europe had hung an impenetrable curtain. For days and days a great steady wind had followed them, sweeter and more constant than any the ships' companies had ever known. Dawns over dew-wet decks tinged the sails with rose-color, and the turning furrow of their wakes. Nights lifted a dome of stars over their gently swaying masts. Starlight moved luminous on the foresails and mainsails only, because the lateens were furled, out of the way of that ever-blowing wind. The three small ships went forward with their steady lift and roll, near enough so that the watch could look over at the shine of the other two poop lanterns. The water of the deeps crushed under those squat bows that were changing the world.

Columbus was always there, on the slant high stern castle. His eyes stared forward. But his inner vision was fixed on the clouded fantasies of medieval ages, with every day now drawing to its end. The inner view had been the goad. The outer was the true secret of his genius. Fame as the greatest of all discoverers rested squarely on this—that he saw what he looked at.

When he had weighed anchor at the Canaries and uttered his one direction, "West," he saw the lonely sea. He saw the strong straight wind come dancing from the east, amazing these Mediterranean sailors, the winds that he believed would blow them to Japan. In ten days they had not failed. He had no idea that they were the northeast trade winds that from summer to winter slide north or south, in their limits north of the equator, with the sliding sun. His

hard-headed Spanish and Portuguese sailors began to be hysteri-
cally afraid this unalterable wind would never let them return.

Columbus saw the yellow weed of the Sargasso Sea as his father-
in-law, Pedro de Velasco, had told him, square miles of heaving
mats. He drove the ships through it, noting it as only surface stuff,
not knowing it lies a long central oval within the circular currents,
in still Atlantic water, the center of an enormous circling of winds.
He saw the birds of the open ocean and described them so well that
later sailors know them. He saw and noted for the first time in history the western variation of the compass.

The trade winds had blown the ships beyond their northern
limits and they no longer made their phenomenal speed. The sea
was glassy. There was a little rain. The men felt they could beat
home against these lighter airs. The canvas slatted. They sailed only
fifty-seven miles in two days. The airs were variable, ruffling the
patches of weed.

Next day, the wind failed completely. The ocean was oily calm.
The sailors muttered there was no wind at all to take them back to
Spain.

They saw a strange thing. Coming up from the southwest was a
kind of deep swelling of the sea, long rolls of slow water, polished
and unbreaking, with perhaps here and there a gleam of gold from
the clouded sunlight. The idle ships violently tipped and heaved.
Men shouted in alarm. The helms were put about to head into the
waves. Then men glanced back at Columbus, on the *Santa Maria's*
high stern, easing to the roll, watching calmy the *Niña* over here, the
Pinta there, both taking it handily. It was a sea to him such as had
appeared to the Israelites fleeing from Egypt, a mark of deliverance.
But to the men he said calmly there must be wind behind those
swells, wind enough to take them home when the time came.

Southwest there must have been a hurricane, sending blue swells
marching straight before it, and to all sides, across that ocean. It
was a marvel of the journey that no other Atlantic hurricane, all
that hushed September and October, came nearer to Columbus than
this.

He would not have been prepared for it. There had been no sea
captain in Portugal, at the court of Prince Henry the Navigator,
where everything that was known of the ocean beyond the Pillars
of Hercules had been studied, who could have warned him there

were storms out there more vicious than Europeans knew. But he had followed the hurricane course westward.

So with men sweating more cheerfully at the sweeps, the caravels crawled forward. For three weeks no one had seen land. The old fears of the unknown flared. Winds were fitful. The course that had been changed was changed again, west by a little more south. They came back into the steady course of the trades and white water talked about their bows.

There were signs of land, doubts, high tempers flaring among the men. The *Niña* and the *Pinta* were close enough to *Santa Maria* so that their captains, the Pinzon brothers, Martin Alonso and the cranky independent Vincent Yañez, could look over and argue about turning back. Later the Pinzons tried to prove Columbus the most doubtful and the faintest-hearted of leaders.

There were false landfalls, more arguments. At latitude 25°45′ Columbus saw great flocks of birds flying steadily and changed his course to follow them.

At sunset, the caravels moved on the wind sweetly into the luminous night, through hushed hours. The watch on the deck spoke only in whispers. The captains stood there. The lookouts were silent at the mastheads. The waters rustled. Columbus, on his stern castle, stared, with his eyes wide stretched across the shadows of the centuries, for the new morning.

The hurricane swells were only important on that voyage because Columbus took advantage of them. But it was the first observation of those amazing climaxes of Atlantic weather which we call "hurricanes."

When Columbus's first voyage was almost over, and nothing became him so much as that magnificent beginning, he sailed home with what was left of his fleet. The *Santa Maria*, that he had disliked, had been wrecked off the northern coast of Hispaniola, now Haiti and Santo Domingo, when on Christmas eve he had slept below.

Returning south of the Azores, February, 1493, Columbus was engulfed by a terrible storm. It has been called a hurricane. That is not impossible for February, but not in that region. It was not a hurricane whirl but a series of vicious winds typical of that eastern part of the ocean off Africa. Columbus's superb seamanship saved everything.

But it has seemed to me at least not impossible that in those storms the original word from which the Spanish derived the word "hurricane," first impressed itself on Spanish ears.

There were Arawaks on board or, as they are called now, "Taino," Indian prisoners from Columbus's island of Hispaniola whom he was taking back to Spain. In the cold dreadful storm, perhaps the Indians cried "Hurricane." Perhaps Columbus heard the word then for the first time. He would use it often later.

There were no storms of any kind, however, in the lovely days of the second voyage when the Grand Fleet of seventeen ships and caravels sailed westward again, but farther south, to the equatorial current. The sea that can be the breeding place of hurricanes was like a silken river. The winds bore that bright company so steadily, blazing with flags and colored sails, that they must have moved in their own enchanted reflections.

The first island rose over the sea, a blue shadow, glimmering in sun haze. They passed into the blue-purple light-struck Caribbean and sailed north and westward. Columbus named for saints the islands as if he told his beads in gratitude on a great rocky rosary, Dominica, Guadeloupe, The Saints, St. Christopher, St. Martin, St. Croix and the innumerable Virgins.

Trouble began as he sailed along the north coast of Hispaniola looking for the fortress Navidad he had left there, with men from the *Santa Maria*. It was gone. He found only ruins and a few Spanish bones.

The genius of Columbus lay always in his ships. His grievous errors of judgment were forced by the necessity of bringing back gold to his sovereigns. He cast anchor within the shelter of a peninsula thick with trees, and built on a small plain by a river, thought to rise among gold-rich mountains, a new town, named "Isabella." The point of land is "Cape Isabella" to this day.

Expeditions to the mountains found some gold, a few nuggets, some worked gold leaf. The marveling Indians were friendly. Half the men were sick. Twelve sail were hastily sent home with the gold and some spices and twenty-six captured Indians.

Spaniards in small panting groups like hounds were already ranging the mountains for gold. Columbus did not check their mistreatment of the Indians. He punished the Indians for their increasing resentment. He turned with relief to his favorite *Niña*,

flagship of three light caravels, and sailed on a new voyage of discovery. He met no hurricanes but the vicious afternoon thunderstorms rolling darkly down the mountains of the Cuban south coast.
Here along the narrow shelf that drops abruptly into almost the
bluest of all Caribbean water he called a maze of lovely wooded
keys and green reefs "The Queen's Gardens." Since then they have
been ravaged by many hurricanes, and their trees are blasted silver
under the sun.

Columbus was sketching the first scant lines of empire on an
empty map. The difficult south outline of Cuba lengthened back
like his own wake. His inner vision insisted it was not an island, but
a peninsula of China. He circumnavigated Jamaica and with un-
erring accuracy traced the four hundred miles of the south coast
of Hispaniola. He met a gale that separated the other two ships
from the *Niña*, met Indians ashore, saw quantities of seals he called
"sea-wolves" basking on a sea all one polished pale steel calm. He
saw thousands of sea birds, rising and dropping down upon the
fish. His men gorged themselves. The other two caravels rejoined
him but Columbus was uneasy. The sea was burning calm or rough
with fitful wind. He was on deck all day, all night. The men could
sleep. His brooding eyes watched.

It was September, the time of hurricanes. The next day the
caravels started, and were horribly startled by, a black sea monster
leaping up out of the water, its black wings beating the foam. Its
body seemed as big as a whale, its head like a barrel. It was probably a basking shark. Columbus spoke of the old sailors' belief that
creatures from the deep often come up to bask on the surface before a storm.

He drove his caravels straight east and found the best harborage
on that coast. Santo Domingo's southern edge is walled by bluffs
and narrow beaches worn by dangerous surf. Off the southeast
point a green island loomed, among reefs. A smaller island still
makes two channels. The main channel has a least depth of twenty-
one feet, a fine shelter for all winds but the northeast. Columbus'
light caravels let go their anchors and furled sails as he watched a
host of birds from the small island rustle over, a roof of wings.

The hurricane drove in from the east. The sheltered caravels
rode as safe as ducks although gusts roughened the bay water and

blew rain like shot. The ships plunged at their cables. Men were idle, but Columbus took no rest.

They were there eight days until he felt it was safe to venture out in the running tides to the west. People from the many Indian villages stared out at the vessels stranger to them than storms. When the sun came out, Columbus took some of his officers and crew ashore for a jolly ceremony by which, with cut turf and planted cross and gallows, he gave the rich island to his Italian friend, Michel de Cuneo of Savona. He baptized it "La Bella Saonese" or "Saona," as it is today. Certainly he asked the people questions about the hurricane.

Today the thirty-seven Indian villages of Saona are gone. But, whether the slavers or the hurricanes ruined it, more we do not know.

The three caravels sailed up the rollicking blue Mona Passage safe. But Columbus broke down. He was taken ashore in Hispaniola, feverish with fatigue and the arthritis that would cripple him. But I think his sickness burned from within, with the frustration of no treasure and no passage to the fabled east. The hurricane was the last straw.

There he was then, back in Isabella, the first city of this world. It had been a frowsy village of two hundred palm-thatched huts, huddled on a sun-baked plain. There was no water. Men were already dying of sun and inadequate food. Under his stern orders Spaniards of noble birth, hidalgos who had mortgaged their moldy castles to voyage with him for riches and for God, were forced to work alongside artisans and stone masons, rebuilding in stone. They were digging a canal to bring water from the river.

Columbus's able brother Bartholemew arrived with three ships loaded with supplies. The whole island was in bloody revolt as raving Spaniards terrorized Indians, kidnaped women, and took slaves. Bitter men sailed home, saying that Columbus was not fit to govern Hispaniola, where, even worse, there was no gold.

More caravels went back and forth to Spain. Columbus rounded up 1,500 Indian slaves, articles of value, to go back in the empty ships. They all died on the voyage or in Spain.

On the island the Indians were beaten down. Columbus was ready to go home, leaving 630 men, women and children in the colony.

It was then, in June of 1495, that the first well-authenticated hurricane hit. The hurricane must have surged across the island on a long course out of the Atlantic across the Lesser Antilles and the intervening sea. The ungovernable violence of the wind was something the Spaniards, except Columbus and his old crew, had never seen before. The great tropic trees of Cape Isabella were twisted out of the rain-softened ground, crashing down in windrows. The gray waves in the bay, the gray light were flattened by the strokes of the wind from the land. Still the water seemed to swell. The vessels anchored in the harbor swung about their strained cables until they broke. Two turned over, filled and sank. Only the *Niña* survived, driven to the opposite shore. Huts were beaten into the mud. When it was over the people moved dazed among sodden debris, with the sun already hot.

In an account of this hurricane written many years later, Peter Martyr, the historian, described it as a "whirlwind." The redoubtable Father Las Casas, outraged by the brutal treatment of the Indians, declared that the hurricane was the judgment of God on the city and the men who had committed such sins against humanity.

Columbus set to work at once to clean up the destruction. From the wrecks of caravels he got enough material to build another, like the *Niña*. She was named the *Santa Cruz*. In nearly ten months he built other forts in the island and exacted tributes of quantities of gold from the Indians under pain of slavery or death. Thousands died or fled and were hunted down with dogs. That was the beginning of the end for all the Indians, on all the islands.

In Spain Columbus's reputation suffered from bitter accusations. In Hispaniola, October, 1495, four caravels arrived from Spain, under the command of Juan Aguado, instructed by the Spanish Court to investigate the charges against Columbus of brutality to the Indians. Columbus sailed home in March, 1496, leaving to the new governor the task of building a better city on the south of the island, at the broad mouth of the river Ozama. So that Santo Domingo city, after historic centuries renamed "Ciudad Trujillo," resulted also from that hurricane. Isabella was left in ruins, haunted.

On his third voyage, Columbus, sailing westward on the equatorial current, on a blue "lady's sea," made his landfall at Trinidad on August 1, 1498, skirted the coast of Venezuela, and was convinced a great continent rose there beyond, if he had had the time to explore it. In Hispaniola, after he had put down a rebellion, his enemy Francisco de Bobadilla arrived with authority from Ferdinand and Isabella to investigate the charges against Columbus. The great Admiral was clapped in irons, and with his brother Diego ordered back to Spain for trial.

Other men of less vision, as he met the accusations of his enemies, were sailing to that west on which his great double vision had been fixed.

Martin Alonso Pinzon, captain of the *Niña* on the first voyage, was a man eaten up with envy of Columbus. He had stolen away from the returning fleet to get home first. The storm that was not a hurricane drove him north so that when he landed in Spain, the bells were already clanging for the triumph of Columbus. Martin Alonso died of his bitterness.

His more durable brother, Vincent Yañez Pinzon, with powerful backing from Columbus's enemies, in the spring of 1500 sailed with four small caravels and a crew of neighbors and friends. He discovered South America at the great bulge of Brazil, and in July rediscovered the low Bahamas. There, without seeing any of the signs, the gray scud going over "low, low, low" as the Bahama people say to this day, or heeding the crying of the birds, his ships were overblown by a hurricane that swallowed up two caravels as a third broke its cable and vanished forever among the hissing gray crests. From the fourth Vincent Yañez and his crew managed to lower away the boats and get ashore, to cling and gasp among broken mangroves, where a few Indians hung, as beaten as they.

In the sun next day one lost caravel, white with salt and weed, came back. They sailed to Hispaniola and so home to Spain, with no treasure but 350 quintals of brazilwood.

Columbus's reputation suffered when such men came home empty-handed from what had been expected was the treasury of the fabulous East. He was aged by more than his fifty-one years. He asked humbly to be allowed one more voyage and was granted four caravels with 140 men. But he was forbidden to put in at Hispaniola, where his enemies were, until he was on his way home.

His last command for the familiar crossing, now thronged by other ships, where already Portugal and Spain, and soon England, France and Holland, were wrangling with the Pope for ownership, was "west by south." He followed the route of hurricanes in lovely weather and after five days among the islands picked up the well-remembered landfall of Saona.

Diamond clear, the river mouth at Santo Domingo opened before him. The blue sea heaved like oil. He saw the round dark heads of seals basking on the clear surface. Long swells from the southeast began to overtake his slow ships in a sunset all copper and blood. At twilight a little rain whispered across his decks.

The Admiral summoned to his cabin his devoted Captain Diego Tristan. "We must put in at Santo Domingo," he said, and gave him letters to deliver to the Governor. "There will be a hurricane."

By dawn, under a sky glittering with fine high streaks of clouds, they could see ships crowded in the wide river, small boats coming and going, masts bright with banners. The Captain rowed in to the Governor. The Admiral of Ocean Sea asked shelter for his ships. The fleet must not sail because of the approaching hurricane.

Don Nicholas de Ovando, the Governor, laughed in the Captain's face. Let the old Admiral sail on. The harbor was closed to him. As Columbus's caravels moved on westward the first of the home-going fleet streamed out of the harbor and turned into the murky east, brave with colored sails and flags and crowded decks and music playing.

The triumphant Bobadilla, Columbus's greatest enemy, sat in the place of honor on the flagship, among the merry nobles, priests, malcontents and returning adventurers. They would all be rich in Spain with the gold all the ships carried, because of the new system of slave labor, and from the Indian slaves packed below decks. Bobadilla's ship alone carried 200,000 castellanos' worth. The smallest and least important ship of all was taking home four thousand pieces of gold which was all there was left of Columbus's island property which his faithful man of business had managed to pry out of Bobadilla's clutches. The brilliant fleet turned to beat up into the gathering shadow of the Mona Passage.

In two days the hurricane struck. The vast winds circling from the northeast blinded and blotted them out with rain and spume blown off the racing waves. One by one the tall overladen unwieldy ships heeled over. Sails cracked and vanished. Masts toppled in a snarl of rigging.

Some men knew only briefly the ship breaking on rocks. Some

knew only the choking water. The flagship, with its gold, its merry nobles, its captives and Bobadilla in his velvets, was broken and forever lost. Ninety vessels vanished, and five hundred men.

A few, three or four perhaps, the last to move beyond Saona, were taken aback and, bailing and praying, managed to return to the river. Only one small caravel rode the hurricane and fled home. It was the *Aguja* with the gold pesos consigned to Don Diego Colon, in Spain. That money kept Columbus in comfort to the last forgotten days of his life. People said he had put a spell on the storm, so that his own ship was saved.

But it was not by spells that Columbus saved his own life and his men and his ships. It was because he was the first white man to learn about hurricanes.

As he sailed west the winds came howling on him over the island from the north or northwest.

By that time under a rolling jostling low hurry of clouds and the light gone and the rain like a river, over the ghostly sucking and rising of the sea, Columbus was anchored in a western bay, snug under the cliffs. The men who had been grumbling because they had been denied a good drunken fling in the city were silent in deafening darkness. The anchors of three caravels were torn loose and the black sea took them.

Columbus's anchors held his flagship safe. He thought he had lost everything, ships, his men, his brother, his son.

By dawn, the sky lifted clear beyond the last torn clouds. The sodden decks steamed in the first heat. Columbus walked there lifting his scalded eyes to stare into the sweet and steady wind from the southeast. The drying sails leaped up the masts. The anchors, to which he had added everything iron on board, came up with a will.

Columbus had appointed a place for the fleet to gather if they were separated, a small harbor within what is now Ocoa Bay. They rounded into it on Sunday, July 3. The anchor was let go in blue water, all calm, all sparkling. Three battered caravels crept in. Every man was safe. It was a miracle, an omen of divine favor. Behind him, in the same hurricane, the small city of Santo Domingo had been mashed flat into the mud.

In a way it was his last triumph.

2 DISCOVERIES

Columbus was never to know how near, on that coast, he came to the passage to China.

His wretched caravels beat their way seaward along the rugged outline of Honduras under high winds that are often hurricanes. For twenty-eight days and nights the aging Admiral bucked the deep rolling northward current, bucked the iron winds. Rain and thunder roared like doom. Sails split. Food was rotten. Salt water cracked the men's bleeding hands. The Admiral was ill with arthritis and malaria, ill with the suffering of his young son and all the men. Nights when they tried to lie nearer the muddy shore line, mosquitoes and sandflies bit them until they bled.

They struggled around a bold headland. Beyond, as the land curved southwest, the winds were behind them and the current carried them sweetly along. "Thanks be to God," they said, and Cabo Gracias a Dios it is to this day. The green seas spouted fountains, breaking among the islands, within which were glassy lagoons where the caravels could rest at anchor.

South still, below mountain jungles, a great bay opened, where now the world's ships stand in toward the entrance to the Panama Canal. Indians brought them fruit and pearls. Ashore, the Spaniards were enraptured with the sight of gold lip- and ear-plugs, breastplates of beaten gold. They heard the rumor of much gold beyond. Columbus pushed south, to a harbor he called "Puerto Bello." But there was no rest. December was dreadful with storms. They turned back.

Afterward there was the Jamaica shipwreck, rescue and oblivion, before the greatest man of his time got home.

The Spaniards who followed him in exploring that coast of Central America he called "Veragua," which became the title of the

Dukes, his descendants, learned what hurricanes were like by living through many of them. Roderigo de Bastidos had survived the 1502 hurricane that wrecked the fleet from Santo Domingo. Diego de Nicuesa lost a small ship there in one after he discovered the fine harbor of Cartagena. What were left of his crew were the first men to push on foot through the heat, the rocks, the cactus, the mangrove jungles of that coast to a wind-assaulted harbor. "In God's Name," they said, "let us stay here." So Nombre de Dios began.

The smell of gold over that land beyond the roughest sea brought Spaniards as thick as blowflies to the colony of Darien, brawling for control. Nicuesa, the self-styled first governor, was forced to sail away with some of his men in a crazy small brigantine. Some said they were eaten by Indians. Some said they were lost in a hurricane.

The favorite leader of Darien was a thirty-five-year-old noble, redheaded, high-hearted Vasco Nuñez de Balboa, who had escaped his debtors in Hispaniola by getting himself smuggled on board a Cartagena ship in a cask. He was a just man, friendly to malcontents and the Darien Indians. He called himself governor.

Balboa sent a man named Valdivia to Hispaniola with bribes to get his election made official. He never heard of Valdivia again in the years he spent hunting for treasure and a great sea they told him about, to the south. His brigantines, loaded with gold, were lost in a hurricane in the Gulf of Uraba, but neither storms nor his enemies rioting in Darien stopped him.

On the morning of September 29, 1519, he started down a path leading from the village of Chiapas high among the mountains, from which he had stared out over a far glitter that was an unknown ocean. Hours later, he and his gentlemen plunged into it from a muddy beach and drank the salt water greedily in their cupped hands, taking possession of the Pacific that would be called for a long time "the Southern Ocean."

He insisted on sailing out on it, although the Indians warned him that the ocean was dangerous in the months of October, November and December. Their crowded dugouts were wrecked on a rocky island where they clung through a terrible night, with the sea bellowing at their heels. In the morning, when the hurricane had blown away, they got to a southern shore. Balboa made friends

with strange Indians and was given rich presents of worked gold
and pearls from oysters thrown up by the stormy winds.

To the south, the Indians assured him, lay the golden country.
But the winds were dreadful. Balboa had had enough of them. So
he turned back. It is hard to imagine how different the fate of the
Incan empire of Peru would have been, if the able, just and intelligent Balboa had discovered it and not his ruffian underofficer,
Pizarro, who despoiled it. Perhaps Balboa would not have met
treachery waiting for him in Darien where presently they cut off
his head and set it up on a pole in the plaza of the city he had built.

But Valdivia, whom he had sent for help seven years before because of another hurricane, had made a great discovery without
knowing it and suffered a more dreadful fate.

Valdivia was a plain, plump, dependable official in a world of
adventurers. When he sailed from Darien for Hispaniola it was the
wrong season of the year. The caravel beat with difficulty against
the roaring trade winds in a squally sea. The captain of the ship
rolling in the thick night refused to be alarmed, insisting that the
southwestern cape of Jamaica was near. Sometime after that, under
a great wall of blackness, a wind hit them like a falling cliff. They
could do nothing but run before it, hoping to keep off the Jamaican
rocks. The hurricane must have been moving in a long curve northwestward, for the caravel was driven by the winds circling counterclockwise north under the rocky belly of Cuba.

The tumultuous darkness went on raging for hours. Then the
caravel was lifted up and dropped, jarring men from the decks like
fallen logs. Rock splintered its keel. The decks slanted and were
still, under exploding walls of waves.

When the darkness thinned a little they heard the captain's shout
like a faint cry. The ship was going under.

Valdivia and eighteen shuddering wet men, all there were left,
got off in the gray light in a boat. They had no sails, no food, no
water. A tide rip between rocks and islands carried them out into
the dirtied open sea.

Some seamen, looking back to the place where the last bows of
the caravel were being broken up, recognized the reef. "Los
Viboras." "The Vipers." Columbus had called them "The Queen's
Gardens." They were a mass of broken and uprooted trees.

The last winds of the hurricane carried the helpless boat into the long current that hurries past the Isle of Pines, past Cape Corrientes, to the brooding Yucatán current. The last of the storm whistled away over the lost men.

The boat turned west as the sun came burning out over the gentle blue sea. In fourteen days six men had died and were thrown overboard. Twelve lived, burned black, starved, raving with thirst. They lived through surf on a line of sunblasted coast, trees heavy over low rocks. They floundered ashore. When the heat dried them they blinked salted eyes to see what no European had ever seen before, the still unknown coast of Yucatán.

Ashore they were seized by breechclouted copper-colored men, strong and stocky, with broad faces under coarse black hair. Their eyes were a little slant in flattened foreheads. They had long curving noses and some wore nose plugs, not gold. The Spaniards were not frightened. Valdivia, no longer so portly, recovered himself as an officer of the Crown. They were given food and water and were marched through deep forests, that opened into sunbaked scrub; two especially, a soldier, Gonzalo de Guerrera, and the young man, Geronimo de Aguilar, a bookish thin chap with keen eyes, who had taken holy orders in Spain but had come out to the fabulous West not as a priest but as an adventurer.

They moved with crowds of people, streaming among huts of a city. There were stone streets filled with people in clean white garments, or trotting under enormous burdens. Ahead were incredible stone buildings going up enormously, rectangles topped with pyramids, pyramids marked by vast ascending staircases. It was a city more strange, more unbelievable, than any Spaniard had ever dreamed of.

They were shut up in painted cedar cages. Some lordly official came to stare at them, a copper-colored man, breechclouted and sandaled. There were gold bracelets on his arms. He pointed at Valdivia, and Valdivia, as became his position, looked back at him haughtily.

Valdivia was allowed to move freely around the courtyard and was served much fine food. Later when he was feeling quite himself again and plumping out, men came and painted him, and four other Spaniards, bright blue from head to foot, evidently an honorable color.

The other seven, including Aguilar and Guerrera, were striped

with black and white and fed well. Aguilar spent his time learning
to talk with their guards.

Early in a morning, other men came for Valdivia and the other
blue-painted ones and set peaked headdresses on their heads. They
let them out into a great plaza where they walked proudly among
the white-clad, dark-faced, smiling people. Valdivia had been given
a drink that made everything splendid. He was aware of gold flashing everywhere and men under headdresses of floating white and
green and scarlet feathers, all set in gold.

Ahead there was a ridged wall of gray stone going up into the
sky. The ridges were steps. The men helped him, respectfully, to
begin the climb. The going up was endless. He glanced up once, his
heart throbbing. It was as if the whole stone sky were pouring down
on him. He was urged upward again and went as proudly as he
could.

He saw rank after rank of white-clad people silent on all the roof
ledges below him, packed on walls, massed on platforms. High up
in the wind he could look far out over the pyramids and temples to
a land level and yellow-green, under moving purple cloud shadows.

They marched him forward to a low stone, among clouds of incense. He could hardly believe the horrible figure that came toward
him, a man whose hair and face and body was stained with old
blood. He saw little else than sun as they threw him backward suddenly, holding his arms and legs, over the sacrificial stone, as the
flint knife chopped down. The priest tore out his heart and held it
up to the sun as the people roared. It was glistening and still beating.

He was the first Spaniard ever to be sacrificed to the gods of the
new world, even, perhaps, one that had begun more humbly as a
god of winds and hurricanes. In that moment they, too, began their
long slow dying.

Back in the cages, Geronimo de Aguilar had learned enough of
the Mayan language to find out what had happened to Valdivia.
The seven escaped southward. They were recaptured near another
great stone ceremonial place but not sacrificed, only made slaves.
Five died. There were left only Aguilar, who had been a priest, and
the resourceful soldier, Gonzalo de Guerrera. They knew the nature of the country now, that there were wars between chieftains

earlier of an empire falling apart. Gonzalo made himself necessary
to a war lord, Nachan Can of Chetumal, the city within a bay of
the forested southern coast. He married his daughter, raised a family. He was a powerful person in that province, tattooed in the
Mayan manner, nose, ears and lips plugged with gold, gold and
jade about his wrists, and over his head a headdress floating of the
green and gold feathers of the sacred quetzel.

Geronimo de Aguilar remembered that he had been a Christian
priest. Yet he served the lord Taxmar with great humility, to keep
his heart beating within his own ribs. It was rumored at least that
other white men in fantastic ships had been seen along the Yucatán
coast. But that was many years later.

3 CITIES AND CONQUESTS

History seems sometimes to pause at the beginning of a great changing action, as if men's minds must have time to grasp the past before
they can go on actively into the future.

In the first twenty years or so after Columbus' discovery of that
brilliant sea, small crowded caravels, singly or in quarreling twos
and threes, were already poking along the coast of South America
and the islands. By venturing only a little farther than Columbus,
they found treasure.

Here and there on the islands whose high jungles and dripping
green ravines they ranged for gold, they set up a few crude villages
along bays where their caravels were anchored. They were no more
than huddles of thatched huts, mosquito and sand-fly infested. Only
the ships careened along some beach were important.

No white man after Columbus gave thought to hurricanes that
only Indians dreaded. They were unaccountable acts of God. Religious men like Las Casas saw in their ruin the sure working of
Divine Justice for the horrible crimes committed against the dying

Indian race. Yet once the dead were buried, the village rethatched, the ships repaired that were not lost, men forgot, sure that no such storm could ever happen again.

Hurricanes were helping or hindering explorations even as the first towns, like Isabella, were abandoned because hurricanes demolished them.

For a while the ruins of the first Santo Domingo lay among the scrub and cactus of the east bank of the river Ozama, where a few small masonry buildings had housed nobles and officials. Soon nothing was left standing but the "Torcilla de Colon" the tower where Columbus was supposed to have been kept in chains. Later hurricanes have left there no trace of any town at all.

The city was moved across the river where it still stands. For a few years it was the capital of the western world, at first only a helter-skelter of Indian huts with a few solid buildings of timbers and limestone. The Spanish Crown that had the growing empire in nets of red tape, licenses, special privileges well paid for, tariffs and taxes, had already laid down such rules for building the cities that their harmonious charm would persist through the ruins and hurricanes of all these centuries.

All important buildings must be set about a central plaza, with shade trees if possible. The life of the whole people focused there, the settled citizens and their families promenading in the sweet evening winds with the sound of bells, or in the blazing noons the adventurers to and from the ships following drums to farther conquests. The plaza of Santo Domingo early attained the dignity that expressed the whole feeling of the Spanish, that life and cities must be noble.

Yet for many years thatched huts crowded along the streets leading to the plaza, no more than footpaths or horsemen's tracks. In the first years the thick-walled cathedral had only a thatched roof, through which the rains dripped on the candles, the altar and the congregation. In 1508 hurricane gusts from the turbulent sea to the north smashed across the newly planted canefields, tore off the thatch in one dreadful moment and beat the walls into lanes of running mud.

Another Ovando, Nicholas the Governor, set himself to rebuild the city with wider streets, paved with limestone, thick stone and mortared walls of newer buildings and a fine small castle called "El

Homenaje." No hurricane has battered it down nor time itself brought it to ruin.

When Diego Colon, the son of Columbus, became the next Viceroy and most powerful official of the western sea, he added monasteries, an Archbishop's palace, a fine palace for the Governor and a new cathedral planned like a Roman basilica. It was not finished for thirty years. But four centuries of hurricanes, crashing down over the forgotten place to destroy lesser houses have not brought the El Homenaje or the cathedral to ruin.

Soon after, on the more accessible south coast of Cuba, on a fine bay cut deep under the lift of mountains, a greater city was begun and named "Santiago de Cuba," and later by the King dubbed "most noble and loyal." It became the gathering place for the greatest expeditions. Farther west, the next year, the city of Trinidad was built of Moorish-Spanish buildings around a plaza, now ancient, that hurricanes have never changed.

An impatient excitable young man with brilliant and searching eyes, lately come out of Spain to seek his fortune, had the job of directing the paving of Trinidad's principal streets and the Plaza de Sarran with small smooth stones. He had a big plantation outside, which, with his allotment of Indians, he worked hard to make pay. But how could farming and street paving long satisfy Hernando Cortes?

When Columbus was stranded without help for a year on the northern coast of Jamaica his men built a village called "Sevilla" on St. Ann's Bay, against the pitted limestone hills hung and matted with jungle. Spanish plantations spread along to Butter or Montego Bay, then up the mountains and along the southern shore. Santiago de la Vega or "Spanish Town" was set inland of the great harbor under the loom of the Blue Mountains. Spanish Savannah-la-Mar would know the tramplings of many hurricanes between the sea and the rising slopes where many a sensible Spaniard was content with gardens and cattle and fruit trees and cane patches. Even now, in the hills, the black Jamaican peasant makes his small house hurricane proof of "Spanish walls," double walls of timber or wattle packed tight with red clay filled with heavy stones.

Ambitious Ponce de Leon, in 1511 given the governorship of Puerto Rico, set his town on a small half-connected island. Not finding gold, he discovered a vaster wealth in Indian slaves. They did not last long under his ruthless exploitation. He resolved to explore lands he had heard of to the northward, setting sail on the third of March, 1517. East of the Bahamas he found America that he thought was another island and named "Florida" because it was the season of Pascua Florida or "The Festival of the Flowers."

They sailed south and fought Indians and filled their water casks in what is now Biscayne Bay and sailed up the Florida west coast, after touching at Cuba. Then they sailed east from Biscayne Bay again, to islands on the edge of the Bahama Banks from which already the slavers had taken all the people but one old woman.

Juan Ponce was already worn out and disgusted with the expedition that had brought him nothing when they were overtaken by a hurricane coming up so suddenly that a bark from Hispaniola that had joined them was wrecked, although the people were saved. That was enough. He sailed back to Puerto Rico no richer than he had set out, but planning another expedition to take Florida from the savages, who would be the death of him.

On the Isthmus of Panama and the immediate coast of South America, now known as "Tierra Firme," or the Spanish Mainland, there were a few haphazard malarial turbulent Spanish camps, and Balboa's town of Darien.

Pedrarias Davila, who had had Balboa killed, crossed the Isthmus and laid out a town and plaza on the Pacific, the dramatic city of Panama. From there, murderous squads of men moved out to extort gold and pearls by tortures from the Indians.

Indeed, as the Spanish frontier grew, the Indian world was dying. The first pearling village among the Margarita Islands off the coast of Venezuela was destroyed by one of those rare hurricanes that sometimes blast through that southern sea. It was never rebuilt, because all the Indian divers were dead of cruelly forced diving. In other places, some Indians saved their lives by escaping into impenetrable mountains. The free Caribs of the Lesser Antilles, the free savage Glades Indians of Florida, learned to watch for Spanish galleons as they watched for hurricanes. Only the teeming heights of Mexico were still unconquered.

A whispered word reached Geronimo de Aguilar, Valdivia's comrade, still a slave in Yucatán, that a cloud of Spanish ships were sailing along the south coast. He escaped to them. It was Hernando Cortes with his great fleet from Santiago de Cuba and the new

Cuban harbor of San Cristóbal de la Havana. Gonzalo de Guerrera, his lips, ears and nose pierced for gold plugs, tattooed from head to foot, could not bear to go back like that or leave his Mayan family. But Aguilar, with the Aztec-speaking Mayan girl, Malinche, Cortes's companion, as co-interpreter, became the man most responsible for friendly relations with the Aztecs, without which all Cortes's amazing conquest might have failed.

He landed with Cortes on the barren northern coastal plain of Mexico, under the far loom of mountains, at the first village of three to be called "La Villa Rica de la Veracruz." The second, behind a rocky island shelter, would be fortified, not always successfully, against recurring attacks by men and hurricanes.

Francisco de Garay, governor of half-settled Jamaica, had reached the river Panuco, where Tampico was built. And in the same year, 1519, when Cortes landed in Mexico, Lucas Vasquez de Ayllon sailed with two caravels for the Bahamas looking for slaves. He saw none; saw indeed no signs, in the bright calm sparkling day before, of a hurricane building. But the dark clouds came racing over and the terrible gusts of hurricanes followed, driving his small vessels north up the wind-harried Gulf Stream, up the long low coast of Florida hidden in gray smother. Ayllon was thrown helplessly up on the east coast somewhere. He called the province where he landed "Chicora" and the cape "St. Elena," and met Indians very different from those he had known in the West Indies, powerful independent Indians, but friendly.

The ship of another man, Juan Bermudez, was blown by a hurricane up along that strange north coast not yet called America, and out into the Atlantic. He was wrecked, but lucky to find himself alive on a rocky island covered with wind-gnarled cedar trees, among others lonely in the rough Atlantic. They were "the Bermudas."

Again, Francisco de Garay, anxious to colonize the coast he had discovered and called "Panuco," set out for Cuba from Jamaica, with 840 men and 36 horses, in thirteen vessels. He left Cuba late in June. No one paid any attention to the time of year. A wild hurricane blew them off their course, over to the long western coast of Florida. Two ships and their crews were lost. He found a river he called "Rio de Palmas." The land was poor. He left his ships to explore the coast westward. This was in 1523. The hurricane that delayed him was fatal to his fortunes. Hernando Cortes had already taken over and settled the province of Panuco, which is now Texas. Garay's soldiers mutinied against him. In Mexico, the unlucky man, or the ignorant, died.

Now the news of Cortes's magnificent conquest, of the teeming stone cities of the heights and their wealth more fabulous than any European imaginings, had swept back to Spain with every returning ship. It burst like an explosion through the courts, the city streets, the very wineshops of every harbor, of Portugal, France, Italy, Holland and England. What Columbus could not do to arouse the old world to his tremendous discovery, Cortes accomplished. The multitudinous face of Europe turned westward.

4 *THE TREASURE FLEETS*

Squadrons of arriving sails filled the river mouth of often-hurricaned Santo Domingo. New men crowded the streets and plaza with loud talk of Mexico. But because Cortes was master there, the hotly ambitious turned their minds to the new land to the north. Where there must be gold, there were certainly slaves.

The most important expedition in many years then left Spain. Its appointed Governor-Adelantado and Captain-General was a red-haired, one-eyed, hollow-voiced man of unsound judgment who had served three years under Cortes and hated him for it. But bombastic Panfilo de Narvaez did one intelligent thing. He took as treasurer the noble Alvar Nuñez Cabeza de Vaca.

Five caravels bright with banners, each crammed with 120 men-at-arms, priests, eager young men who had paid their own passage, made a difficult voyage, June to August, 1527. From the filthy crowded ships, hunger and disease killed off all but 180 men. In Santo Domingo over one hundred deserted.

There Narvaez took on more men and sailed to anchor his ships in the incomparable harbor of Santiago de Cuba, where the cliffs were already marked with the first fortresses. His quarreling gentlemen hurried to climb to the delights of the plaza. But Cabeza de Vaca, with two caravels, sailed along the Cuban coast to the charming city of Trinidad where horses would be cheaper. Its narrow cobbled streets rose up a hill along a shallow river giving poor harborage from the sea.

Early in November a hurricane loomed enormously out of the sea, vaster and darker than the mountains. Under the greeny-gloomy racing clouds the gusts blew over with the shaking sound of cannon. Rain scoured the stony channels of streets. Men assaulted by wind and solid sheets of water kept themselves from falling only by linking arms eight abreast and bracing themselves from wall to wall. Roofs, tiles, church walls, towers, doors, housefronts, trees, crashed down soundlessly in the pandemonium. Spaniards who lived through their first hurricane there said that in quieter times between gusts or in the calm of the vortex they could hear the Indians, packed into some safe building, all night long howling and beating drums, jangling tambourines and shaking rattles to frighten away the hellish demons who had called up the hurricane.

In the glaring sun of the day after there was no city on those slopes, only muddy wet piles of stuff beginning to stink. Along the shores wreckage lay in windrows, tree branches, rags, bodies without faces. Of Cabeza de Vaca's terrified men, sixty were never seen again.

Of Narvaez's ships, only four were left. It took months of hard labor to get the expedition going. They landed somewhere on the west coast of what is now Florida and read the decree of ownership to an empty beach. Narvaez sent his 300 seasick men into the interior with the horses that could keep their feet, to subdue Indians. He never saw the ships again. One ship was wrecked. The other three cruised the coast waiting for him. He never came back.

The expedition struggled northward to Apalache and the Bay of Horses, following Indians who told them about gold beyond. Narvaez ordered crude barges to be built and they all put to sea in them on September 20. A storm that must have been the tail end of a hurricane separated them. Eighty men landed on an island that has been said to be the present site of Galveston, Texas, and died of hunger. A barge foundered on the coast. At midnight winds came up with such fury that Panfilo de Narvaez and two companions, on another barge, were swept out to sea and drowned. Others ate their dead, and died.

Only Cabeza de Vaca and four more were left to wander for months along the coasts of the Gulf of Mexico, eating roots and fish with the miserable coast Indians. Cabeza healed Indian diseases by miracles of faith, as his awed companions believed. For nine years they suffered and wandered two thousand miles into Mexico, where Cabeza was the first to write about the great Gulf like a pale sea where hurricane waves overrun the sandy bird-haunted islands and the barren shores.

In Spain news had just arrived that Pizarro had taken the amazing empire of Peru. The first treasures—gold, silver, pearls and emeralds, had come by way of Panama and the rocky Isthmus to Nombre de Dios and the King's waiting ships. No attention at all was paid to the news from quiet West Indian islands that hurricanes were ruining the first vineyards and plantations deserted by men crazy for the Peruvian splendors. Such storms were only single catastrophes, unheard of today if some careful priest or official or hungry visiting writer had not set down in crabbed Spanish how men died in the waves and the angry winds.

The news from Peru brought crowded ships and crowds of new men to build new cities on the unguarded western coast of South America. By the mouth of the Magdalena River that in a few years would lead men to the right heights of New Granada, the first small port was called "Santa Marta." Just east the fort at Rio de la Hacha guarded the pearl fisheries for the King's pearl ship. Most important still, to the west, on one of the finest natural harbors of that imposing coast, in 1530 Cartagena was founded. In wealth and gray granite, in harmony of proportion and use, in richness and leisure of living and the warm regard of kings, Cartagena for centuries would be the focus for the amazing Spanish kingdoms to the south.

Its warehouses would hold the incoming goods of all Europe that would make the Spanish civilization of the New World ornate, elaborate and pampered as it gathered in for the return to Europe every sort of goods the mountain kingdoms could furnish and the almost endless silver of the mountain of Potosí.

Cartagena has never felt a hurricane. Still in its ancient harmony untouched by them, it looks out north and west to the murk of some hurricane lifting out of the huge Bay of Colombia and always going away.

Already because of the increasing dangers of pirates lurking off Cartagena and the coasts of gold, and the dangers of uncertain weather and hurricanes, the clumsy Spanish merchant ships, carracks and naos, were forbidden to sail alone from Spain to the West Indies or back again. They had to sail together in flotillas, a few of them armed. Not long after this ruling a royal armada of armed galleons was sent from Spain to bring home safe the treasure pouring from the mines and the pearl fisheries and all the growing revenues and taxes from the prospering cities.

In 1533, three years after Cartagena was established, Puerto Rico was struck by three savage hurricanes. The developing canefields, worked by quantities of Negro slaves, were devastated. So many slaves were killed in the destruction of the twenty-sixth of July, August 23 and August 31, that the three hundred Spaniards left set up a great clamor to the Crown that they must be allowed at once to buy more slaves from licensed Portuguese dealers. Slave labor was required for increasing canefields in Santo Domingo. Slave labor rebuilt the city, with masonry walls fifty and one hundred feet across the peninsula, set with fortresses.

A single French ship slipped by Cartagena to storm the Chagres River and its store of treasure. Other Frenchmen cut out nine lumbering Spanish merchantmen from a fleet leaving Nombre de Dios. It was the same year, 1537, that Puerto Rico was flattened again by three terrible hurricanes in two months, July and August.

De Soto's expedition took other Spaniards on his wide, blundering, wandering discovery in the northeast, and to the Mississippi. There he died, never knowing what he had found, except that there was no wealth such as Peru's. But the rumor of an endless land of forests spread back quickly to France where the powerful force of the Reformation had released men's minds for new horizons. French pirates in hordes began to haunt the trade routes of the Caribbean and the harbor entrances to prospering Spanish cities.

San Cristóbal had been a town on the south coast of Cuba. It had never amounted to much. Now its name was transferred to the north, "San Cristóbal de la Habana." At once caravels and small ships found shelter from the pounding trade winds. Buildings were set about the plaza as narrow streets moved out to rich red country, where Spanish planters cleared and cultivated.

Ships that had ventured from Santo Domingo along the rough northern waters to the Atlantic south of Bahama reefs and so called "The Old Bahama Passage" had sunk in many a hurricane. But it was the pirates who leaped out at them from the rugged coast, and took ships and treasure, and killed men, who made the old passage too dangerous. Now out of Havana, past which the currents pour from the Yucatán channel and the Gulf of Mexico as if they poured downhill, ships began to sail with the strong current past Florida, into the Gulf Stream across the Atlantic and so, by the great circle, home to Spain. The press of ships and new business and a Cuban countryside developed by the labor of African slaves, made Havana as great a seaport capital as Cartagena and Veracruz.

In contrast Santo Domingo, devastated again by a great hurricane in '48, never regained its former importance. What citizens were left cleaned up the debris, rebuilt their houses and finally put a solid roof on the cathedral from which the old thatch had been blown away. Most men went away, many to Veracruz in New Spain, behind the island fortress of San Juan de Ulloa, drawn by increasing tales of treasure flowing down to the ships. It came not only from the fabulous teeming cities of the heights but from across the western ocean and the Spanish Philippines—pepper, spices, silks, ivories, and diamonds from China.

A small pirogue, or even a raft with sails, packed with half-naked French pirates, would overtake some laggard ship, to swarm up its main chains like steel-fanged rats. The fat Spanish merchants and landowners would squeal and run helplessly until they died on the decks in their own blood. Their neck chains, their fine cloaks, the bales and treasures below would be taken. The ship itself would become a pirate ship.

The galleons developed to protect them had taken the place of Columbus's fast, handy caravels, not so much ship as fighting sea-castle. Their decorated stern castles rose up in five or six narrowing, slanted tiers, topped with lanterns. Over the broad bows the forecastles stood up almost as imposingly. There was little deck room at the waist. The heavy foremast from which the great foresail bellied had a queer forward pitch. The great mainsail, the lateen mizzen were singularly hard to manage. When any sort of wind caught those great wooden superstructures, top-heavy with cannon, the whole ship was as likely to sail sidewise as forwards, or be so pitched and tossed in the deepening troughs of storm waves that often the masts were rolled out of them.

The galleons carried great fire power. Their supreme advantage was gained by closing with and grappling an enemy ship to pour fire and red-hot shot downward on its exposed decks, its guns, its men. Their unseaworthiness made them the most unforgettable victims of the devious, surging Caribbean currents, its reefs and shoals, its unmarked coasts, but above all, of its hurricanes.

But to Don Luis de Velasco, the Casa de Contratacion, which was the all-powerful royal Chamber of Commerce, and to the Spanish Crown, the galleons were the answer to the problems of piracy.

The New Spain fleet was to be sent in the spring to Veracruz. After they crossed the Atlantic by the familiar southern route and entered the Caribbean south of Dominica, single ships sailed direct with supplies for Santo Domingo, Puerto Rico or, later, for Honduras, guarded by two galleons, the "capitana" and the Admiral's flagship, the "almirante."

The second was the fleet for Tierra Firme which sailed dangerously from Spain in August, guarded with six or eight armed galleons. They moved southward to the Galleons' Passage, north of Trinidad. Single vessels, preceded by runners along the coast, put in at Santa Marta and at Rio de la Hacha, for the pearls. The merchant ships waited at Cartagena. The galleons, with some cargo ships, sailed to the Isthmus of Panama and the fairs, first at Nombre de Dios and then at Puerto Bello, where men from every Spanish province on the Pacific were crowded in those muddy malarial death-traps to buy the goods unloaded from the ships. All the treasure of Panama and Peru, and then of Chile, silver ingots banked up carelessly around the plaza, were as hastily loaded into the galleons rocking on the turbulent water.

Treasure from new provinces in the cloudy heights above Cartagena filled other ships in that harbor, like those at San Juan de Ulloa, rocking all winter long in the warm tropic water, their seams blasted open by sun, their keels and strakes trailing green weed.

All the galleons and the ships they herded, at first about twenty but later on a concourse of as many as ninety sails, were supposed to meet in March in the harbor of San Cristóbal de la Habana for the time of fiesta and big business, banquets, high masses, and processions, that was called "the Conjunction." After that, all the ships, overcrowded with a great company of people and goods, streamed out into the blue light of that sea, banners stinging the sky with color, bright sails painted and blazoned, gilt work glittering while cannon pounded from the fortress and all the city fluttered with farewells.

The difficulty was that, with one delay or another, the fairs, the celebrations, the confusions and waste of such an enormous project, with the variety of bad weather possible to those rough and windy coasts, above all, the panic-making rumor of pirates lurking beyond, the Conjunction at Havana was rarely complete until much later in the year than March. July saw the ships still streaming in to Havana from the west around Cape San Antonio and down the west coast of Florida where the Flota from Veracruz sailed to catch the west winds off the land and the south-going current. It was often as late as September before the Captain-General of the Galleons gave the word for the departure from Havana.

The delay was often deliberate. By this time the French, the English, the Dutch sea-rovers had had plenty of experience with the incredible Atlantic-Caribbean storms they all called hurricanes. The English particularly had a healthy respect for their incredible release of force. So that, as the hurricane season was understood to be approaching, more and more pirates went home or laid up their ships in some strong harbor until the last hurricane had blown itself away before the dry, cool, tropic, sparkling winter.

The Spanish people of the coasts and islands had for centuries faced the beginning of the hurricane season, the visits of those "storms of the four winds" with superstitious terror. They believed them to be the work of devils out of hell and a foretaste of the destruction of the world.

The full rites and powers of the Catholic Church had therefore for centuries been called upon to oppose the stormy devils. Oviedo, an early Spanish writer, stated that since the Holy Sacrament had been placed on altars throughout Santo Domingo, hurricanes had not happened there. He wrote too soon. Later, the Holy Sacrament was carried in procession through the streets of many Caribbean cities when hurricanes threatened. A special prayer was offered in certain islands in the months when they were most subject to hurricanes, August and September in Puerto Rico, Cuba in September and October. It was called "Adrepellendas tempestates" or "To repelling tempests."

The leaders and directors of the great Spanish fleet system were less afraid of hurricanes than they were of the English. Therefore the fleets were ordered to sail, with masses sung in all the Cathedrals, the blessing of ships, without which the sailors would not go on board, the incense, the chanting, the pealing of bells. Perhaps that year a hurricane would not strike. Perhaps if it did, the ships would survive.

Since hurricanes are frequent everywhere in the once Spanish islands of the West Indies in October, the month dedicated to Saint Francis of Assisi, a whole body of legends and lore grew up which invoked against the evils of hurricanes the powers of the humble and beloved saint whose brotherliness encompassed all nature. It was believed that he used the knotted cord around his waist to drive away the devils of the storm. Knots became important, as perhaps they had always been since the Greek god Eolus tied up the winds in a great bag. So knots were tied to control the hurricane. The "cord of St. Francis," a little rope of three knots with three turns apiece was displayed in many houses in the dangerous season. Or knots tied in the dried fronds of palms blessed on Palm Sunday. Prayers to St. Francis were held to be especially effective in the season of the autumnal equinox.

For the same purpose, the descendants of African slaves in the West Indies tie up under their rafters bundles of certain leaves, as they tie up branches of trees that have been struck by lightning, to avert thunderstorms. "Saint Francis of the Hurricane," as he is often called, has become a lesser deity of great power in the Congo cult, called "Tata" for "saint," "Pandu" for "Francis," "Kimbungila" for tempest. His symbol, too, is the knotted scourge.

So, in spite of all the fear of hurricanes, protected by the help of the Church and all its rites, the fleets every year were ordered to sail in the hurricane season. The hurricanes came. The ships were wrecked. They say that a ship was sunk for every mile of that unmarked, hurricane-threatened Florida coast. But somehow, some ships, some men, much treasure, got home.

5 *FLORIDA AND THE WRECKS*

We would know less than we do about the early wrecks and the fate of thousands of men cast away with them, if in 1546 a single ship from New Spain, in some storm unknown but for that, had not been wrecked on a Florida key. Among the merchants and grandees taking home their wealth, it carried a remarkable boy of thirteen, Domingo Escalante Fontaneda. With his brother, his rich parents had sent him from Cartagena, by way of Veracruz, with twenty-five thousand pounds in gold, to pay for their education in Spain.

The overcrowded ship was driven in a hurricane on one of those mangrove keys. In the furious blackness many people were drowned, including Fontaneda's brother. The survivors pulled themselves up here and there among broken trees to the littered sands. They saw tall Indians coming at them, the fierce, rangy, muscular, copper-brown people of the Florida Keys, who from their mounded villages watched for Spanish wrecks.

They wore only some kind of plaited palmetto breechclouts, with raccoon tails behind, to sit on. Shell ornaments hung clinking from their belts, and their black horsetail hair was pinned up on their heads with carved shell pins.

They searched among the wreck for metal, iron and steel, hatchets, knives, kettles, nails. They saved the spilled coins, the minted gold bars, the silver ingots, the gold plates and necklaces, the temple ornaments and the curious gold figures set with turquoise and jade and rough emeralds.

All those huddled white people and the loot were taken northward in canoes to a village on a wide bay by a river called "Mayaimi." The village was called by the same name as the chief, a huge brown man sitting on a log among his wise men as all the others stared and pointed. His name sounded like "Tequesta."

Working as slaves for the Indian women, many Spanish people died of heartbreak and homesickness. But not bright-eyed young Escalante Fontaneda. He had been quick to learn Indian words, quick to do what he was told, merry and cute. When they told him to dance, he danced like anything and they laughed and liked him for it, letting him live as they did, brown as an Indian.

He saw ship after hurricane-wrecked ship taken on the Keys or the long sandy east coast and the captives brought in to the village to face the cold eyes of the chief. Fontaneda's whispered Spanish gave them hope. He saved all that he could from being clubbed to death. But again and again, in the great annual ceremonies, he was forced to watch them led to the top of some temple mound and burned to the greater glory of the sun, the giver of power.

He saw a Spanish captive named Don Pedro Vizcaino, whose ship was wrecked in the bay by the river Mayaimi. Later, the bay was called "the bay where the ship of El Vizcaino was wrecked," or "Bay Biscayne."

Shortly after Fontaneda was captured he must have been surprised to see wrecks of Spanish ships that were laden entirely with small silver ingots, from the greatest silver discovery in the New World, the almost inexhaustible Silver Hill of Potosí.

He must have heard with sorrow the news from the west coast Indians that a strange Spaniard in a long brown gown, wading in with crossed sticks in his hand, had been killed by one blow of a war club. It was Fray Luis Cancer de Barbastro, coming to save Indian souls. The ship from which he had landed, returning in grief to Havana, was blown to the Mexican coast by a hurricane of that year of 1549.

The young Fontaneda had a good life with the Glades Indians, learning for the first time their unique civilization, which had no metal tools but only heavy shells with which to pile up sand mounds for protection against high water and to dig canals through the mangroves for shelter from hurricane winds and waves. He learned to know what hurricanes were like over that flat shape of land, where the endless acres of saw grass were flattened under the whistling sea winds and the leaves and birds flew before the steely gusts, as they do now. The Indians huddled wretchedly among the wrecks of their platform houses.

Afterward, as the battered birds drifted back to lagoons littered with trash, and the raccoons and deer poked timidly out of their shelters, the Indians rebuilt their mounds and their platform houses, burying their dead in silent places far away from the renewed human cheerfulness of their villages. To them, it was all part of the evil to be averted by sacrifice and prayer for power from the Master of Breath.

Rescued and in Spain years later Fontaneda wrote the first known account of these early Florida Indians, to whom he felt no gratitude. They were all heathen, he insisted, who should be taken and shipped away as slaves, so that Spaniards could colonize their land and protect the people and ships sailing past on the blue strong current.

The same hurricane that wrecked on the Florida Keys the people captured after Fontaneda, about whose death he wrote, brought about the strange voyage of the great galleon *San Miguel* that had brought to Mexico from Spain the new viceroy, Luis de Velasco. For the voyage home the *San Miguel* was packed and jammed with too many people, too many goods, besides its crew and a company of men-at-arms guarding the King's Fifth of all the treasure of the New World. It would save the King from his debts and losses to the increasing menace of French pirates.

The *San Miguel* sailed up the Gulf of Mexico, the honorable last of a long convoy of ships. After the first week of sun they were lost in the murk and winds of two storms. Her mainmast broke and her opened seams drank salt water. The half-wreck drifted for weeks, in which changing currents carried them helplessly here and there, within sight of Cuban mountains or the reefs of the Bahamas. A sudden gray northeaster forced them to try to sail back to Havana, past the frightening Martyrs. That wind flatted out and they talked of trying to turn back toward Spain.

What the wretched people were worried about was the safe delivery of the King's bullion. Then came another wind, a murderous true hurricane. The rudder broke. They prayed and threw over all their goods but the King's. The ship was breaking up in the seething darkness.

Yet she lived, a floating wreck hung with seaweed, salt glittering where once there had been gold leaf. The emaciated people had the eyes of sleepwalkers, staring at the calming sea. They struck on a reef. The tide worked them off, lower in the water.

They saw land and could not speak. The Captain sent a boat. A caravel rescued them, first taking off the King's treasure, nine boxes of bullion to be sent home in a safer ship.

Of the other ships that had sailed with them, weeks before, the leading ship from Veracruz sank in that hurricane that caught up with them at Bermuda. Twenty-five survived, with enough gold to save the feeble King from bankruptcy.

The next year French pirates swarmed west of the Azores and France and Spain went to war again. Ships were taken like puddle ducks, and undefended peaceful cities about the Caribbean burned and looted and ravished.

The tale of wrecks in hurricanes went on, every one with a different story.

An enormous fleet carrying one thousand people, about which a priest had prophesied doom as he went on board, sailed from Veracruz. One passenger was a rich widow convicted of having murdered her lover. A hurricane carried them up the west coast of Florida, where all the ships and treasure were lost and the three hundred survivors began the terrible march around the Gulf to Panuco.

All the women and children died, including the murdering widow. The few naked men left took refuge from Indians in long grass, from which they were driven out by fire ants for the Indians to kill them. The survivors drowned trying to swim the last river. Only a priest, Fray Marcos, lived, half-buried in sand and rescued by friendly Indians he thought were angels.

Some people believed that the hurricane struck because there were priests on board, some, because of the wicked widow.

Part of the treasure was salvaged when the war was over, in time to be of use to the new King of Spain, energetic Philip the Second, who agreed with the viceroy, Luis de Velasco, that the Spanish seas could not be kept free of pirates and the mainland of savages unless the North American coasts could be taken and settled.

They remembered that province called "Chicora," with its port, Santa Elena, to which a hurricane in '26 had blown the discoverer, Ayllon. The King ordered that both coasts must be held and settled, the Gulf Coast first.

In 1559, therefore, orders came by which Don Luis set up a great expedition to take and hold that country. Captain-General of the fleet, and the new governor of Florida, was Don Tristán de Luna, a rich elderly widower who mortgaged his estates in Spain, because, as usual, the Crown provided no money from its own coffers. Don Tristán was ambitious, conscientious, brave, if pompous. He gathered, in New Spain, a motley population for his ships and the new settlements, five hundred soldiers, many of them untrained and rebellious, and one thousand assorted colonists.

At Veracruz they crowded on board thirteen beautifully dressed vessels, already loaded with supplies and 240 horses, and sailed on June 11.

For seventeen days the ships sailed pleasantly upon the winds, until they reached the longitude of the Mississippi River. Abruptly, a wind rose that drove them south to the Alacrán Reef, off Yucatán. When the wind was favorable again Don Tristán directed them to sail northeast to the Bay of Miruelo, thought to be Tampa Bay, and on July 17 sailed west looking for the port known as Ochusa.

On August 14 he entered a bay and named it "Bahia de Santa Maria Filipina." It was the finest port yet discovered. There was a high reddish bluff on the eastern side. The town was to be set on high land overlooking the anchorage.

Before any boats could sail with the good news, however, on the 20th of August a hurricane blotted out their world. All the ships in the churned harbor were heeled over, washed out, drowned in seething white. Hundreds of people were killed.

Less than a thousand escaped, including Don Tristán, although it made an old man of him. When the bay was sweet blue again, he found one caravel, high on a bluff, dry and trim as if it had been picked up and put there by demons. Everything else was ruined. It was the end. Don Tristán remained but the people were hungry and angry.

A supply ship brought orders from the King, in triplicate, to give up all idea of a Gulf Coast settlement. There were too many hurricanes there. What he wanted now was a stronghold on the Atlantic, at Santa Elena. "And so I command you," the King wrote.

Poor old Don Tristán in desperation sent out one small fleet, two frigates and a bark, under an inexperienced nephew of his, to go around Florida, now thought to be a peninsula, and find Santa Elena. The fleet was overtaken by a hurricane and wrecked on Yucatán. The settlement was abandoned that would have been, but for that hurricane, the first city of what is now the United States. Two hundred years would go by before the present Pensacola would be established there.

The stories of all these losses and disasters came constantly to the ears of Philip II. He faced the fact that Spain had not been able to set up a single outpost or hold one foot of ground in that northern continent he called "Florida."

The nation of the envious daring French was growing stronger. They had long since sailed to the rich cod fisheries of Newfoundland, and claimed those cold coasts for France. The French would be in Florida soon.

6 *FRENCH INTRUDERS*

Philip of Spain was right. France of the Reformation was passionately anxious to snatch the control of that long Florida coast line from Catholic Spain. In 1562 powerful Admiral Coligny sent out an expedition of Lutherans under the first French seaman of his day, Jean Ribaut. He came from the city of Dieppe on the channel. He was forty-two, magnetic, shrewd, well-educated, often pigheaded, but always daring.

One hundred fifty seasoned soldiers, all passionate Lutherans, set sail from Dieppe with a tiny fleet on the 18th of February to a place called "Newfoundland." As the translator of that time wrote in English the equivalent of Ribaut's French, "Albeit the wynde was for a long tyme verye much against us and troublesome, yet at the end God giving us through his grace and accustomed goodness a favorable wynde, I determined with all diligence to prove a newe course which hath not byn yet attempted, traversing the seas of the oction 1800 leagues at the least which indede is the true and short course that hereafter must be kept, to the honour of our nation. . . . God, by his onlye goodness, hathe given us grace to

make the furthest cut and traverse of the seas that ever was made in
our memory or knowledge in longitude from the east to the west.

"Thursday, the last of Aprill at the breke of the daye, we discovered and clearly perceaved a faire cost, stretching off a great
length."

So they made it, having as far as we know sailed across south of
the Gulf Stream and found land at 29°30', although their latitudes
were not accurate. They landed in Florida somewhere near Matanzas
Inlet. They discovered the river we know as the St. Johns and
called it "River of May." Ribaut set up a column by which he
claimed all that coast for France. North from there, within green
islands deep with oak and dogwood, he found the Broad River of
South Carolina, set up another column at Port Royal, left a settlement called "Charlesfort" with men totally helpless to keep alive
there, and sailed for France.

On the Florida coast they picked up Escalante Fontaneda, who,
after twenty years with the Indians, resumed his interrupted journey
to Spain. It is highly likely that what Fontaneda told of the French
invasion of Florida reached the King in time for him to take action.

Philip needed a leader. In all that kingdom of Spain in America,
now a world of fat officials and taxes and regulations of every sort
of trade, there was no one able to carve a Spanish foothold on the
Florida coast. Except one man in prison in Seville, the great Admiral
Pedro Menéndez de Avilés, denied by his enemies all communication
with the King. He was still raging in prison in the fall when one of
those great convoys of laden merchant ships sailed from Havana,
under the Captain-General, Pedro Menéndez de Avilés the younger,
his son.

A hurricane was boiling up out there in the Atlantic. Years later,
someone spoke with a Florida Indian who wore a necklace that
might have come from one of those ships. That was all that was
ever known of them.

In France, Coligny determined to hold Florida. Jean Ribaut was
in England—in jail or out of it, helped by the English or not, it is
hard to tell. For the moment the war was over between the Catholics
and Huguenots. At least in Europe. Coligny sent René de Laudonniere to the Florida coast where the Spaniards had already knocked
down Ribaut's column and burned Charlesfort. Laudonniere set a

fort called "Caroline" on the river about where Jacksonville is today.

So Jean Ribaut, in France again, sailed for Fort Caroline with four companies of arquebusiers, laborers, women and children. Six hundred people. His flagship *Trinity* led the *Emerillon*, the *Pearl*, three Dieppe transports with provisions, the *Leviriére*, another *Emerillon*, the *Shoulder of Mutton* and the *Trent*. They carried eighty-one pieces of artillery.

They arrived at Fort Caroline on August 14, and a few days later landed in such small vessels as could get up that leisurely river, leaving four large ships with few men aboard, anchored a mile off shore.

At the fort they were building, a man cried out. Men ran to look. Five high-towered Spanish war ships moved at the river mouth, between the fort and the anchored French ships.

"Who goes there?" a Spanish voice shouted, as the famous story goes.

"France."

"You are in Spanish territory. Get out."

"Who is your general?"

"Pedro Menéndez de Avilés."

There he was then, the man the King had sought out to make Florida, once and for all, Spanish. High on his galleon, he was a grim great figure in his armor, his velvet, his stars of office—Pedro Menéndez de Avilés, seaman-adventurer, pirate fighter from boyhood, war leader, admiral, passionate doer of the King's will, passionately Catholic.

Over all the swarming political captains and corrupt colonial officials, over the lords of the Council of the Indies, the King lifted him from prison to the supreme command of Florida, the Newfoundland fisheries, the coasts, the rivers, the passage to India. He was, however, to conquer and hold it at his own expense. In the first year, the enterprise would cost him a million ducats. But in July, as the news of Ribaut's new venture came to him, he sailed from Cadiz with only eleven ships.

On the twentieth of July, full in that southern course along the equatorial current, the fleet was overtaken by a monster hurricane.

The winds were a solid screaming force by which sails, masts, men, out of their wits with terror in the violent dark, were blown away. One ship lived through the blackness from Friday to Monday noon, not seeing any other.

When it was over three ships limped into harbor at Puerto Rico. Two more came in the next day. With five hundred soldiers, two hundred sailors and a hundred colonists, the Adelantado drove on to Florida.

So now, before Fort Caroline, what there was left of Menéndez's fleet found the French. A French ship cut its cables, made sail, exchanged a few shots with Menéndez, and by adroit sailing got away to sea. Menéndez returned from chasing it to find the whole French fleet drawn up to oppose him, many more ships than his.

He sailed south to a good harbor within sheltering islands and sandbars. It was nearer than Fort Caroline to the northward surge of the Gulf Stream that here widens away from Florida. He named it "St. Augustine."

Ribaut, at Fort Caroline, ordered every man on board and with all his ships, four large ones and eight smaller ones, sailed to attack Menéndez before he could entrench himself.

This is the moment when a hurricane, perhaps more than any other, changed the course of American history. It was the nineteenth of September. No man of all these, French or Spanish, or even the Indians with whom the French were in touch, saw anything to indicate a hurricane was drawing near.

Few hurricanes have ever struck from the Atlantic that coast of Florida at St. Augustine and Jacksonville, from the east. They usually come across by the back door, blowing in nastily overland from the Gulf of Mexico.

This hurricane seems to have moved like that, west to east by north, an irresistible slashing wind, and rain, solid torrents of rain, rain hurled in level sheets like glass with broken edges, fine rain, harsh rain, stinging rain, rain as white and cold as hail. Rain. And more wind.

Now it is clear that Ribaut's forces were superior to the remnants of Menéndez's fleet. Ribaut, in courage, quickness, daring, seamanship, was the Spaniard's equal, if not perhaps in authority and in the grim steeled drive of the Spaniard's purpose. Success depended entirely on chance. That was the hurricane.

The Spaniards saw the French sails stand outside St. Augustine. In the same hour they saw the first gusts darken the bay, the wind begin driving the fine rain, the gusts strengthening, the white water of hurricane swells racing and smoking up the outer beaches.

The center of the hurricane must have hit just about there. The whirling wind struck from the north. The helpless French ships were swept down the coast.

It was then that Menéndez struck his blow. He was sure that Ribaut had risked all his men on the ships, leaving only a handful to guard Fort Caroline. It was a long, difficult, rain-sodden struggle to get there, through swamps and tangled scrub and across rivers, where the highway goes so straightly to Jacksonville now. But he and his five hundred men got there, on six pounds of biscuit and a canteen of wine apiece. He took the fort easily enough, killing one hundred and forty-two. Some escaped to the two vessels left and sailed for France.

Menéndez sailed back to St. Augustine in a ship he had sent north, although his own fleet was badly damaged and some were lost. Eight days later he learned there were Frenchmen wrecked on an inlet and long island now called "Matanzas." Matanzas means "massacre." There, where the bleak naked dunes rise white and sunblistered, the starving Frenchmen saw the Spaniards coming. As they surrendered, their hands were tied behind them. They were marched along the dunes and were shot, every one.

Jean Ribaut and many others of his men in his flagship had been driven on other shoals. His masts had gone by the board. This may have been farther south on Matanzas, or Daytona Beach. They tried to get north to Fort Caroline. There again Menendez found them, sodden, injured, miserable and starving, but still with fire in their eyes.

When he asked, "Are you Catholics or Lutherans, and are there any who wish to confess?" all but a few said flatly, "We are Lutherans."

Jean Ribaut began to sing a hymn. Their hands were bound. Ribaut was stabbed and his head was cut off. The rest were shot.

By that one stroke of brutal, undeclared warfare, for which a hurricane gave the opportunity, Menéndez took Florida. If France had been able to grasp and hold the Atlantic seaboard, it is impossible to imagine what the history of the United States of America would have become. As it was, in the Caribbean, life for the Spanish at once became more dangerous. French pirates at once increased their robbings and burnings of undefended Spanish island cities and their attacks on laden vessels on the fringes of the armed fleets. Many Frenchmen who had escaped Ribaut's fate in Florida were hiding on the east coast, inciting the Indians to greater savagery against the Spaniards and their ships. The provinces of the Spanish main and the islands, strangled with royal restrictions, could do little to defend themselves.

Against all this Pedro Menéndez de Avilés, Admiral and Adelantado of Florida, was the dominating figure of that world. That extraordinary force he had, the supreme Spanish quality they called nobility, compounded of brilliance that was almost genius, unsparing energy, utter devotion and imperious ruthlessness, was directed entirely to making Florida, from the Mississippi to the Chesapeake, a great Spanish kingdom. By controlling it, he meant to bring the souls of Florida Indians to God, to develop its gold mines, fill it with Spanish cities, and make its most dangerous coasts safe for the home-going wealth of the New World.

At once, he put down the mutinies of discontented Spanish soldiers in St. Augustine, and got the fortifications going. He proceeded swiftly against the few Frenchmen at Cape Canaveral, took them, fed them, marched them down the coast, charmed the Ais Indians and left men building a fort at Santa Lucia or St. Lucie.

In November he was returning with two small vessels, fifty soldiers and some Frenchmen to Cuba. They must have been caught by the edge, not the full force, of a hurricane which even then was surging slowly up on its curve from the Windward and Leeward Islands. Menéndez snatched the long tiller from the frightened helmsman and by ordering his sails taken in and finding the inshore current, brought his ship in safe, down the Straits of Florida.

In Havana, he had other troubles. He had no more money of his own and the jealous governor refused him any for the starving forts of Florida. But as he was borrowing money from his wife the rest of a hurricane-scattered armada came in, commanded by his friend Esteban de las Alas, seventeen ships with men and food and equipment, with letters from the King to Menéndez.

His first concern was to study in calm weather the dangerous channel between the Florida Keys and the Dry Tortugas, to make Florida safe for the ships, especially in hurricane season. Carlos, the fiery, sensitive chief of the west coast Indians called "Calusas," dominated all the tribes of lower Florida and the Key Indians, the salvors of wrecks. Menéndez sailed to impress Carlos with his flag-dressed fleet, the scarlet and armor of his soldiers and his own majestic presence. Carlos saw the point so clearly that he swore friendship with Spain and embarrassingly offered the thoroughly married Menéndez his sister to wife.

He was forced to make the long voyage around Cape Sable and up the east coast quickly, on receiving word that dissatisfied soldiers were mutinying at Fort Santa Lucia, at San Mateo, which had been Ribaut's Fort Caroline, and at St. Augustine itself.

Menéndez asked for priests to convert the Indians to peaceful acceptance of Spain. The King sent three Jesuit missionaries who were wrecked by a hurricane on the Florida coast and walked north to try to find St. Augustine. Father Pedro Martinez was killed by Indians. Menéndez rescued the other two and sent them to convert the Calusas of the lower west coast. He set up forts in Guale, now Georgia, in Orista, now South Carolina, and San Pedro on Cumberland Island.

It was not until 1568 when Menéndez had gone back to Spain and was appointed Governor of Cuba, which then included Florida in its jurisdiction and paid him two hundred thousand ducats toward his expenses, that he sailed back to Florida with ten more missionaries. The Spanish superstition that priests were unlucky on board ship was proved again, for they were overtaken in the Atlantic by vast waves and dreadful winds from which his ship just managed to save itself. The priests insisted that it was by their prayers that the hurricane spared them so that they came into Havana harbor at last over a tranquil sea, rose-colored by a tremendous and quiet sunset.

Dominic de Gourgues, a powerful and independent Huguenot, sailed the direct route to St. Augustine, burned it to the ground and killed and hanged the soldiers. He could not hold it. Menéndez rebuilt it and strengthened his line of forts and tried to establish missions. Still French pirates haunted the Caribbean.

And in the world from which the treasure was all that kept Spain victorious in its unending wars with the Turks in the Mediterranean and its garrisons in Italy, a new kind of invasion by a very different people from the French began, on whose fate hurricanes would have their unrelenting effects.

7 *ENGLISH VENTURERS*

The wealth of America was safer for Spain by the control of Florida, but the Crown itself was strangling the economy of the western kingdoms with red tape. It refused to provide the clamoring people with more than small quotas of goods at high prices, goods such as flour, clothing and mercury necessary to their canefields, mines, tanneries, plantations and industries. Above everything the New World people demanded they be allowed to purchase more Negro slaves to replace those constantly dying of hard work. Equally importantly, the Crown refused to allow the provinces free and competitive trade with other European nationals, which would have made them all prosperous.

At home, the flood of gold and silver was floating Spanish prices to a dangerous inflation. There was increasing unemployment among the people.

The Crown had goods delivered to governors of colonies, who resold them at big profits for themselves. In consequence, all officials were hated and the island and seacoast people learned to get what they needed by trading with smugglers.

England of the young Elizabeth was too weak still to dare so bold a venture as Ribaut's against Spain in the West, or for piracy and landgrabbing. What England wanted, and needed, was work for men and ships in the way of trade.

The free merchants of English ports like Bristol and Plymouth knew very well, from English merchants allowed to trade in the Canaries and Lisbon, how often the Spanish-Americans begged the Crown for supplies they so badly needed to buy. It seemed to the English Queen's Privy Council that Spain could be convinced that English trade for sugar and hides in the Caribbean would be profitable to everybody. The unprotected Spanish colonies, the unarmed

Spanish merchant ships, could be protected by English guns from the increasing ravages of French pirates.

In fact, the prospects of good trade by sea and perhaps a little treasure burned in the breasts of English merchants and idle young seamen as the passion for treasure and for saving souls had burned in the hearts of Spanish conquistadores and discoverers.

In none was that passion more intense than in a rich old Plymouth family of shipowners and sea captains by the name of Hawkins. The family had power at court where the tall-boned, red-frizzed, still nervous young Queen, her long fingers snapping with jewels, listened intently to men from the guilds of cloth merchants, flour millers, ship chandlers, dockmen, and all the others clamoring for work.

The rich Caribbean market for slaves was going begging. If the Portuguese had established excellent relations with West African tribal chiefs anxious to sell their war prisoners, why not the English? The merciful Spanish priest Las Casas had convinced Isabella of Spain that Negro slaves imported into the New World would prevent the deaths of countless Indians. Elizabeth of England saw nothing wrong with the common European practice of slave-dealing.

John Hawkins, the ablest of the sons of that well-to-do Plymouth family, had proved himself resourceful in a trade voyage to the Canaries. All the Hawkins ships were always clean, seaworthy and well found. John Hawkins hated the wasteful practice which crammed ships with too many men so that more than half died of bad water, rotted food and filth below. The pride of the Hawkins was to keep their men as well as their ships able.

The pictures of John Hawkins in his early days show him ruddy, his blue eyes wide open, his dapper beard and moustachios not hiding the merry quirk of his lips, a man ready to sail far and fight hard for a fair profit.

His first venture was backed by high navy officials and London business interests. With his own family ships and one or two loaned by the Queen, he sailed as the Queen's officer, under her flag. He captured Portuguese slavers or dealt for slaves with African middlemen. He did a brisk trade with West Indian islands. He paid customs duties in additional slaves and traded all his cloth and flour for pearls, ginger, indigo, sugar, and hides. On a later voyage, nervous officials of certain islands and cities off the coast of South America begged

Hawkins to put up some show of forcing them to buy, with some harmless shooting off of guns. For that, and the quality of his wines, flour, clothing and strong Africans, he was given certificates of character, and often banqueted. But the Spanish government never gave its permission to English trade.

An unexpected strong sea current pushed him up the Yucatán Channel and the Florida Straits. He dropped in to help the starving French colony at Fort Caroline. When he got home with his profits, the Queen and all his noble shareholders were delighted. He sent out three trading ships with his young cousin, Francis Drake, as an officer, and Captain Lovell, who was not so careful not to act like a pirate. But as a loyal official wrote back to the Spanish court, neither fines, threats nor regulations could stop the colonists from buying secretly what they so much needed.

For his third venture Hawkins had the most impressive shareholders. The Queen let him have another navy vessel besides the leaky, impressive old galleon, the *Jesus of Lubeck*, which suffered in a storm just beyond the channel and from fighting off the coast of Africa.

In February, 1568, Hawkins sailed west with his unforgettable ships, the *Jesus of Lubeck*, the *Minion*, the *Swallow*, the *William and John*, the *Angel*, Francis Drake's *Judith*, a captured Portuguese caravel, the *Grace of God*, he had bought from a Frenchman, and two cargo ships. Four hundred and eight English names were listed aboard including certain humble ones which the fortunes of this voyage were to keep unforgotten, among the thousands of nameless seamen who would suffer in desperate centuries on this bloodied sea. They were Job Hartop, a gunner; Miles Philips, a boy of thirteen; and a man named David Ingram.

Trade was brisk at the first cities along that steep Venezuelan coast, governors amiable and the people happy, with good English cloth and African slaves and because the well-armed English ships kept off pirates. There was a little trouble at Rio de la Hacha but Hawkins paid with extra slaves for the houses that took fire. He stayed there a month. It was all right at Santa Marta, too. After a fake attack the governor let him trade and gave him a banquet.

But at Cartagena its grim military governor ordered its grim forts to fire and Hawkins sailed away. In eighteen years Francis Drake would storm and take that white Spanish city.

Outside in a glassy sea where no wind blew, the fleet swung wakeless. Hawkins had eight empty ships left. One was the *Jesus of Lubeck*, with her seams opening in the baking sun. It was July, time to go home. The time for hurricanes.

John Hawkins hoped the same strong current might carry him around Cuba, and east, northeast and by east, in two months, by the Gulf Stream, home.

But the seas were roughening under the trade winds. Some disturbance in the rushing upper air troubled the stiff sails, streaked the rising greeny black waves with livid foam. Men shivered in the chill, staring up at cloud scud tearing over fast and low. There was the sharp rattle of rain on wet and bucking decks, the sting of sharp drops on sunburned English skin. It was the middle of August and the empty ships yawed and reeled as the men hurried to take in sail.

Slow dark waves foamed up behind them, rolled them forward and glassily, weightily, went by. In the driven middle of the Yucatán Channel the wind was a solid hurrying force, with voices yelling and screeching in it.

It has been said that that storm was not a hurricane, because John Hawkins' ships were still manageable. It could have been nothing else but a hurricane there, at that time of year. Probably the eye with its devastating winds was not immediately upon them, and caught the English fleet with its reaching waves and outer wind bands.

They were vicious enough almost to wreck the old warped *Jesus of Lubeck*. Hawkins and his crew worked frantically to strip her of canvas, but the planks of her stern opened and shut with every sea she careened to. Water spouted inboard. A man said he could see fish swimming in the ballast.

Her helm was put hard down so that she ran before the wind, west. The *William and John* beat to windward and disappeared toward England. Six other vessels fled with the old flagship. They were stopping her leaks with cloth, and kept the pumps working. It would have been easier to abandon her. But she was a ship of the Queen's navy and the honor of the Hawkins family depended on his bringing her back safe.

The fleet was blown somewhere upon shoals of a northern coast of the Gulf of Mexico. For three days more the counterclockwise outer winds of the hurricane blew them from north toward west across the Gulf.

At last, the raving sea grew quiet. Hawkins spoke a Spanish ship who told him the only decent harbor of the long Mexican coast, fifteen miles from old Veracruz, was within the island of San Juan de Ulloa. The Spanish fleet from Spain was expected there the first of September. Hawkins took that ship and two others with him, to prevent their outsailing him and raising an alarm. His desperate hope was to repair his ships and get away at once.

Elizabeth's royal standard at the masthead of the poor old *Lubeck* was faded and salt-bleached but it flowed bravely in the calmer air. The storm-flogged English ships rounded the famous island of San Juan de Ulloa, only 240 yards long. Its beach had been cut down steeply so that ships could lie rail to rail like hooked fish, lashed ashore to great rings in the rock and anchored astern. Over them at the top of the dune the blank mouths of a few cannon bellowed suddenly in salute.

When the echoes and the smoke had blown away the dismayed captain of the island made out on those small decks rows of grimy, hungry blue-eyed English faces. He took to his boats hastily, leaving John Hawkins master of the situation, the island, the cannon and eight heavy Spanish merchantmen already tied there, quiet as fat sheep. He asked only to be allowed to buy food and water and time to repair his ships.

His luck was holding, he must have thought, taking a look around from the *Lubeck's* high stern castle before turning in for the first good wink of sleep in weeks. In the luminous tropic dark he could peer along the decks, eased now in starshine and lantern light. The after-supper voices of the off-duty watches mumbled quietly. The watch, the deck officers moving in the streaked shadows, could look down at the black water that merely joggled the close-packed hulls. The Devon crews, the men of Plymouth and Bristol whose fathers had sailed with his father could look up at Hawkins there, against lantern light.

The fierce eyes of his headstrong young cousin, Francis Drake, watched, hooded with his own thoughts. Among those hundreds of forgotten men Job Hartop the gunner, the boy Miles Philips, and David Ingram were only three of all of them thinking of home.

It was the last peaceful night some would have in years. For many, it was the last of all.

The hot tropic morning glared over the guns and the English ships alive with men at work in the rigging, loud with hammers. The channel tide glittered. A lookout screamed.

There turned majestically a huge Spanish galleon. It stood high and dangerous as a fort, with its gun ports open, under the canvas painted with kings and angels, its scrollwork glittering gold, gold on the officers' uniforms on the high deck about the Viceroy of New Spain. Beyond, the whole fleet waited—eleven unarmed Spanish merchantmen heavy with cargo and thick with people. And another great galleon beyond that. The trumpets snarled under the sky rippling with Spanish banners.

Hawkins' men waited by the island cannon, slow matches alight. The gunners of his six armed ships were crouched ready. His position was strong enough to have blown the Spaniards to splinters. But as an officer of the Queen and a familiar of navy councils he knew he was not here to start a war with Spain.

He sent officers to speak politely to the outraged Spanish Viceroy, promising he would leave as soon as his ships were ready. He asked the Viceroy to give pledges that they would not attack if allowed to enter. The Viceroy had not fighting men enough. He sent Hawkins a letter full of promises and gave and accepted hostages. But a messenger to Veracruz brought soldiers aboard secretly by night, to all the anchored ships.

The Spanish fleet entered the channel some days later while Hawkins' caulkers and riggers, his carpenters and his sailmakers, were working desperately. From the twenty-eight ships packed tight under Hawkins' island batteries, Spanish and English crews had begun to fraternize. But John Hawkins thought that from the Spanish ships an ominous activity was sounding. The Spanish gun ports swung open. The Viceroy answered Hawkins' protest by swearing on his honor he had no idea of firing.

On board the *Lubeck*, as Hawkins sat down to dinner, a Spanish hostage was caught in the act of drawing a dagger. Hawkins rushed on deck, saw a Spanish ship closing in and shot an arrow at the Vice-Admiral. Spanish trumpets screamed and gunbursts thundered.

The incredible fight, deck to deck, went on for six hours. Hawkins ordered the *Minion* to clear and fought off the boarding Spaniards.

The Spaniards overwhelmed the English at the island batteries. Hawkins ordered the *Lubeck* and the *Minion* off shore, bringing their guns to range. They sank the Admiral's ship, burned the vice-flagship and a merchantman. The Spaniards sank the *Angel*, the *Swallow* and the Portuguese caravel. Drake in the *Judith* got clear and stood by outside. Hawkins began to reload supplies from the useless *Jesus of Lubeck* to the *Minion*. As the Spanish sent down a fireship, the English, Hawkins last, went overside into the *Minion* which moved away with the *Judith*. The night glared with burning ships and the end of all English hopes for peace.

Many Englishmen died. Twenty-nine Englishmen and two Frenchmen were captured and taken to Spain, where some died in prison, hungry and suffering. Two were burned alive by the Inquisition. Four died as galley slaves.

But that was not all, either. Hawkins in the *Minion* with 200 men had practically no food. Francis Drake in the *Judith* sailed home and left him, without a word. Hawkins' hopes of getting the leaky heavy-burdened *Minion* home across the Atlantic were bad. Ninety-six men begged to be set on shore. Hawkins landed them somewhere on the coast of the Gulf of Mexico, with goods for barter, and so left them.

Once more on the way home John Hawkins and his men, starving and dead on the battered *Minion*, forced by high winds off course, faced Spanish capture off Vigo Bay. Hawkins put on the best he had, standing tall and amazing, gaunt, glowering, defiant, in scarlet velvet, scarlet leather, silver braid and long gold chain, and roared at the officials sent to capture him. He scared them out of their wits. So he got home at last, with fifteen men left, famous.

The story of that hurricane of John Hawkins, which changed the course of history for the English in the Caribbean, went on for years more, in the lives and suffering of unknown and humble men.

Of the men he had left on the coast of Texas, where so many shipwrecked men had already suffered, some went south and were captured by the Spanish at the new settlement of Tampico. Later they were freed to live as they chose. In 1571, however, the Spanish Inquisition came to Mexico. Hawkins' Englishmen were re-arrested and examined. Many were condemned to be burned alive, first being half-strangled. Many were lashed and sent to the galleys for as long as twenty years. The boy Miles Philips, imprisoned at eighteen for ten years, was sent to Spain to be tried by the Inquisition there, but he managed to escape and so got back to England.

All the others died but the unkillable Job Hartop. He wrote his extraordinary story at last and Mr. Richard Hakluyt printed it in his great work of making the New World known to the English people, *The Principal Voyages and Discoveries of the English Nation*. Hartop listed his twenty-three years of suffering by imprisonment: in Mexico, two years; in the prison of the Casa de Contratacion in Seville, two years; in the Inquisition House in Treana, one year. Twelve years he served in the galleys, and lived. Four years he was imprisoned "in the everlasting prison remediles." He was a slave for three years until 1590, when he was helped to escape in a Flemish boat that was captured by an English galleon. So, by Christmas, he came home.

No story of all those of Hawkins' men, however, is so little known or had such far-reaching effect as the extraordinary long walk of David Ingram. Twenty-three of Hawkins' men, put ashore on the Gulf Coast, did not go south. They began to walk northeast. Years later, Ingram and two others, Richard Browne and Richard Twide, appeared in Nova Scotia. They were the first Englishmen, almost the first white men, to travel across deserts, rivers, mountains, through the continent of forests, in cold, heat, rain and snow, attacked by hunger, disease, Indians and, surely, despair. An English ship took them home. At first, Ingram's story was told only to a few. Then a few more. Then what he told about that enormous land began to have an amazing effect.

It is true that David Ingram's story has been doubted. They said such a journey was impossible. They said he reached a nearer coast and was picked up first by some other ship. That is not important. His stories of North America kindled a growing excitement in England for the new land.

In the meantime, John Hawkins had returned home in his single battered ship, with the ruin of his hopes and the sorry remnant of all his courageous crews. He petitioned, begged, argued and bribed to get free those men still alive in Spanish prisons. As they came home their tales of suffering blew up the smoldering rage of Protestant England against Spain into a fire of ruthlessness. It was a long effect for a single hurricane to have worked.

When France was not at war with Spain, she called home all her important privateers or pirates. England was not yet strong enough for open war but from that time on English pirates, lesser and greater, began to stream out to the Caribbean with Elizabeth's tacit permission, to carry on a kind of unacknowledged guerrilla warfare by burning cities and ships and to take treasure.

In the years of blood and gold, the myriad and terrible drama which burst upon the Caribbean then, when no cities, no ships were safe, the catastrophes wrought by hurricanes seemed unimportant. Yet recorded or not, they were there, as inevitable as the sun glaring and the winds flowing over the waters of that troubled sea.

8 THE SPANISH ARMADA

Hurricanes troubled the first Spanish garrisons, the farmers and Jesuit missionaries set where the French had built their forts, among the magnolias and oaks on the pleasant river islands of Georgia. The rivers wander among green marshy tidelands to greener sea islands fronting the Atlantic. The Spanish settlers complained of great winds and high tides that drowned their pigs and washed away houses and gardens. The devoted Jesuit Fathers could not keep the Indians within sound of the mission bells in the dangerous season.

The first known hurricane in Georgia was recorded in letters of Father Sedeño and Brother Villareal from St. Augustine who struggled in despair a long time with mission difficulties in Florida and in Spanish Guale and Orista. They caught the plague from soldiers they nursed. Then the ship on which they had sailed for Havana was wrecked by an unmistakable hurricane.

The wretched people who got ashore walked south, dogged by Indians through matted growths of scrub oak, loblolly pine, myrtle. Indian arrows struck them down as they waded across rivers. Nights, the Indians howled like fiends around the starving refugees' camp fires. A few exhausted men and women got back safely to St. Augustine.

In Spain, Philip the Second was frightened by reports that his old enemy John Hawkins, now chairman of the English Navy Board, was improving and enlarging the Queen's fleet. He was getting rid of graft and incompetence. He was building new and sea-worthy ships. In fact, by cutting down the unwieldy top hamper of the impractical old galleon, making more room for guns below, John Hawkins was developing the able, handy English galleon with which would be established the whole power of England in the seven seas.

Philip was also frightened that "El Draque," the fiery, intractable Francis Drake, had been nosing about the Isthmus of Panama, making friends of French pirates and Cimarrones, the wild Indians who hated the Spanish, and finding a harbor for an English base.

To Philip the Second, all the English were pirates. He had Pedro Menéndez draw up a plan to fortify the defenseless Spanish Caribbean cities. He tried to stop the graft and corruption that overloaded and delayed the Plate Fleets. He reorganized the Plate Fleet system, but grafting merchants made such an outcry against Menéndez that the fleet control was taken away from him. He sent ships and supplies to islands devastated by pirates or hurricanes. Both took a greater and greater toll.

Like Hawkins, he well knew that the height and clumsiness of the galleons made them a prey of hurricanes and difficult coasts. They were built in graft-ridden shipyards, of green timber, badly outfitted and left for months to rot in the warm waters of tropic harbors. He therefore built a sturdy small vessel of deeper draft such as the light vessels called "brigantines" he had used among the Florida Keys, not over twenty tons, equipped with a fore-and-aft rig of lateen sails and a single bank of oars. He put thirty-five excellent oarsmen aboard, five seamen, twenty-five nobles and sailed it across the Gulf Stream to the Azores in seventeen days. He called it a "galizabra."

It took the King's treasure straight home safely. It improved communications, outsailed pirates and fled before hurricanes. In 1572 he was back in Florida. In Havana, late in the fall, he sailed in command of the combined fleets.

South of Bermuda, in a dirty sea, the bar of a hurricane crept

over the horizon. He only just managed to keep his ship alive
through the night. After two days of pumping, all his ships were
in sight again, but the great galleon, the *San Lazaro*. His nephew
Menéndez Marqués, who had taken the place of his lost son, had
sailed on it.

Twenty-two days later, the damaged *San Lazaro* crawled into
Vigo Bay, where the captain tried to unload without paying duty.
As they were taking the captain to prison they were horrified to
learn that a passenger, one Pedro Menéndez Marqués, with his wife
and servants, three coffers and a heavy chest, said to be carrying
eight thousand ducats, got ashore without a certificate of entry.
But when the Corregidor of the Port wrote in passionate protest to
his Majesty, there was no answer.

There was shocking news from Nombre de Dios. "El Draque"
had taken it with two small ships and sixty blood-thirsty Englishmen.
They stole gold and silver from the King's Treasury. Drake found
shelter on that coast at "Port Pheasant" during the hurricane season.
After it, he raided Santa Marta, Cartagena and the Isthmus Gold
Road, taking 21,000 ducats' worth of booty home to a jubilant England.

Nombre de Dios was abandoned by the Spanish and the Treasure
House and the Governor's Palace moved to a better fortified harbor
at Puerto Bello. There for another century or two the great fair
was held at the arrival of the galleons. All the goods were displayed
and the men from Panama, the Pacific Coast, Peru and even Chile,
crowded in for three days, bargained, shouted, fought and dropped
down dead of fevers or plague on the stones walled with chests and
treasures and piled silver ingots. Those who lived tried to get away
before the first hurricane.

Now Menéndez de Avilés was set to work to carry out Philip
the Second's burning desire to invade and crush England. He had
assembled twenty thousand picked men and three hundred ships,
when he died. There was no one else capable of that command. But
that aging English spinster, Elizabeth of England, was profoundly
alarmed.

Menéndez's nephew, Pedro Menéndez Marqués, was not a very
able administrator, a tall, thin, worried, careful man of about forty,
who made the first survey of the Florida coast. In his memorial he
wrote that all the Indians of Florida ought to be captured and sold

as slaves because they had taken prisoner or killed more than three hundred Spanish people from the wrecks.

He bought from the Indians as many as he could find alive and the people from two ships blown from New Spain and wrecked on Canaveral in the hurricane of 1572. In 1574 he himself was wrecked by a hurricane on that same dangerous Cape. With seventeen others, Menéndez Marqués had to walk the beaches, cross the swamps and inlets, to reach St. Augustine. They were followed by a threatening pack of Indians whom Menéndez Marqués kept off by waving his long arms and making an interminable Spanish speech. The Indians followed them all the way to St. Augustine, listening respectfully. They always admire an orator.

There was no war between Catholic France and Catholic Spain now, since Catherine de Medici had killed off all the Huguenots on St. Bartholemew's Eve. But the scum of French privateers turned pirate and devastated more islands than the hurricane of 1575, called "the San Mateo," that ruined only quiet Puerto Rico.

The English were trying the Arctic ice for a passage to the west and Drake had been heard of, taking booty in the Pacific. He was home in '80, having sailed around the world and brought back more than two millions in gold ducats. The Queen went royally down to Plymouth, a fabulous aging woman in cloth-of-gold and a red wig and knighted him on the sea-battered deck of his small *Golden Hind*.

She could not forget Philip of Spain, who by seizing Portugal had made Spain the world's greatest power. For all that Spain, deserted by workmen, overrun by hordes of nobles too haughty to work, fields exhausted, cold medieval castles filthy and rat-ridden, with an enormously expensive army, was bankrupt.

In England, a new tide of hatred for Spain had been rising slowly out of the stories that followed John Hawkins's hurricane, and a new vision of an enormous and unoccupied continent.

Ships that began to sail to those northern coasts were not turned back by a hurricane that loomed over the Atlantic in '83. A man named Humphrey Gilbert sold all his property in London and bought five ships and sailed the next year to take possession of the rough, darkly wooded Newfoundland. Ice floated there in summer and there were polar bears about the good, if rocky, harbors. When he and his men had eaten all their food, they tried to sail home, careless of the season. Even so far north, a hurricane found them, not yet diminished in its terrible course up from the tropics. His vessel sank off Sand Island, and Humphrey Gilbert and all of them were drowned.

It made no difference to all those sea-faring Englishmen, eager for ventures in the Atlantic, in the Pacific. Private ships, ships of powerful syndicates of men like Hawkins who dominated Naval affairs, privateers to take what Spanish vessels they could find, sailed and returned to Plymouth, Portsmouth, Bristol, London. No man did more to spread an excited interest in the new country of the west than Richard Hakluyt, in the first effective piece of American advertising, "A Discourse of Western Planting." Rich men, poor men, sailors, merchants, hungry men, in teeming overcrowded England found the idea of American colonies as desirable as Spanish treasure. So Sir Walter Raleigh sent out seven vessels under Sir Richard Grenville, with 100 settlers who began the ill-fated settlement of Roanoke within the Outer Banks on Pamlico Sound.

The English failed to intercept the two huge treasure fleets of '85, that got safe home with a treasure equal to over eight hundred millions of pesos.

Drake never made up for its loss, either by taking Santo Domingo or Cartagena, which he could not keep, or St. Augustine where Pedro Menendez Marques took to the woods leaving Drake to burn the town and take the soldiers' pay. He burned San Mateo on the St. Johns and would have burned Santa Elena on the Edisto but he had to run before the hurricane of 1586 that overtook him at Roanoke. It drove some of his ships on the beach and wrecked the colony's supply ship. His own ship weathered the hurricane and he took away in it Ralph Love and his starving men.

Drake convinced Philip the Second, as Menendez de Aviles had not been able to do, that the cities of the New World must be strengthened and fortified. The work was immediately begun that brought to the old cities of Puerto Rico and San Domingo, to Cartagena, Puerto Bello and Panama, Veracruz and Havana and even remote St. Augustine, a new nobility in stone, that would outlast the invasions and hurricanes of all these centuries.

Philip of Spain took Drake's venture for what it was, an act of war. His answer was the Armada for the invasion of England.

There were only about twelve days of summer in the North

Atlantic, in the year 1588. In those months all England was roused
to a frenzy of anxiety but it was not by wild weather.

In the Caribbean, the heavy heat of the tropics was invaded by
rougher gusts and whips of pewter-colored rain. The dangerous
season was beginning early that year.

A hurricane raked slowly across Cuba, coming from whence,
going where, the houseless people did not know. Hurricane waves
were pushed out to assault the coast of Europe and a concourse of
one hundred and fifty Spanish ships colored like circus wagons,
bannered like palaces.

There were sixty-four tall castled galleons, some huge, decorated
galleasses, top-heavy with turrets, chapels, pulpits, state chambers
hung with arras; twenty fighting caravels and towing galleys that
on a calm sea ran like spiders, four or five trained men to a long
oar. There were fast pataches and despatch boats, and square-rigged
hulks heavy with supplies. They moved with the slow motley pomp
of a land army, and carried jammed in, seven thousand sailors, more
than seventeen thousand soldiers, innumerable noble officers and in
command, who knew himself no seaman, the military Duke of
Medina-Sidonia. It was "The Invincible Armada."

When the hurricane-engendered gales smashed into those tall,
wobbly, creaking and gilded tenement houses, they were advancing
toward England. Some got safely into harbor at Corunna. Some
fled away north to rendezvous at the Scilly Isles. The Armada was
badly hurt.

Drake's fleet, stopped by the lashing weather from a raid on the
Spanish Coast, was only just back in Plymouth. John Hawkins had
been building England a navy fit to fight anywhere, on any sea.
His idea had long been to stop a Spanish invasion by blocking
Spanish ports so that the treasure fleets could not get in. But Elizabeth of England was a nervous woman, although she had the best
navy England had ever known, a country full of ambitious, sea-
minded people, a great array of fighting admirals, and John Hawkins.

Elizabeth had kept England safe when it was weakened and confused by the bloody times before her own, not by her bluff father's
grasp of military affairs, but by unparalleled diplomatic subtlety.
She had gained no boldness from England's new strength nor from
the male directness and effrontery of her sea-adventurers. She

wanted her ships and men at home, guarding the narrow seas, "plying to and fro" while she tried to head off Philip by negotiation.

Spain had the hurricane as handicap. England had her great Queen's cautious spinsterishness.

The Armada was at last able to sail from Corunna. The winds had dropped before the fleets were joined at the Scilly Isles. Twelve days of beautiful summer had begun.

The Lord Admiral, Charles Howard of Effingham, had joined the fleets at Plymouth, taking the high command. Unpredictable Sir Francis Drake accepted the place of vice-admiral. As the ships crowded Plymouth's Cattewater and Sutton Pool, all the captains were there, including rough Martin Frobisher, who hated Drake. John Hawkins had joined them in May with ships from the Queen's dockyards at Chatham, with guns and ammunition for all the ships, from the Tower arsenal. His energy drove them all, fitting, loading, signing up thousands of able men from Cornwall, Devon, Kent.

All along that south coast the towns boiled with nervous excitement, that reached up the crowded roads to London to the anxious and pacing Queen. The white cliffs were dark with people staring out west over the blue, wrinkling Channel water as bees in the warm summer zoomed on the furzy slopes.

A fishing boat fled into Plymouth Sound with the shout, "They're off the Lizard."

Behind it, in the afternoon light a band of pearl glinted and grew on the horizon. On the morning of July 20th the Armada stood out there, a white cloud of sails beyond sails, a wall looming toward Plymouth. Just in time the English streamed out like hawks, wheeling and beating up the light airs to windward. The huge array of the Invincible Armada went past slowly far off.

The Lord Admiral watched them from the poop of the beautiful flagship the *Ark Royal*. Drake had his perfect *Revenge* under his stamping heels. Martin Frobisher had the old-fashioned high-charged *Triumph*. There were twenty-five fighting ships and eighteen sea-going pinnaces. There they went, taking the brief sun on clean English canvas as they came about, one by one, in the eye of the wind. And John Hawkins brought up the rear on the roomy ship *Victory*.

He had seen Spaniards before. Surely now his gaze was only for the ships that he had built, refitted, made over, furnished, new to the last strake: *Mary Rose, White Bear, Golden Lion, Swift Sure, Dreadnaught, Philip and Mary, Hope, Elizabeth Jones, Elizabeth Bonaventure,* how many more—*Vanguard, Rainbow,* and the *Foresight.* He had the same keen ship-keeping eye for the clutter of small vessels footing it past like a flight of terns, coasters, luggers, small merchantmen, fishermen. He would not have noticed especially among the hired craft a small ship called *Mayflower.* They all made a moving criss-crossing flashing host, 190 sail.

How could he know that he was staring at the beginning of the glory of the English nation?

Instead, Hawkins was probably deeply worried, knowing that it was the first time in history so many great English ships had sailed together, with not one man in command, including himself, who had the slightest notion how to maneuver so great a fleet. Of the guns he had had placed on them, the man-killing short-range swivels, the heavy long-range battering guns, culverins, demi-culverins, sakers, minions and falcons, not one had been fired in a single practice shot. Powder was too dear.

The English idea was to keep to windward of the Armada, to cripple the high ships with long-range fire. The Spaniards seemed to hang there, turning a little, waiting for the English to come up. The fighting Duke of Medina-Sidonia wanted only to sweep in close, fire down from their towering castles on the English decks, grapple, order the boarders over and fight it out, man to man, dagger to throat.

The English could not do it. For two hours they carried the fight to the Spaniards, with splintering round shot. The watchers on the far cliffs strained toward the booming guns' thunder.

One Spanish ship was damaged in a collision. One blew up. The English took both but won no more.

The Armada was slowly sailing eastward, the English following. The next day there was a real fight. The heavy firing must have been heard in France. Not one ship was hit but both sides used up almost all their ammunition.

The next day, the unwieldy English fleet was broken up into four squadrons under the four commanders. The weather was blue and calm. The sun shone on that sea-garden of white sails, fluttering and idling. Hawkins had his crews out in small boats, towing his ships to cut off a Spanish galleon, motionless as a picture. A sharp little breeze edged the sea. Sails filled. The high rudders found steerage way. Firing began again—*pow—ka—pow, blam*. Smoke dulled bright water. They all moved in the same helpless eastward drifting.

Things were so quiet that on July 26, on board the *Ark Royal*, the Lord Admiral conferred knighthood on six men, but first on John Hawkins.

The ships drifted near to Calais. The great duke was trying frantically and uselessly to get in touch with the Prince of Parma and his land forces, who were to help take England. By night the English brought up the fireships, their long forward tubes gushing and boiling flame. The chief galleass lost her rudder and went aground.

The twenty-ninth, off Gravelines, was a long day's battle, the great day for Drake's brilliant attack. Spanish masts hung in a cobweb of rigging. Their canvas showed the sky through torn holes. Men were killed by cannon balls, died pierced by exploded splinters. Blood reddened under bare heels as hoarse men, powder burned and sweating, served the insatiable guns.

Everybody was valiant. The Spaniards astonished the proud English by their steady fire, their discipline, their passionate devotion, their high chivalry. Somehow the great crippled galleons kept afloat. Drake's fleet pressed in, delivering terrible broadsides. He had them cut off. They could have been captured.

A wind roared up suddenly, cold and strong, blowing hard, a gale. Summer was over, and dirty weather piled up the narrow seas. What sails the Spaniards had, filled. They moved off, wind driven.

The English followed but they had no more ammunition. On their decks and below, thousands of English seamen were dying of Hawkins' horror, jail fever, that comes from overcrowding, filth, bad water. They were dying of dysentery, poisoned by the grafting contractors' rotten food. The sea was making up in great tumbling swells. July 30, the Spaniards were almost on the lee-shore of England. If the English were suffering, how much worse were the Spaniards? They died like flies.

The English, for all their wounds and their sickness, piled after them. Even the dying cheered.

Then the wind changed. There was the last shift of a hurricane in that. It blew furiously out of the Atlantic from the southwest. The dark sea mounted. The ruined Spanish ships, rolling like drunken men, fled north. The English followed to the Firth of Forth and then hugged the coast, beating home. While they carried the dead ashore and the dying filled the houses of coast towns, cheering ran over the English countryside and the bells, the bells, sounded, all the way to London, to the ears of the flushed victorious Queen.

Still the great Spanish ships were driven like leaves, like ragged ghosts north, up Scotland, around the Hebrides into history, into legend. Dark nights saw the galleons sinking among the rocks, the driven mists, the surf, the rocky islands, the passages hissing with black water. Some galleons drove into the Atlantic along Ireland where the black savage winds wrecked them and drowned them. Some who were saved were butchered. Some were hidden and cherished so that the dark Spanish handsomeness lives still in the West Country, stronger than the sea. England was safe.

BOOK THREE
THE STRENGTH
OF THE ENGLISH

1 *THE TEMPEST*

Nothing so shocking as the defeat of the Armada had in all these years of conquest happened to Spain. Philip had pledged everything he had to money lenders to equip it. Now the treasure from the New World meant everything to him. Yet now Dutch and English privateersmen swarmed in the Caribbean even as hurricanes seemed to grow more constant and more disastrous.

In the years 1589 and '90 hundreds of Spanish ships were wrecked by one hurricane after another in the Yucatán Channel, the Straits of Florida and all over the Atlantic. The ships that got home brought five million ducats' worth to pay Philip's debts. He had learned at last to use galizabras. In consequence, Hawkins and Frobisher were at last allowed to try to blockade the Azores and the Spanish coasts.

Spanish fleets sent to attack Hawkins were driven back by another hurricane. The English Lord Admiral Howard lay blockading the Azores but his fleet was not in good order. Some ships were being overhauled, some were scrubbing out their bilges. Many crew were ashore, some ill, some amusing themselves. This was the end of August, 1591. There was a long howl that the Spaniards were coming, and there they stood in, fifteen high-charged galleons.

Howard ordered the English ships to slip their cables and get away beyond. Only the vice-admiral, Sir Richard Grenville, in his perfect small English galleons of 100 tons, the *Revenge*, stayed for the men on shore, sick or well, now swarming on the beach. The Spanish ships were on his weather bow. He could cut his mainsail, they said, and drift off on the current, stern to the enemy, leaving the men behind. He said he would rather die than dishonor his command and his country so.

The Spanish galleons, like blazing fortresses, closed in. The fight that began at three o'clock in the afternoon of July 25 was one of the greatest sea battles in English history. The little *Revenge* fought them all, two galleons to a side, moving up and falling away, all the glaring, thundering night long. But for the *Pilgrim*, a small supply ship, Jacob Whidden master, who hung about as long as he could to help, it was alone. A thousand Spaniards died.

An hour before midnight, on his shattered deck, Sir Richard Grenville was shot through the body. Then he was shot through the head. He lived.

The guns of the *Revenge* fell silent at dawn. The damaged Spanish galleons ringed around the blackened shell, heaped with forty bodies out of a hundred men. Grenville ordered his ship, with all alive, blown up. The men refused and made honorable terms of surrender. Grenville was carried aboard the Spanish flagship and lay on the afterdeck alive, for three days more.

They said in Tercera, as Richard Hakluyt reported in England, that "so soone as they had throwen the dead body of the Vice-admirall Sir Richard Greenfield over-board they verily thought that as he had a divelish faith and religion and therefore the divels loved him, so he presently sunke into the bottom of the sea and downe into hell, where he raised up all the divels to the revenge of his death, and that they brought so great storms and torments upon the Spaniards because they only maintained the Catholic and Romish religion."

Over a hundred ships, galleons and merchant ships of the just arrived fleet which the galleons had been sent to guard, were wrecked, their crews drowned, their riches lost. "For 20 days after the storm they did nothing but fish for dead men that continually came driving on the shore. . . . It may well be thought," Hakluyt went on, "that it was no other but a just plague purposely sent by God upon the Spaniards and that it might truly be said, the taking of the Revenge was justly revenged upon them."

Five great hurricanes that year sent the English privateers home with less booty than ever. After that the galizabras carried all the Spanish treasure and the merchant fleets were better protected.

The great days of that first English sea power were passing, with the deaths of the great captains, Drake and Hawkins. Elizabeth was aging. Her indecision, her fears, her confusion, worked confusion and depression in England. But Spain, like one of her rat-ridden, half-rotted outdated galleons, crammed still with the greatest revenues the New World had ever produced, somehow lived on. Philip the Second died in 1598, like a dried-up beetle lost in the gloom of the Escorial, dead of worry.

In Havana, they were saying that because of hurricanes that wrecked St. Augustine, it might be better to abandon the site altogether. "The Bishop of Cuba," it was written, "does not go to Florida any more because of the threats of pirates, the dangerous character of the sea, and so many hurricanes." Yet in a few years of a more aggressive policy, St. Augustine was headquarters of four districts of Christianized Indians and had given help and shelter to more than five hundred people cast ashore by hurricanes or marooned by pirates on that interminable coast.

When Elizabeth of England died, James Stuart, the Sixth of Scotland, the First of England, "the wisest fool in Europe," immediately made peace with Spain. In England, hidden private capital was brought out and invested in an outburst of enthusiasm for the settling of Western lands "not effectively occupied" by Spain. But hurricanes still wrecked ships; in 1605 a fast Spanish frigate on the Florida Keys and in 1606 a London ship blown into a Florida river and captured, and the men ill-treated, by a Spanish vessel.

The English were learning about hurricanes now. They pronounced the name variously, "haurachana," "uracan," "herocano," "hyrracano" or, as the early Spanish and the Portuguese did, "furicane." The French had long adapted the Indian word to call it "ouragan" and the Dutch "orkan."

Virginia was a territory even vaster than Florida then. It reached from Cape Hatteras to Canada and west to the Pacific. Two companies to promote Virginia land had been set up, one in London and one in Hawkins' Plymouth. Richard Hakluyt put on an enthusiastic advertising campaign, insisting there was more gold in Virginia than had yet been discovered anywhere, and rich lands for everybody.

Three small ships, the *Sarah Constant*, the *Goodspeed* and the twenty-ton *Discovery*, with 140 people under Captain Christopher Newport and Captain Benjamin Gosnold, sailed from East London for Virginia in the teeth of a September gale. They were three months sailing the impractical Azores-Canaries-West Indies route to reach, at last, the "Bay of Chesupioc" or "Chesapeake."

In another day they anchored at Point Comfort, which indeed it was, and sailed up a broad pleasant river, just coloring with spring. They landed on an island which Captain John Smith, always talking big, announced was a "Verie fit place for the erecting of a great citie." It was too marshy, too heavily wooded, with no fresh water. But they were anxious to get out of the foul ships. That settlement, which was to starve and suffer many things, was Jamestown.

Philip the Third of Spain took this very ill. He was told it was to be a base "for privateering and making attacks upon the merchant fleets of your Majesty—not to plant colonies but to send out pirates from there."

The next year two ships went to scout Maine, reporting on abundance of furs, ship stores and codfish, which as Captain Smith said later, would be a rich mine. That year also Samuel Champlain sailed to occupy Canada for the French.

There was a rugged old sea captain of the late Elizabeth's, Sir George Somers, sixty years old, rich from many a bloody venture he had made against the Spaniard, yet kindly and public-minded. He was vice-admiral to the joint stock expedition under Sir Thomas Gates, who, in 1609, sailed for Virginia with three ships overloaded with five hundred people. On the southern route through the tropics in summer, eighty people died of the heat below decks.

They were crawling north in July when a huge "hurycano" swelled up the sky behind them, and beat down the ships in the troughs of terrible waves. The smallest, a ketch, sank with twenty people on board. The other ships were scattered all over the calming ocean.

They had planned, if anything happened, to rendezvous at Bermuda. But nothing was ever done right on these blundering, pitiful ventures. Four ships, the *Blessing*, the *Lion*, the *Falcon* and then the badly damaged *Unity*, found each other. The wind behind the hurricane was fair for Virginia, so they sailed for the Chesapeake. Two other ships presently came in.

But not the *Sea Venture*, on which, surprisingly enough, all the quarreling officers had sailed—Gates, Somers, and Captain Newport. In Jamestown it was given up as lost. The colony was wretched. The people were starving. There were not enough huts, especially for the newcomers. And the people of the ships could not help them, for the hurricane had ruined all the supplies that were not already rotten. The result was disorder, dissension, almost mutiny.

Captain John Smith, braggart, furiously hated, was sent home in disgrace. The adventurers starved through a dreadful winter, glad to eat dogs, cats, rats and shoes. Two out of three died. They were about to abandon Jamestown for good when they saw two small ships sailing up the river. They carried Sir George Somers, Sir Thomas Gates and Captain Newport. It was a full year since they had disappeared in the hurricane.

The *Sea Venture* had almost foundered. They kept her up by pumping, for four days, and then gave up, in that "hell of darkness," deciding to get drunk before they died. But George Somers was at the helm. When something loomed up ahead, he thought at once it was the "dreadful coast of the Bermoothes . . . inchanted and inhabited with witches and devills . . . and wunderous daungerous Rockes and unspeakable hazard of ship wrack."

She struck a half mile off shore but the sea lifted and wedged her so tight between higher rocks that she was safe. At low tide, they all escaped to shore.

Bermuda was the loveliest place they had ever seen, with plenty of fish and berries and wild hogs from a wrecked Spanish vessel. Although they yearned to stay in that paradise they managed to make two vessels out of what was left of the *Sea Venture* and in ten months sailed, bringing with them to wretched Jamestown supplies for only two weeks.

Under Gates's orders all abandoned the unhappy colony and sailed downstream for home. But at Point Comfort they met the arriving ships of Lord de la Warr, who ordered them all, cursing and groaning, back to Jamestown. Worse things followed the pigheadedness of de la Warr. But Sir George Somers had gone back to Bermuda. In a week he died "of a surfeit in eating of a pig" in that happy place.

An account of the Bermudas and the fate of the *Sea Venture*, based on a letter of Sir George's, was published in 1610 by Sylvester Jourdain. Its title was, "A discovery of the Bermudas, otherwise called the Ile of Divels, by Sir Thomas Gates, Sir George Sommers and Captayne Newport and divers others." In 1612 a fuller account was written by William Strachey of London, the manuscript of which was read by a well-known playwright for the court of James I. He was William Shakespeare. He had already written in *King Lear*, "Rage, blow you Cataracts and Hyrricanos spout."

It is evident that he was fascinated by the Bermuda story. He bought drinks dockside for sailors who told about the mysteries of the Western oceans and how ships must be sailed, in tempests, among strange islands and lonely rocks. He needed an idea for a new play, a short one, to be acted as part of the festivities attendant on a marriage of royal personages.

He wrote *The Tempest*. It was about "An Uninhabited Island" that was obviously Bermuda, made immortal in his phrase, "the still-vexed Bermoothes." The first scenes are laid on a ship about to be wrecked in a storm. The orders shouted by the ship's captain are correct, in the nautical terms of the day, for the handling of a ship in five increasingly dangerous positions.

The test of genius is what great art it makes of the stuff of this world. The hurricane is here from the beginning. "What care these roarers for the name of King?" Or Miranda's speech,

> *If by your art, my dearest father, you have*
> *Put the wild waters in this roar, allay them.*
> *The sky, it seems, would pour down stinking pitch*
> *But that the sea, mounting to the welkin's cheek,*
> *Dashes the fire out.*

Or "the never-surfeited sea," "twixt the green sea and the azured vault set roaring war," and after the storm,

> *The isle is full of noises,*
> *Sounds and sweet airs, that give delight and hurt not.*

It is a play and great poetry like the islands, surrounded and permeated by the sea.

But it is no ordinary island. The imagination of no matter how many seagoing Spaniards, who believed it was the "Ile of Divils," where the English, from that time on, conjured up hurricanes to destroy the Spanish ships, could not have supplied such magic as Shakespeare's. Here were such creatures, kingly magician, demons, hags, faery messengers as have peopled our minds from that time forth. No sprite in literature is lovelier than Ariel, whom Prospero rescued from a wind-cleft pine tree. The twisted trees, the sea-worn rocks, are no more strange than the fancies of the demon-drudge Caliban, in whom there is surely something of the "salvages" of mysterious America, dark, tormented, probably all evil, who must be conquered.

The early discoverers had already made "cannibal" out of "Caribbean." From it Shakespeare derived "Caliban," the perfect name for the creature of that place, "all torment, trouble, wonder and amazement." Surely *The Tempest* is the loveliest thing ever to come out of a hurricane.

2 PILGRIMS AND PIRATES

For thirteen years after William Shakespeare's hurricane only one is recorded, in Puerto Rico, with its sad old history of neglect and disaster.

Henry Hudson, an Englishman sailing ships for the Dutch, discovered Hudson's Bay, and far south, the most important river of that coast. The boat-shaped island lodged in its mouth, the Indian "Manahatta," at once became a Dutch barrier between the French at the St. Lawrence and the feeble messy English colonies Raleigh had set to the south.

The fate of those colonies was more uncertain after James the First of England beheaded Raleigh in sudden anxious friendship for Spain. While it lasted, the Spanish missions to the Indians in Georgia and South Carolina extended their peaceful influence.

In Holland, English people who had left England because they wanted to appoint their own religious teachers and be free of ritual and the bishops, bargained with the Virginia Company of London to allow them to occupy land in Virginia as a joint stock company.

So the Pilgrims, as we have learned to call that rather motley assembly of tailors, shopkeepers, carpenters and plain men who cared little for religion but a lot for freedom and land, sailed from Plymouth on the fifth of September, 1620. The *Mayflower* was a small, sturdy, duck-bowed ship in which the people were crowded below for four sick and weary months. The weather was cold. They had not been sailing many weeks before they had to endure a black gale of wind from the northeast, which changed suddenly to a furious head wind from the west. There are some accounts of a lull in this storm after which the seas lifted enormously and a wind more terrible than any they had known tossed the ship and the unfortunate people battened within.

The ship was disabled. But by morning the storm, or hurricane, had blown on its way. The ship was repaired. They sailed on.

By the twenty-first of December, they saw land.

It was not Virginia. It was Cape Cod. The men stumbled in dismay over the blowing pale sand, the stunted trees of the great thin Cape that seemed to shake a fist at the whole Atlantic. Whether it is true they were blown off their course, or the captain betrayed them into a settlement called "Plymouth" is still being argued.

But with courage and endurance they made the place their own. They also had the luck to arrive at a time when a plague had killed off hostile Indians and they had an English-speaking Indian without whose help they could hardly have lived through that first winter.

In Spain, Philip the Third depended even more on the treasure fleets from the New World, which for a few years seemed to be spared the ravages of both pirates and hurricanes, until 1622.

Two great processions of ships, the "Galeones" carrying an enormous mass of silver from Potosí with the Tierre Firme fleet, and the New Spain "Flota," all sailing for the Havana conjunction, were caught by a hurricane that drove many up the Florida coast. Some did not beat a painful way back for thirty-nine days. One ship, the *Candelaria*, was discovered to be overrun with rats that fouled the drinking water, ate the supplies and bit the sleeping people.

At Havana twenty-two ships sailed out as they could into contrary winds over the rolling Florida current. On the third of September, twenty-eight ships, eight galleons and many other vessels ventured forth. They were at once caught by a hurricane that then swept over Havana, beating down everything into the streets. Debris matted the torn harbor.

Until the tenth, nothing was heard of the ships. Then eighteen half-wrecked weed-hung vessels struggled into the harbor. Fifty people had been picked up from wreckage on the Dry Tortugas. Sixty people had been found floating on planks in calming Florida waters.

Near Bermuda, the first ships that had sailed were overtaken on the ninth of September by the same hurricane that threw them about until the twelfth. The crew and passengers on the sinking *San Augustin* were saved by the *San Ignacio*. Then the *San Ignacio's* seams opened up and its crowded people were taken off by other vessels. Others were lost or abandoned.

The weather was still violent as the few ships kept going east. The *Candelaria* lived, but the increase of rats ate all the food.

At the Azores there were only eight worn-out ships left out of the fleet of twenty-three that had left Havana one hundred and six terrible days before. A ship was wrecked on the bar at Cadiz. The people were taken off, who had been on four other ships, each of them sinking under their heels.

But the long boat from a Campeche ship had the most remarkable tale to tell. It was sunk at Bermuda. Twenty people and two friars fought for places in the long boat, as eighty-three others drowned. As the old Spanish account says, "Those who arrived first did not make room for the others, it being inconvenient for all to perish." The twenty-two survived a voyage back to Havana in that twenty-seven days in that boat, on a hamper of hardtack and a little water, over two thousand miles. One other man floated off the Florida keys on a hatch cover for five days. All he had to eat was a sea bird that alighted on his head.

Up and down Florida, men were sent to burn wrecks for what treasure could be got out of them. There must have been four hurricanes which circled over almost the whole Atlantic from September to November.

A hurricane on September 19, 1623, that walloped the Windward Islands, was of no interest to Spain who had abandoned them as worthless, but destroyed the first huts and tobacco plantings of the first English colony of St. Christopher.

Only the savage Caribs had resented the intrusion. Thomas Warner set up cannon on a fort and the French under d'Esnambue helped the English drive off the Indians, and each held half the island. The English occupied Nevis with its perfect volcano peak in a snow of clouds and Antigua for its good harbors. They had already settled Barbados, then covered with great trees bearded with moss, fronting the blue rollers of the Atlantic.

The furious Spanish recaptured, for a while, Nevis and St. Kitts. The St. Kitts governor fled to the rock of Tortuga Island, north of Hispaniola. From that high rock and harbor, Dutch and English, French and Portuguese outlaws, cattle killers turned buccaneers, and every sort of bold or sneaking pirate swarmed out against the fleets and seaport cities. Between the pirates and the hurricanes of the coasts many undefended cities were moved, for safety, high up the mountains, where they are today.

The Dutch seized Curaçao and Aruba and Bonaire, and in the Lesser Antilles the high extinct volcano of Saba with its crater villages, and St. Eustatius.

Dutch ships busily traded among the islands, smuggling in slaves and supplies for the tobacco crop from starving English islands, bringing in food to islands ruined by hurricanes. Two Dutch ships were driven on the shore of Sebastian inlet in Florida by the hurricane of 1626. And in 1628 the daring Dutch admiral and pirate, Pieter Pieterszoon Heyn, in Spanish "Pie-de-Palo" and in English, "Peg-leg," was blown by a late August hurricane from the western Cape of Cuba to the Florida east coast.

No hurricanes stopped English ships from trading everywhere, putting out from the safe harbor of the newly founded town of Boston in Massachusetts Bay Colony, or interfered with the busy life of forty-three Spanish missions in Florida and Georgia, or the two ships of Lord Calvert, sailing up between the green banks of the Potomac to begin Maryland. Roger Williams, idealist and dissenter, never heard of them, kicked out of Boston already and rowing a boat down the Seekonk River to the pleasant Salt River at the head of a jagged bay, to set up the free-minded town of Providence in what would be Rhode Island.

The water was alive with fish—mackerel, bluefish in their season. Shad and herring climbed every spring to spawn in the clear brooks. Clams squirted at low tide in the mudflats, oysters and quahogs for wampum lay in plenty on the reefs. There were mussels in the eelgrass and eels in the river mouths. Soon there were hip-roofed farm houses among apple trees and sea gulls in a salt wind cried over stone walls among pointed firs running down to blue tidewater.

The turbulent, hard-working Rhode Islanders gained for Providence Plantations, from the Crown, the right of absolute freedom of worship. They always liked to say that Massachusetts had religion without liberty, but the elders of Boston retorted that Rhode Island had liberty without religion.

Both had hurricanes, but Rhode Island, facing the sea to the south, took the brunt of them first.

In Delaware Swedes were building log cabins that would enable men to live everywhere in winter ice, sleet, snow, rain and hurricanes. Log cabins were built in the wild forests west of Boston, up the Connecticut at Weathersfield, in Dutch New Amsterdam and up the Hudson. They would help move the frontier west.

And in Virginia John Rolfe planted the first tobacco that gave the colony its first money crop. No hurricanes ruined those small plantings.

Hurricanes assaulted the beautiful arc of islands standing guard between the Atlantic and the Caribbean, that Englishmen had long desired and now held, having fled Oliver Cromwell's revolution in England, and made Barbados, St. Kitts, Nevis and Montserrat strongholds of loyalty to King Charles. Newly arrived ships were wrecked there at once by a whole series of hurricanes. The young tobacco was ruined.

New Spanish cities, like Maracaibo on the Gulf of Venezuela, that almost never felt a hurricane, and Santiago de la Vega in Spanish Jamaica that knew them too well, were alike ravaged and looted by English pirates who did not give a curse for Cromwell or for Charles, in their greed for treasure.

None of them took treasure more famous than that which the hurricane of 1643 blasted into history. A fleet of thirty Spanish ships and galleons from Tierra Firme laden with treasure, and seven galleons bristling with guns, managed to get into Havana harbor. Rotten with leaks, the great treasure ship, *Nuestra Señora de la Concepcion,* was unfit to go on. Over the protests of the captains, loaded to the waterline with treasure and 540 people, she was ordered to sail out, unrepaired.

In the night of the twenty-eighth of September, violent gales suddenly blew from the south, in which the *Nuestra Señora* was kept afloat only by the wildest efforts. Suddenly, it was becalmed under a blue sky within a great circular wall of boiling cloud. They were alone in the hurricane's central eye.

They had to go through the other wall, savage winds, blinding and deafening rain, waves that rose above them. Everything was swept overboard in the violent pitching. Everybody manned the pumps. The winds blew themselves out. The terrible sea was more quiet.

They turned the patched bow of their floating wreck toward Puerto Rico, under a little ragged sail. For a month they crawled nearer, watching the currents and the shoals. On the first of November they found themselves in white water flashing over a sea of reefs. When they let go the anchor, the galleon was dragged by a savage current nearer and nearer the harsh ridges of coral.

That night, among the bursting foam, they heard her keel grate. She began to break up at once.

There were two canoes, many planks and boxes, a crude raft or two which the people in panic fought to fill. Hundreds drowned. Some men found foothold on a rocky reef a little higher than the gentling sea. They piled up there what treasure they saved, boxes of gold, silver ingots carelessly stacked. They decided it was the reef, northeast of Hispaniola, called "Los Abreojos," the rocks of "Keep Your Eyes Open" or "Watch Out." They lie at the end of that long scattering of the Bahamas, between a passage leading northeast to the Atlantic and the dark blue depths.

The last men to leave saw the broken shell of the *Nuestra Señora de la Concepcion* slip down and disappear in the water foaming and eddying among the rocks.

The loss of the treasure was a blow to the Crown. The Admiral was ordered to salvage the bronze cannon. Once he was wrecked by a sudden storm, once he was captured by pirates. The next year, another salvage expedition was driven back by a violent norther. Nothing succeeded.

Twenty years later, a Dutch ship picked up some bars of silver from the reef where the unfortunate Spaniards had left them. But that was all they could find.

But in that time, and for years thereafter, the reefs were re-named "The Silver Shoals" as the channel north of them is still called "The Silver Passage." The treasure that went down with the *Nuestra Señora de la Concepcion* became the most famous of all the treasures, wrecked and buried by the sea, in the gold-haunted Caribbean.

3 ENGLISH COASTS AND ISLANDS

The English were giving no thought to sunken treasure in those days. Charles the First was beheaded in 1649. Oliver Cromwell, as Lord Protector of the Commonwealth, set his grim mind on the conquest of the Dutch and of the rebellious Irish but especially on a plan for the conquest of the Catholic New World which was called "The Western Design." Thomas Gage, the English priest and turncoat, caused a furore in Protestant England by his book, *A New Survey of the West Indies*, in which he asserted that the licentiousness, graft, superstition and incompetence of Spain in the New World made their wealth ready for plucking.

The passionate King's men in Virginia, in Barbados under Francis, Lord Willoughby, and the new settlers in Nevis and Montserrat defied Cromwell and especially his Navigation Act of 1650 which ordered all trade with the English colonies to be carried on only in English ships. The Loyalist islands got no supplies from home.

They were near starving after the hurricanes of 1650 and '51 when a few Dutch slipped along to smuggle them both food and supplies. Fifty-two was a bad hurricane year for the French islands as well as the English. They were all affected when Spanish Puerto Rico felt the last of the storm that devastated them, because that neglected and always independent island was the center for all the smuggling trade by English, French and Dutch.

Because there was more money in smuggling than in piracy, the American towns, Boston, Newport, New Amsterdam, Philadelphia, and Charleston, joined in the trade with enthusiasm. Hardly a hurricane swept on its long curve about the islands that did not sink some of their nameless ships in harbors, roadsteads, or in open sea.

An important part of Cromwell's Western Design was to dump the surplus population of English jails, poorhouses and London slums, and thousands of Irish rebels, in the West Indies, where they all died like flies.

Thirty-eight English ships sailed with a rabble army of misfits and malcontents to Barbados, where three thousand small planters, ruined by hurricanes and monopolistic sugar production by great estates, joined up with the army of General Robert Venables. The Admiral, William Penn, was the father of an odd Quaker son who would found Pennsylvania. St. Kitts, Nevis and Montserrat, ruined by repeated hurricanes, added more discontented and hungry men to the disreputable expedition.

It failed to take Puerto Rico and Santo Domingo. In Spanish Jamaica, five hundred men, the only able-bodied planters and cattle raisers of that almost abandoned island, could not defeat them. That was 1655, a turning point in the history of the sea of hurricanes.

Penn and Venables left their miserable troops to starve and die in Jamaica or live off the land if any had the wits to. For a while they were spared hurricanes.

The settlers in the Lesser Antilles, struggling to rebuild houses and replant crops, were not so lucky. In 1656 Guadeloupe was terribly ravished. In Spanish Florida there had been a most unusual hurricane in January, that year.

On September 13, 1659, a hurricane banged the shutters of the house in England where in guttering candlelight Oliver Cromwell lay dead. After him, with a rising sound of trumpets and shouting, came Charles the Second, Royalist triumph, and the released, turbulent energy of the Restoration. He granted a patent to "The Royal Adventurers to Africa," which became the powerful "Royal African Company" that delivered increasing numbers of Negro slaves to the clamoring labor markets of the West Indies.

On the London market suddenly the price of sugar went up like rockets. All over Europe, as well as in England, the demand for sugar was so much greater than the supply that English speculators piled up fortunes. In the islands nothing was thought or talked about but sugar.

To make more canefields, jungles were cleared halfway up mountains. Cane was planted right up to the walls of plantation houses. Indigo, a quick and easy crop, its feathery low green much less likely to be damaged by hurricanes, was given up for sugar. Vegetable gardens in which the slaves raised what food was not imported, were plowed up. With every harvest the phrase became more common, "as rich as a West Indian sugar planter."

On the other hand, as great estates bought up smaller holdings of men dispossessed or ruined by hurricanes, the West Indies were filled with a wash of discontented, landless and restless men, who became petty adventurers, smugglers or pirates.

A group of respectable planters from Barbados, who wanted to find new and cheaper land to plant to sugar, took ship in 1665, with their wives and families, intending to settle in Carolina near Port Royal, now abandoned by the Spanish. They were driven by a hurricane, or a very severe storm, northward and found shelter near the island-guarded mouth of the Cape Fear River. What is now North Carolina saw their sails reaching up between the sunny green marshes and ridges shadowy with live oak and magnolias. The men from Barbados introduced to that good land the West Indian plantation system. The great house, the fields, the gangs of dark, almost faceless slaves directed by overseers, the slave huts, were almost what they had been used to, except the cold, dank winters. What they had not imagined was that hurricanes would find them here also.

The English, under Charles the Second, took New Amsterdam on the island of Manhattan from the Dutch, and filled it with criminals, wasters, Catholics, Huguenots, Quakers. The Swiss were settling on the mainland south of that magnificent harbor, on the rocky outcroppings among the swamps and the fertile country of New Jersey.

England knew herself at last as a great maritime power, restricting all the commerce of its colonies, as arrogantly as Spain had ever done, to English ships, goods, men, merchants and ports. The independent American-English, on the endless American coastline, took to smuggling as fish to the sea.

So many hurricanes from 1664 through 1667 again and again scoured bare Guadeloupe, Martinique and St. Kitts, leaving no houses or sugar works standing or any food crop in the ground, that the governor of the French half of St. Kitts wrote to Colbert, Louis Fourteenth's able minister, that if peace was not made soon so that cassava could be brought in from nearby islands both settlers and troops, stunned by disaster, "like men totally ruined," would die of hunger. Many left for America and, in the peace that finally came between England, France and Holland, settled in New York.

Henry Morgan, the Welsh governor of English Jamaica, had taken Puerto Bello and a huge treasure from Spain, which began to realize that England was too powerful to be shut, like Holland, out of the New World. By 1670 English settlers under the Lords Proprietors, including Albemarle and Anthony Ashley Cooper, whose names would live on that coast, were building a colony in Carolina where the Ashley and Cooper rivers meet, on a point of land on sand and clay and the "pluff" muds that are worked by ceaseless tides and currents. The town looked out to the rivers' mouth to sea between coastal islands thick with trees. Plantations began to spread through tidewater country for which the city of Charleston, at once granted a local court, its own government, and religious toleration, would be the focus of a unique and proud way of life.

At the same time the Lords Proprietors were granted letters patent to the scattered islands of the Bahamas. About five hundred people lived here, fishing, scratching gardens, looking for wrecks to salvage, offering harborage and services to all the pirates that auctioned off their booty among the shacks and blistering sands along the beautiful bay at Nassau. Hurricanes crossed them often as they did Barbados in '70 and Jamaica in '71.

They went unheeded as the official age of piracy came to a fantastic climax when Henry Morgan and his starving ruffians that year crossed the Isthmus, burned the "fair cedar houses" of Panama, and tortured the Spaniards into giving up an incredible treasure.

England did nothing for her West Indian colonies, offering no help to Barbados, destroyed by hurricanes again in '74 and '75, from which more ruined men left for Carolina and the strengthening American colonies.

English pirates in the Caribbean were growing more cautious. They were learning enough about hurricanes to go home in the dangerous season, leaving the seas to the Spanish, who still held the great Conjunction of the Tierra Firme and New Spain fleets in late August and September, as if the losses to hurricanes, still enormous, were less fearful than those to pirates.

Spain could not afford them. Soon the fleets began to sail only every three years and Spain's power, for lack of revenue, deteriorated more rapidly. The people of the Spanish New World grew more independent as among the neglected islands life was carried on by a network of smart French and American smugglers.

By 1678, when the Anglo-Dutch war ended with a treaty, a ten-year peace began in Europe, with Spain and England promising to defend each other against France. The hurricane that ravished Santo Domingo in '80 swept up to batter the last of the discouraged Spanish missions in Georgia where American sails were steadily working their way among the sea islands.

A Mr. John Smallbone, English gunner, wrote one of the first eye-witness stories of a hurricane in the English islands after the disaster of August 27, 1681, at Antigua.

Before the hurricane, it rained excessively. It was fair for three days. There was little wind. Smallbone's ship, half-laden with sugar, molasses and rum, moored in the harbor of St. Johns, Antigua, was made fast ashore to trees. At seven o'clock that evening they all went ashore to a poor planter's house. "The wind came on very fierce at N.E. and veering about to the N. and N.W. settled there, bringing with it very violent rains. Thus it continued about four hours and then fell flat calm and the wind ceased."

They found the ship already driven ashore, dry on the sand on her side. Returning they were overtaken by a whipping violent wind from the southwest. By morning, drenched when the thatch roof had blown away, they found the ship upright again, but the sugar had liquefied and the rum washed away.

During the northeast wind the sea ebbed so prodigiously, Mr. Smallbone wrote, that some ships "riding at 3 or 4 fathoms were aground until the S.W. gusts dashed them on the shore." The whole island suffered. "Neither was there any green thing left, but all looked like winter."

A second hurricane scoured viciously at Antigua. "The day after the storm," Mr. Smallbone wrote carefully, "the shore was strew'd with Fish of diverse sorts, as much great as small; such as Porpoises, Sharks, etc . . . and abundance of Sea-Fowl also were destroyed by it."

The ruins of Nevis, and St. Kitts, after the first hurricane, were blown over by the second, which chiefly affected small Montserrat. Hurricane water roared down the slopes from the old volcanic chimneys, washing the soil away and deepening the rocky gullies called "ghauts" or "guts." Many of Montserrat's poor planters were Cromwell's Irish exiles, who lost land, huts and their few hogsheads of sugar. Many were forced to hire out in other islands as indentured servants again. Many died, leaving only their Irish speech to the tall Negroes of Montserrat, a curious immortality.

Mr. Smallbone would not have described the hurricane if it had not been for a remarkable seaman-scientist named William Dampier, the first man since Columbus eager to know the natural curiosities of the Caribbean world. He was a large-nosed, lean, quiet, keen-eyed man, an excellent navigator, a careful and accurate scientist. He was also a pirate.

To his fellow Englishmen Dampier was a privateer captain's mate, who was present on innumerable bloody occasions when the English took their revenge on the Spanish in America. It would have been wonderful to see William Dampier going about his work of studying the earth, in the wild company of pirates, Campeche loggers, desperadoes and ignorant adventurers, watching the sea-currents and testing the winds. He walked strange beaches to take notes on mangroves, alligators, turtles, trees, mountains, capes and harbors, and always the weather.

He must have gone without sleep ashore, or on a disorderly buccaneer ship, or a pirate expedition, to keep the orderly, precise and wonderfully faithful notes of his "Discourse of the Trade-Winds, Breezes, Storms, Seasons of the Year, Tides and Currents of the Torrid Zone throughout the World."

He wrote:

Stormes within the Tropicks are not so frequent there, as they are in Latitudes near the Poles; yet they are nevertheless expected yearly in their proper months; and when they do come, they blow exceeding fierce, though indeed some years they do not come at all.

He described the "Tuffoons" of the East Indies, which he knew very well, and the violent north winds "that frequently blow in the Bay of Mexico from October till March . . . most violent in December and January," and in other parts of the West Indies.

The Hurricane-clouds tower up their Heads, pressing forwards as if they all strove for Precedency, yet so linked one within another that all move alike. Besides, the edges of these Clouds are gilded with various and afrighting Colours, the very Edge of all seems to be of a pale fire-colour, next that of a dull yellow, and nearer the Body of the Cloud of a Copper-Colour, and the Body of the Cloud which is very thick appears extraordinary black; and altogether it looks very terrible and amazing even beyond Expression. . . . I know no Difference between a Hurricane among the Caribbee-Islands in the West-Indies, and a Tuffoon on the coast of China in the East-Indies, but only the Name: and I am apt to believe that both Words have one signification, which is, violent Storm.

Dampier, on a long voyage to the East Indies, did not see or have any reports of an Atlantic hurricane in 1683. Nor was it noticed by a New Englander named William Phips, who had scraped up enough money in Boston to go to England for the purpose of raising money to try to find the famous lost treasure of the Silver Shoals. For two years he importuned the Duke of Albemarle and other big-wigs to get the support and permission of King Charles the Second.

Phips was there in 1684 when Robert de la Salle, the able French explorer of Canada, coasted Florida and went ashore at Apalache Bay, and found the Indians friendly. He was convinced he had found the country of De Soto's long-sought Mississippi, fertile, filled with game, a valuable land.

Such clouds as Dampier described rose before a hurricane late in July, at "Fort St. Louis Bay." La Salle's small fleet was all but wrecked. He wandered beyond the Mississippi, intent on the great purpose of France, to hold all the vast country of the mammoth river from Canada to the Gulf of Mexico.

La Salle had not come to his death yet when in Europe the Truce of Ratisbon was signed by England, France, Holland and Spain, that in one stroke made all piracy in the West Indies illegal. But in the rum shops and along the wharves and ports of the south of England men talked only of sunken treasure.

For at last William Phips, the persistent Yankee, sailed from England, with the approval of Charles the Second, in a fine 13-gun frigate, the *Rose,* to find the treasure of the Silver Shoals.

After weeks of sailing among the dangerous Bahama reefs with a rascally crew, he failed to find the right place and had to sail back to England with empty hands. James the Second was now king, and a penny-pincher. In his fury he had Phips thrown into prison.

Phips bounced out again, soon enough, thanks to friends in high places. There must have been something electrifying about Phips's New England energy, because a group of rich and noble backers calling themselves "Gentlemen Adventurers" bought him two ships, the *James and Mary*, and the *Henry of London*, loaded with goods to be sold in the islands.

They sailed in the autumn of 1686, bucking turbulent winds. The two ships arrived in Puerto Plata in Puerto Rico, where the survivors of the *Nuestra Señora de la Concepcion* had found help so many years before. Phips sold his goods, bought supplies, and to avert suspicion, sent off the *Henry* alone with Captain William Rogers with a few Indian divers, to scout the Silver Shoals.

A message came that they had found seven ingots of silver, two bars and about 2,000 doubloons. The Captain had been paddling in a canoe slowly along a reef, staring through sea water clear as green glass down to the coral heads furred with waving purple sea-fans. The Captain sent down an Indian diver for a fan; he came up gasping that it was rooted in the coral shell of a great bar of silver.

The two ships sailed west before they made their way back to the Shoals, unobserved they hoped. The divers worked until they fell nearly dead on the decks, among their trove of two thousand pounds of ingots, pieces of eight, bars of silver, rotted bags of pearls and jewels. There seemed to be no end to the wealth tumbled there among the old guns.

By June, fearful of pirates, both ships were home in London River. The Duke of Albemarle, a guard of soldiers, the Gentlemen Adventurers and the financial officers of the King came aboard. The total of recovered treasure was 22,196 pounds of silver ingots, 30,326 pounds of pieces of eight, 336 great bars of silver with the mint marks, and jewels and worked gold to an enormous value.

William Phips, a rich man with his one-sixteenth share, was knighted by James the Second.

Phips's third expedition to the Shoals found a crowd of vessels, making an untidy shouting village in the green foamy and sparkling water over the hidden shoals. When Phips drove them off, his divers brought up only a few ingots more.

Modern diving equipment has proved that in all these centuries the old ship has rotted apart and, weighted with coral, slipped down the steep edge of reef and dropped into the purple-black, channeled deeps.

Sir William Phips became sheriff of Boston. When his last backer, the Prince of Orange, became William the Third of England, he made Phips the first native-born governor of Massachusetts Bay Colony.

Long before that, a New England ship captain brought from Madagascar to the tidewater Carolinas a bag of rice seed. The rich mud swamps and slow rivers, marked with canals and dikes, produced the great rice crops which, from March to August, made plantation owners prosperous, and trade important with the West Indies. The only enemy was the hurricanes which drove in from the Atlantic, ruining the harvest and the green fields with salt.

To the English colonies themselves the Spanish in St. Augustine and the missions of Georgia were an even more constant menace, after an English pirate named Agramont looted and burned St. Augustine.

About noon of the seventeenth of August, 1686, therefore, three small Spanish galleys sailed up the Port Royal River and landed 200 armed men below a settlement called "Stuart's Town" on an island below the present town of Beaufort. As the English guns fired the alarm, the Spaniards attacked. The English left. The Spaniards looted and burned for three days.

Lord Cardross, the founder of Stuart Town, ordered the whole country alarmed, the militia out, and the Council to meet him in Charleston on the twenty-third of August.

The night of the twenty-fifth was black and menacing. Word came that the Spaniards had destroyed a house on the Edisto River, and were burning and carrying away Negroes from a plantation near New London. Captain Daniel and ninety men went out to their assistance in weather violently windy.

Suddenly, a full hurricane blew down on them. The high winds and piercing rain continued only four or five hours, but it "was attended with such dismall dreadfull and fatall consequence that the hand of Almighty God seemed to concur with the malice of our enemies to hasten our ruin and desolation," as the letter written after the event to the Lords Proprietors in London testified. "All the ships and vessels in the Roads and harbours were driven up on the land and whether any of them can be fitted out again. The whole country is one entire map of Devastation. The greatest part of our houses are blown down and still lie in their ruins many of us not having the least cottage to secure us from the rigours of the weather. The long incessant rains destroyed all the goods in the houses. The corn beaten down lyes rotting on the ground. What corn escaped was eaten by the cattle, and many cattle were killed by the fall of trees. The rest were running wild. Four miles of trees were down over the paths. Everybody," the letter went on, "was depressed because the Spaniards sent word they would return and destroy Charleston."

The letter asked for thousands of pounds for reparation and "a ship of force to lye along our coasts with ammunition of all sorts." "More English have gone off than have come on," the letter concluded. "Neither is this (as we humbly conceive) a tyme for yr. Lordships to stand on niceties and punctilios if yr. Lordpps. think your interest in this country be of value great enough to deserve your regard. We resolve not to quit the country. Our natural courage is not lost."

Charleston was in a bad way with its hurricane, the first of a long line. Its first pine dwellings were down, the cedarwood furniture broken, its West Indian sugar melted away, as the waves and spray and rain washed up its low early streets. But the hurricane had drowned out the Spaniards also. Charleston was never in such danger again.

The hurricanes of 1691 and 1692 wrecked four fast Spanish treasure frigates below "Los Viboras" to be picked over by a cloud of pirates and plowed across Cuba to Havana. It was less famous than the earthquake of '92 that drowned Jamaica's Port Royal as Spain conquered Guatemala in the last burst of her old energy.

4 THE RETURN OF THE FRENCH

The same hurricanes often linked with a pall of desolation nearby islands of the Antilles, as remote from each other as England and France which occupied them.

After William Dampier, there were no scientists at all in the English islands in any way like the two remarkable Dominican priests who, successively, for more than half a century, observed and wrote about the island birds, plants, trees, fish, rivers, Carib Indians, Negro superstitions, and especially hurricanes.

"They never used to come except every seven years, but they have become much more frequent since the Antilles have been inhabited," wrote gentle, keenly observant Father du Tertre, in his *Histoire Générale de l'Establissment des Colonies Françoises dans les Ant-Isles de l'Amerique*. Of course he meant inhabited by white men. "L'ouragan," as the French called them, he said was, "an impetuous wind which runs through all the courses of the compass, that is to say, that blows from all points of the horizon one after the other. . . . Before the coming of the storm, birds seem to be filled with anxiety, flying everywhere, gathering on houses and cliffs as if they tried to find refuge from something. . . . Four-footed beasts bunch together as if they felt an earthquake coming, pawing and bellowing as if overtaken with terror. . . . After a hurricane, the birds try to find food among the broken trees and plants stripped of seeds. Those of one island fly to the next, and vice versa, until they fall exhausted and can be picked up in the hand."

He described three otherwise unrecorded hurricanes in 1637, at Martinique, of which the third ruined what the others left. "It began with a noise in the trees as if one heard distant wagons rumbling over cobbles. For three hours there were such whirlwinds that it seemed as if the whole island would be swallowed up. Forests were blown down and only those houses spared that were banked with stones. The sky was like molten metal with a continued crackling of thunder and lightning so frequent that one was forced to shut one's eyes or fall flat on the ground. . . . The wind changed so suddenly after six o'clock that ships and sailors were blown on the rocks. All trees but a few were thrown down, all the domestic and native fowl were killed, rabbits, dogs, pigs. The manioc was uprooted from the ground. There was famine afterwards."

After the 1656 hurricane he wrote that there was infection in the air and a plague of worms so covered the ground that they were afraid they would have to abandon the island. Of hurricanes he wrote again in his second volume, "They are the most horrible and violent tempests one can name, true pictures of the final fire and destruction of the world. . . . If this disorder occurred more often,

I don't know who would have the heart or courage to go to the Indies."

He was the first person to set down what the Carib Indians thought about hurricanes. "Many people believe that the savages perceived the coming of hurricanes long beforehand and are warned by their witch doctors; at least, since the Isles have been inhabited, no hurricane has arrived that the savages have not predicted. For myself, I think this is pure fable because the savages have not failed to predict one every year, even if they have been proved false."

Twice in 1694, at Barbados, in '95 once at Martinique, monstrous Atlantic hurricanes struck. It was twenty years after Louis the Fourteenth had put a stop to the fights between private owners that had held back the islands' development, by taking them all for the French Crown.

The brilliant Dominican, Father Jean-Baptiste Labat, arrived in Martinique in '94, having observed everything on his voyage which he set down in his vivid narrative, *Memoires des Nouveaux Voyages Faits Aux Isle de l'Amerique.*

He was certain hurricanes were caused either by the movement of the earth around the sun or the sun around the earth. "Or this compression and rarefaction of the air is the cause of the winds. They are not here," he announced firmly, "by accident."

Father Labat was in Martinique for the hurricane of October 20, 1695. When the winds began, Labat galloped on horseback to his church, snatched the Sacrament from the altar in its covering and fled through the tempest so strong he had to hold on to the neck of his horse, through the open meadow like a sea of waves. Father du Tertre was a merciful man, who prayed that owners of slaves would have pity for them. But Labat was a big, energetic, square-faced man, ruddy, tireless and ruthless, whose driving energy made him a great administrator of Dominican property in the islands, built sugar works, plantations, mills, canals and churches. He ate with gusto such special dishes of the island as wild parrots roasted with honey and spices, befriended the smugglers and freebooters on whom the islands depended for most of their supplies, and whose traffic was increased after every hurricane.

He was a magnetic and terrible figure to the Negroes, whom he worked almost to death. He believed implicitly in their black magic and punished it by flaying with whips and rubbing the raw flesh with lime juice and red pepper. He lives today in the islands as a figure of extraordinary legend, galloping his horse through hurricanes, moving with a light up inaccessible cliffs, no longer man or priest but an evil demon, responsible for many of the ills of the Negro people he hated.

The coast of Florida, so long known to shipwrecks, in those days would have been almost unknown to us, if a very different sort of man, a respectable Quaker merchant by the name of Jonathan Dickenson, had not, with his family and servants, taken passage from Jamaica in the barkentine *Reformation*, for the Quaker city of Philadelphia. In the Florida Straits they were wrecked by a hurricane among wet sand and blown scrub about at Jupiter Inlet, on that "wilderness country looking very dismal" as he wrote later in his journal. The bedraggled and wretched party were captured by Florida coast Indians, now friendly to the Spaniards and hating the English whom they knew chiefly as slavers. They were forced to march northward to St. Augustine in the drenching cold rains that followed.

The Scots from the ill-fated colony of Darien suffered an even greater wretchedness from a hurricane in 1700. Seven half-rotting vessels finally got away from that place which all Scotland had been enthusiastic to colonize, and straggled up past St. Augustine in Florida to founder on the third of September before the small town of Charleston. The five hundred English people, as well as Indians and Negro slaves, peering fearfully through the rain and the hissing wind, as trees and steeples crashed down soundlessly in the tumult that sunk ships at the docks from Boston and the West Indies, knew well it was a hurricane.

By daylight, they saw that the waves and the terrible undertow had sucked away the timber pilings before the new fort on the river. A new inlet had been opened into Winyah Bay. And a crazy Scottish frigate from Darien, the *Rising Sun*, had broken up, with ninety-seven men and the captain lost, out of 220 people aboard.

The Scots left alive, rescued by pitying Charlestonians, were the luckiest of all that expedition. They stayed in Carolina, and became the ancestors of a sturdy line of Scottish citizens who made names for their energy and fair dealing with Indian tribes all the way to the Mississippi, and left their marks on the histories of that colony and of such towns in South Carolina as "Darien."

That same hurricane ruined the rice planters up the Cape Fear River, who moved at once to Charleston. But with every hurricane that howled across Barbados out of the Atlantic, more ruined men moved up the Cape Fear River to settle in America.

More Europeans were moving up the rivers of Carolina, Virginia and Delaware with every new war that blew up in Europe as the feeble-minded Charles the Second of Spain died. William the Third of England died also, as England, with the failure of her expedition against Cartagena, established the British Empire firmly in the Mediterranean and in the slave trade, by taking and holding Gibraltar.

All this time the French were pushing steadily down the Mississippi from Canada and up from the French islands to the Gulf of Mexico coasts. For one hundred and fifty years since Tristan de Luna's hurricane, Spain had kept only an old sand and log stockade at Pensacola.

Now the first of four remarkable French brothers, Jean Baptiste Le Moyne de Bienville ably serving the ambitions of Louis the Fourteenth, had visited Pensacola disguised as a servant, had already decided Pensacola harbor was useless, filled with shifting sand bars. But the French dodging about the Gulf of Mexico convinced Spain that they were pirates with designs on the fleet from Veracruz. Two hundred Spanish soldiers were sent to rebuild the Pensacola fort, San Carlos de Austria.

Bienville, who had also scouted the Texas coast in vain for a harbor to guard the mouth of the Mississippi, built the first French fort at Biloxi, with shelter for many ships within Ship Island. He ran up the French flag over the live oaks, palmettos and camphor trees about Fort Maurepas. The first houses on the mainland were built of stout clay walls stuffed with moss, to defy the Spanish and the autumn hurricanes. He made friends and fighting allies of the Southeastern Indians, who promptly moved away from Spanish Pensacola to be near the more generous French and brought with them down the rivers the valuable trade of all that inland Indian country.

Although the end of the war in Europe put a Bourbon on the Spanish throne, making France and Spain loyal to the same family, in America Spain refused to give up Pensacola. Bienville's brothers, Le Moyne d'Iberville and Le Moyne de Seringuy, were ordered to fortify Dauphine Island by the mouth of the Mobile River, a good anchorage and excellent hurricane shelter.

For three years no hurricanes troubled that often troubled shore. But in the meantime, Spain was so worried about the English drifting down from Carolina into Georgia, that the Castillo de San Marcos at St. Augustine was strengthened to guard the home-going Plate Fleets.

Meantime, everywhere, from Boston or Newport to Philadelphia and Charleston, to St. Kitts, to Barbados and back, from Venezuela to Cartagena, Veracruz to Havana, Jamaica, Santo Domingo, Puerto Rico and the French islands, went the coastwise and increasing commerce of the great Bay of America, in Chesapeake Bay schooners, luggers, sloops, French pirogues, English "periagers," shaky old galleons, carracks, snows, the elegant French fighting frigates, hookers. They caught the worst of the hurricanes now.

5 STORMS OVER ENGLAND AND FLORIDA

In November of 1703 there was a hurricane which plowed from the Atlantic across southern England and was made famous by an obscure political pamphleteer, Daniel Defoe. He was just out of prison for jibing at Whigs and Tories in the same article. It was six years before he wrote *Robinson Crusoe*.

A middlesized spare man about forty, with a brown complexion, a brown wig, a sharp chin and gray eyes, of course he needed money. The storm gave him the idea of collecting eye-witness accounts to add to everything he wrote. He printed and sold it as a pamphlet under the title, *The Storm or a Collection of the Most Remarkable Casualties and Disasters which happened in the late Dreadful Tempest both by Sea and Land*. Like his histories of the plague and of the great fire in London, it was the forerunner of *The Tatler* and *The Spectator* and the modern newspaper.

It was clearly a hurricane. He wrote:

It had blown exceedingly hard for about fourteen days past: and that so hard, that we thought it terrible weather: several stacks of chimnies were blown down, and several ships were lost, and the tiles in many places were blown off the houses; and the nearer it came to the fatal 26th of November, the tempestuousness of the weather increased.

On the Wednesday morning before, it was fair weather and blew hard; but not so as to give any apprehensions, till about four o'clock in the afternoon the wind increased, and with squalls of rain and terrible gusts blew very furiously . . . had not the great storm followed so soon, this had passed for a great wind.

On Friday . . . about ten o'clock, the mercury sank lower than ever I had observed it.

About 12 that night, [according to Defoe's correspondent, the Reverend Mr. William Denham,] the storm awakened me which gradually increased till near 3 that morning; and from thence till near 7 it continued in the greatest excess: and then began to abate and the mercury to rise swiftly, It was very dark and Mr. Denham's wind vane blew down but by information from millers and others forced to venture abroad, it had blown about S.W. by S. or nearer to the S. in the beginning and to veer about towards the west towards the end of the storm, as far as W.S.W.

Defoe continues:

About one, or at least by two o'clock, few people that were capable of any sense of danger, were so hardy as to lie in bed. . . . Most people expected the fall of their houses. And yet, nobody dared quit their tottering habitations: for, whatever the danger was within doors, it was worse without. The bricks, tiles and stones from the tops of the houses flew with such force and so thick in the streets. . . . The force of the wind blew the tiles point blank; where there was room for them to fly, the author of this has seen tiles blown from a house above thirty or forty yards and stuck from five to eight inches into the solid earth. Pieces of timber, iron and sheets of lead have from higher buildings been blown much farther.

In the last part of the storm, according to Defoe, the greatest damage was done.

Several ships that rode it out till now gave up all, for no anchor would hold. Even the ships in the river Thames were all blown away from their moorings and from Execution Dock to Limehouse Hall there was but four ships that rid it out, the rest were . . . huddled together and drove on shore, heads and sterns, one upon another.

There was a prodigious tide the next day but one . . . that brought up the sea raging that in some parts of England the water rising six or eight feet higher than it was ever known to do in the memory of man; by which ships were fleeted up upon the firm land . . . and an incredible number of cattle and people drowned.

There was evidently some sort of lull at sunrise, proving that the center of the hurricane passed over London River. After some hours it began to blow hard again, an extreme storm with violent gusts, a black cloud, thunder and some rain. It blew hard for days. Chimneys fell, ships were sunk. It had blown hard, in all, for nearly a week.

The hurricane came from the west across the Atlantic, some thought, according to Mr. Defoe, from Florida and Virginia in America. He learned "they felt upon that coast an unusual tempest a few days before the fatal 27th of November . . . continuing its course, we find it carried a true line clear over the continent of Europe, traversed England, France, Germany, the Baltic and passing the northern continent of Sweden, Finland, Moscovy and part of Tartary must at last lose itself in the vast northern ocean."

Seventeen ships were lost at sea. English ports, Grimsby, Hull, Yarmouth, the river Thames, Gravesend, Portsmouth, Cowes, Plymouth, Falmouth and Bristol, were filled with fleets swept home by the first winds. The havoc there was terrible. The Russian fleet of a hundred sail was scattered along the English coast. Many foundered and all their men lost. Sir Cloudesley Shovel was just arriving with the Mediterranean fleet which was driven off as far as the coast of Norway. The Virginia fleet, the Barbados fleet, lay scattered in all the ports. There were many others. "Horror and confusion seized upon all." Some said 30,000 seamen were lost in the ports alone and 300 sail of ships.

As for England itself, houses were untiled, hovels leveled and trees and orchards down everywhere, too many for counting. The city of London was a strange spectacle. The price of tiles rose from 50 shillings per thousand to six pounds. The charges for bricklayers were so extravagant that an "incredible number of houses remained all the winter uncovered. Whole ranks of buildings were covered with deal boards. . . . Above two thousand stacks of chimneys were blown down." Twenty-one people killed, many more drowned or buried or beaten to pieces by falling bricks and tiles. Hundreds were wounded or maimed. Like any good reporter, Daniel Defoe gives names and addresses and stories, for page after page. In Threadneedle Street, one Mr. Simpson "refused to get out of his bed as his family urged him. They left his room, the chimney fell, broke through the roof and killed him."

Brick walls, parts of her Majesty's palace, many public edifices, were down. The lead on the tops of the churches and other buildings was in many places rolled up like a roll of parchment and blown clear off. Christ Church spires and pinnacles everywhere were down and "above a hundred elms in St. James's Park, of great growth, said to be planted by Cardinal Wolsey."

There was incredible damage in the country across which the hurricane cut its swath; in Suffolk, Oxfordshire, Northampton, Gloucestershire, Somersetshire, where an eight-foot tide was forced up the Severn; Wiltshire, where a stone of 400-pound weight was carried seven yards; Worcestershire, Warwickshire, Surrey, and Sussex, where a wagon of hay was forced down a field through a hedge and so far into the clay road six horses could not pull it out. In Kent above 1,107 houses, outhouses and barns were blown flat. Barley, oats, corn, hay were ruined everywhere. At Cranbrook, sixteen miles from the sea, the rain was so salt the cattle could not eat for days.

The most remarkable of Defoe's stories is his matter-of-fact narrative of the men on the Goodwin Sands. They were seamen of the many hundreds of wrecked ships who found foothold upon the Goodwin Sands when the tide was out. "It must have been a sad spectacle to behold the poor seamen walking to and fro upon the sands, to view their postures and the signals they made for help, which, by the assistance of glasses, was easily seen from the shore. Here they had a few hours reprieve but had neither present refreshment nor any hope of life for they were sure to be all washed into another world at the reflux of the tide. Some boats are said to come very near them in quest of booty, and in search of plunder, and to carry off what they could get, but nobody concerned themselves for the lives of those miserable creatures."

One man alone, evidently, a Mr. Thomas Powell of Deal, a slop-seller by trade, made application to the customs-house officers for the assistance of their boats and men, to save the lives of as many as they could. They refused.

Mr. Powell then made a general offer from his own pocket of five shillings a head for all the lives anyone could save. He and some willing men took the customs boat by force and with a few other boats saved two hundred men. The others were all drowned when the tide came back. Mr. Powell had the greatest difficulty in getting part of the money from the government, which he spent out of his own pocket not only to save the men but to feed and clothe them and send them home. Nobody else seemed to care, or even think they should care, in that ruthless and indifferent age.

Still, a hurricane in old England was a very different thing from a hurricane in the young settlements of the West. Le Moyne d'Iberville had chosen for his city up the Mississippi a muddy ridge within a crescent of the great yellow river, sloping off to green swamps and willow jungles to a pale lagoon he named Lake Pontchartrain. The city was New Orleans. Almost at once there were nearly one hundred bark-roofed houses overlooking the river by the Place d'Armes and excited men talking and slipping in the muddy streets. In 1711, it was added to the growing list of hurricaned cities. That vast engine of wind and rain had a long way to churn in from the beaten sea, over coastal islands and delta swamps and bayous, to flatten the houses into mud. After it came the problems of drainage, sewage, polluted drinking water, and disease that for centuries would plague that city more constantly than hurricanes.

A group of Germans, who had ventured upriver as far as the great rock cliffs narrowing the Arkansas River, had been flooded out by the rains of the hurricane's right sector, hurried back to New Orleans to beg for a ship to take them home. The mud was dry by that time. Houses were being repaired. A supply vessel had come in with more people from France, and the first men were showing the newcomers the sights. This, after all, was New Orleans. There must already have been some charm in it, some heady spirit that kept men gay. The Germans stayed.

The next year was Havana's turn. It was being rebuilt in stone when this new hurricane burst over it. To the east, by the village of Jaimanitos, a great painted Spanish galley lay among the scattered broken boxes and canvas rags and drowned men within the wave-blasted mangroves. Three out of six such galleys had managed to run into harbor. This one had carried treasure to the amount of three million gold pesos of which the Admiral Diego de Alarçon managed to salvage only one million.

The same year the English of Jamaica learned about hurricanes. The experienced planters from Barbados and St. Kitts, brought in to bring some sense to the new colony, knew them too well. But the unfortunates from London jails and slums were scared out of their wits. New colonists and old pirates and seamen were drowned in hurricane waves and river floods. Many others were killed in the wreckage of English houses built of flimsy boards. Only strong old Spanish masonry was left standing.

The hurricane of September 15, 1713, searched out the weakness of the city of Charleston, Carolina, impoverished by the war in Europe. The half-built roof of "the new church" was blown off and walls knocked down. Waves bursting white filled the darkened streets. Suddenly the wind chopped about and spared them worse damage although their losses in standing crops and full warehouses amounted to one hundred thousand pounds. The church would stand roofless a long time.

Because the Spanish king was poor with wars, Don Rodriguez de Torres, Admiral of the Veracruz Flota, sailed from Havana with fourteen galleons late in June, 1714. The ships were blessed, Masses were sung, the bells clanged.

For all that as the overloaded vessels entered the Florida channel, bitter gusts drove the ships along the water. Don Roderiguez de Torres clung to the bucking rail of his after castle, blinded by rain and salt spray. There, where many of his ships were blown, they sank behind a key now called "Carysfort" for a later English ship that was lost there. Or perhaps it was Key Largo. Don Roderiguez and many men got somehow to land.

The sun came out hot next day over the littered sand and the naked mangroves, over the lime-green sea beyond and the milky waters of the lagoon where many men and women floated dead, or on planks feebly tried to reach shore.

A Spanish vessel or two that had run to safety carried the living, and the news, back to Havana.

At once, the Governor of Cuba sent sixty soldiers and Indian divers from the Pearl island and what ships he could get, to salvage the lost treasure. They set up huts and a storehouse under palmetto

fronds on the sands. They even brought in Florida Indians and
trained them to dive with rocks to take them down, in crude diving
bells from Spain. All day the naked brown men flashed down among
the shadows of the wrecks. All night there were flares on the beach.
Silver bars were stacked up in the storehouse, with chests and
casks, and bags of pearls and worked gold ornaments and emeralds.
A supply ship had carried back two million pieces of eights' worth
of mixed salvage. Sixty men still guarded 350,000 pieces of eight.

Now Nassau on the Bahama island of New Providence was infested by the dregs and scrapings of piracy, English, Dutch, mixed
bloods, forced to leave their old haunts in the West Indies by the
stricter regulations of nations. Old pirates retired to Out Island hide-
outs came in for a carouse with some younger Brethren of the
Coast, along that crowded, noisy drunken bay-front street. Now
they gathered like buzzards.

A powerful pirate captain named Henry Jennings, master of
a small sloop, *Bathsheba of Jamaica*, let go her anchor in Nassau
harbor. He liked the looks of pirate Benjamin Hornigold's larger
sloop, *Mary*, which had been snatched from a man named Anthony
Goulding off the Cuban coast. Jennings took the *Mary* and sailed
with 140 men and six guns to scout the Florida Keys, where he
captured a larger Spanish ship, sailed from Nassau in it with 200
men and was back with a big French ship, 32 guns and a rich cargo
of European goods. He loaded all these vessels with men and
sailed to the Florida Keys as commodore of as big a fleet of pirate
craft as this coast had seen. Benjamin Hornigold was there on the
Mary again, and Charles Vane and a pirate called Archer and a
Captain Cuthbert, whose name somehow was given to an enclosed
blue lake among mangroves in south Florida.

In broad sunlight an orderly army of pirates crept up the sands
to the Spanish camp. When they began firing the astonished Spanish
soldiers backed away into the scrub, and kept going. The pirates
took everything, burned the huts. They spread on the sands scarlet
satin cloaks and their own ragged shirts and knelt in a great wolfish
ring around Henry Jennings, dividing the ingots and wedges, the
discarded weapons and clothing and food, according to the strict
laws of the account.

That year the Spanish Crown did not get all his revenues. The
pirates, scattered to Jamaica, St. Kitts, Barbados or back to Nassau,

where they got drunker than ever and gambled away their silver, stole supplies and burned houses, and ravished the wives and daughters of the agonized settlers.

In Charleston, where they had raised money to repair the church and put on the roof at last, a hurricane, on the tenth of September, 1714, knocked the church flat. The raging sea cut a new inlet across one of those long islands to the marshy inland waterway. The discouraged people asked for help from England. There is no record that they received any. The concern of the English government now was all for the troubled Bahamas, from which, as more pirates flocked there, the frightened settlers put their families and goods into whatever honest vessels they could get and sailed to Virginia where they hoped to be safe.

Many men would get excited about that treasure lost in the hurricane. As late as 1855 a number of Harvard students from Boston in a Salem ship are said to have sailed down to the Keys and recovered $1,000,000 worth of silver. This ship was lost in a storm or hurricane off Monomoy Point in Massachusetts and the men barely escaped drowning.

The current European war was over, with the Treaty of Utrecht, 1713. Queen Anne died. And briefly, Great Britain declared war with Spain again.

Spanish Admiral Don Juan de Ubilla had orders, that year of 1715, to get the treasure home without fail. He sailed from Havana on July 31 with fourteen galleons and a hired Dutch ship. A hurricane found him and wrecked them all on the east coast of Florida, about where Sebastian is today.

The Spanish sent up their salvage crews. The Bahama pirates gathered around like buzzards. Apparently everybody got some of that treasure, but not all. Even to recent years Spanish silver coins called "pistareens" have been picked up on Sebastian Beach.

The English government could not let the pirates ruin the Bahamas. They were too important, both as outlooks on the Florida channel and as refuges to English ships in times of hurricanes. Captain Woods Rogers, with whom Dampier had sailed on a famous Pacific voyage, came blazing into Nassau harbor like the incarnated wrath of George I and nearly one thousand scared Brethren of the Coast capitulated. He swore he would hang every men of them at once who would not then and there give his oath never to go pirating again, not even against the Spanish. After that, if anyone ever reverted he would be caught and hanged promptly on any gibbet from Jamaica to Execution Dock.

Many got away. But more than two hundred villains, including those leaders and veterans, Henry Jennings, Benjamin Hornigold, Charles Vane, Cuthbert and Archer, Matthew Low and the rest, crowded the sand before Captain Rogers on his platform to hold up their tarred hands and give their solemn oaths. He gave them, singly, the King's Pardon.

Many of them, who took to planting, complained they could not make decent livings except by piracy. Many reverted. Some found safe harbors up Carolina rivers or among the lonely sand islands of the Outer Banks of Hatteras. For a while many colonists took shares in their ventures. So Edward Teach, alias Blackbeard, was said to have found backing among influential Carolina citizens. But in time the pirates were all caught and hanged.

When the colonists themselves grew rich, pirates, no longer even secretly useful, were shot.

The Spanish Crown failed in a frantic effort to take Nassau in the Bahamas. Already Spain had hurried to strengthen the rotting stockade and rusting cannon of Fort Santa Maria at Pensacola. An expedition from Spanish St. Augustine was sent to build a fort at Apalache.

John Law's loaded ships were coming in to Mobile village, crowding Dauphine Island with troops and assorted colonists. The French had six garrisons below the Illinois, three on the Mississiippi, three on Mobile Bay and River, all manned by 1,000 troops and Paris guttersnipes. They were pushing garrisons to Natchitoches on the Texas frontier. The narrow streets of New Orleans were full of new people.

Pensacola, taken and retaken by Spanish and French, at the end of the current war was given back to Spain. The Mississippi Bubble blew up, leaving the Le Moynes in peace to develop Louisiana.

Hurricanes were everywhere. In 1723 New Orleans lost its new hospital and the next year a more terrible blow leveled houses and cleared swaths in the forest. In '25, many French ships in Martinique's fine harbor, then called Fort Royal, ready to sail to Haiti which had been given to France by the Treaty of Madrid, were wrecked in a hurricane that blasted the plantations up the mountain slopes. Jamaica in '26, Antigua in '28, among others, were hurricane stricken, and Charleston in America where the wind backed the tide up the rivers and ships rode the wild waters up against crumbling house walls.

Life was a changing pattern around those islands and along those coasts but hurricanes, unpredicted, relentless, inevitable within the range of their courses, went on as usual.

BOOK FOUR

TIMES OF

CHANGE

1 PEACE FOR THE SUGAR ISLANDS

The English sugar islands, Barbados, St. Kitts, Antigua, Montserrat, Nevis and Jamaica, began to boil with excitement over the sudden fortunes made as all Europe, as well as England, demanded more and more West Indian sugar. Prices went higher every year. Every island stripped its slopes of all growing things but sugar cane. Planters, dizzy with new wealth, left their termite-ridden plantation houses, their fields, their hordes of slaves, to overseers and agents, and flung their money away among the extravagances of Paris, Bath and London.

Less fortunate men, with their idle families, endured with impatience the heat, malaria, yellow fever and boredom until the next harvest. Their houses were bare boards, furnished with slave-made furniture. Their towns were dusty, hot and nondescript, their roofs shingled or even thatched. Streets were narrow and rutted, roads fit only for cane carts or horsemen.

There were some intelligent and able men, like the Pinneys of Nevis, who retired, after generations, to country places in England. But most resident planters, with the white overseers and young English bookkeepers wasting their absentee employers' hopes in idleness, ignorance and incompetence made up a curious society. London fashion, they wore silks and velvets, both expensive and hot. They ate enormous meals from silver dishes: turtle, turkey, fowl, fish of all kinds, stringy local beef, always highly spiced; they were served at every meal with coffee, tea, chocolate, wines and rums. They were served badly by incompetent house slaves, barefooted, not long from Africa.

The men, whether they could afford it or not, drank to excess, fought duels, gambled on cards, horses, cockfights, kept Negro mistresses and often lost them and whole plantations on a single wager. In a society beset by disease, and which valued extravagance more than anything, many went to the devil and died of it.

Yet when the English fleet came in to Nevis in the winters, no watering place was gayer. Well-to-do people flocked out from England to Charlestown for the season, the sulphur baths, the balls, the banquets. There were moonlight horseback rides up mountain trails to some great estate houses blazing with candles. There was feasting, gaming, dancing, music and lovemaking. Beyond the laughter lay the long slope of cane fields and the breathing silver of the sea.

Only a few of the hardworking planters had any feeling for their own islands. Most estates were loaded with debts. Land was mortgaged to buy more slaves, since they died constantly, and slaves were mortgaged to buy more land as the heavy cane yield exhausted the soil. Estates encumbered with debt were handed down from father to son, making the heirs all the more ready to spend on high living what cash they could get their hands on. And still sugar prices went up.

The only real menace to all this was the hurricanes. Hurricanes made kindling of plantation houses and slave huts, tore off the roofs of sugar works, even leveled masonry walls. Hurricanes waves undermined wharfs, warehouses and waterside streets, cut great gullies in fertile slopes and washed the good soil into the sea. Hurricanes overturned sugar ships in harbor, leaching the sugar out of the hogsheads. Hurricanes sank ships at sea carrying sugar to England or bringing the supplies on which all the islands depended: New England salt herring and Carolina rice for slave food, cheap Osnaburg cloth for slave clothing, navy cutlasses for cane knives, sugar mill equipment, even the oxen for the carts and the mules for turning the grinding mills, windmill parts, copper boilers, sugar mill machinery, barrel staves, building material, shingles, bricks, lime for the fields, and all the luxuries demanded by the planters and their families.

Hurricanes sank slave ships, reducing the supply from Africa of the slave labor necessary for every detail of sugar production, and increasing the profits in slavedealing made by the English Royal African Company and its noble shareholders.

In fact, everything about the production of sugar was dependent on hurricanes. Hurricanes set the schedule for the entire year.

Planting began after October and the hurricane season, and continued until Christmas. Then the slaves were allowed their brief riotous holiday. The fourteen months' cane was ripe for cutting in January. It was hauled to the heavy rollers of the mill, turned by oxen or mules, waterpower or windmills as in Barbados. The clear juice ran along a wooden trough to the coppers of the boiling house, over fires hot with cane trash. Boiling went on day and night until the tense moment when the skilled Negro sugar boiler thrust his finger and thumb into the seething mass. If it threaded right, the sugar was made. The cooled raw crystals, bright yellow or straw colored, gray or low brown, were shoveled into hogsheads, tierces or small barrels to be shipped to England.

The sugar market itself, first at Bristol, later at London, was all a gamble. Prices varied as the quality of sugar varied from year to year, according to the demands of grocers for Christmas, of refiners, and of the raw-sugar dealers who sold great stocks to northern Europe. The British government grew rich on heavy sugar duties.

The first sugar shipped in spring, when English ships raced out and back for the first sales, got the best prices. But the best sugars might be deteriorated by a rough voyage on the edge of an early July hurricane. Sugars let to stand too long in Bristol warehouses, as the molasses drained off, fetched inferior prices.

Technically, prices were high for fine sugars, less for middling or low sugars. But gluts or shortages made a difference. The long green fields of Barbados, crawled over by oxcarts, made very fine sugars, and excellent prices, if a hurricane did not ruin them or there were not too many Demerara sugars unloaded at Bristol. St. Kitts from the sea halfway up the wooded ridge of Mt. Misery produced good muscovado sugars but so did other islands. If one was hurricaned, another was made rich.

The best market began when the first ships carrying spring sugars docked at Bristol before the end of May. Nobody knew what the prices would be. For four months, as the sails of sugar ships whitened the Channel, prices fluctuated madly. There was a great moment of suspense before the last ships came in and the hurricane season began. On the first of August insurance rates were doubled. The very rumors of wars, earthquakes, slave insurrections, hurricanes in one island or another, set the prices see-sawing.

The older sugar islands, their lands exhausted, crowded with

Negroes who must be fed, began a long decline into hopelessness after some hurricane's devastation. Often, after a hurricane which wrecked the supply ships and ruined the garden patches, the white people ate the slaves' herring and rice and the Negroes died of hunger.

It is only rarely that one reads of some strange good a hurricane brought. The more level slopes of Santo Domingo were commonly enriched by mountain soil washed down by hurricane rains. Once in Dominica and Martinique a plague of red ants was drowned out by a hurricane.

This English frenzy about sugar was not shared by the French and the Spanish. They were settlers, proud of their islands, their houses, their Catholic traditions. The French restored Martinique and Guadeloupe after the Seven Years' War, planting not only sugar but food crops, rebuilding cities and churches in stone, planting parks and making good roads.

In Haiti, which the French had quietly occupied in 1696, cane-fields spread along rich valley floors and mountain water poured from stone aqueducts. Plantation mansions were French, among avenues and terraces and gardens, furnished in French styles copied in tropic hardwoods, imported armoires, gilt mirrors and crystal hurricane lamps.

Hurricanes have struck often along the southern coast, like a thrust jaw, of Haiti and on the rocky north coast thrashed by the trade winds. But no hurricane has passed the ramparts of the northern mountains or overtopped, from the south or southeast, the greatest height of the Antilles, the purple-brown rock massif of Morne La Selle. No hurricane has ever smashed the rich green flatness of the Cul-de-Sac valley, or washed away the white dust of hidden valleys, the dust on rocky paths, on thatched hovels behind cactus hedges, on black voodoo rags hanging motionless in the heat on crosses in roadside cemeteries.

Perhaps it is not too much to believe that the deep-rooted Haitian uniqueness, blended of French and African, has developed in the valleys because no hurricane has ever interrupted it with ruin. The fragile, tinted wooden-lace charm of Port-au-Prince, poverty-stricken but not grim, all rusty tin, fading paint—lemon, pink, lavender, dusty white, under the blossoming flame trees, would have blown away long, long ago.

It was not so with the often-hurricaned Spanish cities. To get away from pirates and from the winds and the terrible hurricane waves, many were moved from the seacoast inland, up mountain slopes, leaving only the ruins of some ancient port to recurring destruction. All were rebuilt more strongly, rosy tiles for thatch. Throughout the New World Spanish houses were built in much the same way, thick walls of stone, clay filled with small stones, called "tabby." In St. Augustine they used slabs of heavy coquina shell, and everywhere, even in Spanish Jamaica, timber frames filled with rough stones set in red earth and lime mortar, known as "Spanish walling."

The cities themselves never changed the pattern of their immemorial plazas and promenades, cathedrals and public buildings. Cobbled streets might lead out between houses growing meaner, past deserted convents, old hurricane and earthquake ruins to a dusty country side or down to the idle port. The façades of governors' palaces were no more elaborate with stone lace than the town mansions of rich old families.

The change worked by hurricanes now was more subtle. Such cities, increasingly cut off from communication with Spain by the hurricanes which destroyed even the three-year fleets, were forced to act for themselves, under their own leaders, in their own ways. Their thinking grew more independent, less Spanish, more American.

In the same way, the hurricanes of 1732 could not weaken the hold of the French on Mobile and Biloxi, their plantations inland and their rich trade with the Indians.

A June hurricane of 1733 had ruined the island and the sugar plantations of St. Kitts. In July a Spanish fleet of twenty-one heavily loaded merchant vessels and several stately worm-eaten galleons under Admiral Don Rodriguez de Torres, was wrecked at Matecumbe in the Florida Keys. Don Rodriguez saved his galleon, thirteen ships and a great deal of silver, but he was forced to burn all the other wrecks to keep their cargoes from the Bahama pirates. Many important people were drowned. It was an old, old story.

But not all the English were concentrated in the Sugar Islands. They had inched into Georgia with Oglethorpe and set the first village, Fredericka, on St. Simon's Island, among shaggy live oaks within sound of the surf, and a fort on Cumberland. They smuggled

so profitably in the West Indies that a Spanish war blew up called
"The War of Jenkins's Ear" over a bit of gristle shown to the
English Parliament. An English smuggler named Robert Jenkins
claimed his ear had been cut off by a Spanish officer who captured
Jenkins' ship.

The war in Europe was about the Austrian succession but in
America England felt Spain was weak enough to be attacked.

Yet Spain clung tight to Florida through war and the hurricane
of 1740 that blasted Pensacola.

Hurricanes for eight years sank more ships and hurt more people
than the haphazard fighting. But the energetic coastal English never
lost a chance to harass their ancient enemies the Spanish.

Admiral Don Juan Manuel de Bonilla's hurricane of 1750 made
that clear. His ships were overtaken in the Atlantic and pushed
north toward Hatteras and the surges boiling over the deadly
Diamond Shoals. The broken timbers of five great Spanish ships
were scattered from Currituck Inlet, Hatteras, Drum Head Inlet
to Topsail Inlet by Cape Lookout. The great *Nuestra Señora de
Guadeloupe* was broken on the outer beach of Ocracoke.

Admiral Don Juan Manuel de Bonilla, however, was furiously
aroused at the threat to *Nuestra Señora's* reputed cargo of a million
pieces of eight. He sent men to hire the sloops of seagoing Englishmen, even then living on the Outer Banks, to carry the silver back
to Havana.

The Bankers remembered the Spanish raids of '47 and shook their
heads. A schooner from up north fled with a load of silver. Governor
Johnson had to send over men from the mainland to take the
Spaniards' silver back to Havana, at a good round price.

The Bankers were like that, already a unique breed along that
long, sparsely settled Atlantic coast. They had lived on the Outer
Banks since 1728, driven ashore in storms, and living on the narrow
sun-colored sands or beyond the dunes, in deep pine woods on
quiet sounds. Their houses were built of sea-worn timbers the tides
left on the endless white smoking beaches. Their furnishings had
been flotsam. They scratched out vegetable gardens in pockets of
leaf mold. Their dooryard flowers bloomed all year round in the
warm air. But their lives were all salt water, fishing, oystering, salvaging wrecks, slipping down to the West Indies like other coastal
people and there richly smuggling or even pirating.

Their little villages felt the hurricanes of the next two years when hurricanes turned up along the Sea Islands of Georgia, the Carolinas and the many-armed Chesapeake. Planters of rice, the excellent money crop, suffered ruin that was years repairing, when the voracious winds blew salt water over the rice fields. In New England the fisher people, their boats, their villages, suffered. And especially the farmers and fishermen along the south shore of Long Island, that bore the thundering weight of rollers hurricane-driven all the way up the Atlantic. Small water mills set along Connecticut streams, up rivers from Narragansett and Buzzards Bay, for the grinding of local meal and flour, were smashed by seaward-rushing hurricane floods. The small farms among the rocks of Maine, the lonely hamlets of Cape Cod, endured the additional hardship.

There was only a little time of peace along the hurricane coasts, in which the Spaniards hastily rebuilt their fort on Santa Rosa Island at Pensacola, blown to pieces by the hurricane of 1754, before France and England were fighting again everywhere. In the West Indies, the Seven Years' War added to the debt-ridden English islands the fear of French invasion. But it was the terrible hurricane of 1756 over Barbados that brought its worn-out and mortgaged estates finally into the possession of the Crown.

The English survivor from the Bahamas, William Gerard de Brahm, studying the Florida coast and changing the old Spanish names to English ones, reported a hurricane in '59 which swept sea water over every bit of land from the Dry Tortugas to Key Largo. The master of an English snow, the *Ledbury*, thought in the screaming uproar he was anchoring in the Hawk Channel. Next morning he found himself high in the mangroves of Elliott's Key. Mr. de Brahm doubted that story, but the people of the Keys know that the *Ledbury's* master was not only truthful but lucky.

A hurricane in '61, when Spain was dragged into the war on the side of France, blew across the Cape Fear River and the plantation houses among live oaks and magnolias, looking out over rice fields whitened with salt water. But even that rueful world heard at last that England had taken Havana, for which Spain hastily traded all Florida. The French kept Martinique and Guadeloupe and "the island of New Orleans." But now everything was English to Canada and the Mississippi and there was fine new trade in the English colonies.

In the brief time England held Cuba, the English brought in thousands of strong slaves and cleared and planted thousands of acres for cane fields. After the Treaty of Paris, when it was Spanish again, Cubans went on raising the sugar crops that would exceed the English islands and dominate the world market. Hurricane damage to sugar cane became the most serious loss Cuba had to endure.

English interest in Florida was only that of removing the Spanish menace to Georgia and Carolina. Grass grew in the streets of St. Augustine. English Florida and the English Bahamas controlled the Florida channel. Pensacola and Mobile were almost abandoned.

The only Englishman with any interest in Florida was Dennis Rolle, who obtained from the Crown a grant of forty thousand acres of previously unclaimed Florida land. With one hundred families he sailed from England for St. Marks in Apalache, with that carelessness as to the season which no colonial Englishman would dare. On his way down the inshore current, he was caught off Georgia or Florida by a north-swinging hurricane and forced to put in for shelter up the broad mouth of the St. Johns. He sailed upriver, and took his forty thousand acres where half a mile of cliffs were topped by shell and clay Indian mounds, crowded with shadowy oaks, magnolias, and Spanish orange trees gone wild. Beyond lay open meadows. He called his town of cypress-plank houses Charlotia. The swamps seemed good for rice but too many people died of malaria. The living fled to Georgia or Carolina.

Because of hurricanes, 1765 and '66 were bad years in the French West Indies. St. Pierre, with its lovely harbor filled with ships, its charming parks and French houses, was so badly damaged then, that little attention was paid to hurricane effects on the exposed rocky cape to the south, far across the harbor of Fort-Royal.

There today still is the small, very French village of Trois-Islets, a few narrow houses and an old worn church about a cobbled square. Cane fields go down hill and back toward the mountains and scarlet flamboyants and palmistes shimmer in the sun dazzle.

It was much the same when Joseph-Gaspard Tascher, of an impoverished island family, came home from artillery school in France to work on the harbor fortifications, which failed to keep off the British. Joseph-Gaspard, out of work during the British occupation, was fortunate in marrying a young woman who inherited a sugar plantation at Trois-Islets, "La Pagerie." The Treaty of Paris gave the island back to the French and Lieutenant Tascher turned to his cane growing. In June, 1763, his wife gave birth to a second little girl, baptized Marie Josephine Rose and called "Yayette." But Napoleon Bonaparte made her Empress Josephine of France.

The estate buildings of La Pagerie were impressive for Trois-Islets, a mansion with a gallery and courtyard. The little Yayette lived there for three years, spoiled by her own nurse and the house servants among the one hundred and fifty estate slaves.

In the black dreadful night of August 12, 1766, Trois-Islets was rocked and beaten by the unleashed force of the hurricane whose worst sector demolished St. Pierre. Frightened slaves escaped from their smashed huts to the mansion where the family huddled as tiles blew off and rain and wind rushed in. One wall began to crumble.

Joseph-Gaspard bundled up his wife, three small children in the arms of their hysterical nurses, and hustled them all downhill in the soaking ravening darkness, to the old stone sugar house, walls two feet thick, down in a ravine. Inside was a cavern of quiet where the pointed flames of candles burned without wavering, among the crowds of black people shivering in the strange hurricane cold. The candlelight brightened the bright eyes and honey-blond hair of little Josephine. Perhaps that night was her earliest memory.

The next morning when Joseph-Gaspard Tascher struggled up hill to look over his estate, he saw he was ruined. He had nothing left but a small pension and the slaves which he sold. The great brown-roofed old sugar house was Josephine's home for ten years.

The only good fortune offered the impoverished family came then, when their great-aunt, in favor with the powerful Marquis de Beauharnais, sent hastily from France for the oldest daughter to marry the son of the house, Alexandre. She had just died of a fever. There was Yayette, not considered pretty, who might do as Alexandre must be married in order to inherit a fortune. So Josephine was in France, unhappily married, until the French Revolution cut off Alexandre's head and sent her, with her children Hortense and Eugene, back to the old sugar mill and her mother in Martinique. It would be two years before Josephine, the dashing, magnetic young widow, went back to France to seek what fortunes she might, and caught the eye of the young officer, Napoleon.

In the meantime, there had been hurricanes everywhere among the islands. The last hurricane of 1766, in October, caught off the Texas coast a Plate Fleet from Veracruz, with five armed vessels they now called "register ships" because they carried gold reg-

istered by the owners, of which the Crown took its immemorial
fifth. They were blasted across the bar at Pass Cavallos and were
lost in St. Bernard's Bay, as the French called Galveston Bay then.
For all anyone knows, the treasure is there yet.

The same hurricane raved northward-eastward to wreck at
Pensacola forty deserted Spanish huts, a rock-and-sand bastion and
a roofless cistern, all that the English had there. In the twenty quiet
years in which they held Florida, marked everywhere with the signs
of listlessness and disuse, we have only one vivid description of that
country, written by a young Philadelphia botanist, William Bartram, who traveled through it. His father was John Bartram, the
more famous botanist of thriving Philadelphia, friend of Benjamin
Franklin.

Sailing south from Charleston, William Bartram observed "prodigious bands of porpoises, foreboding tempests, that appear to
cover the ocean." He saw the new capital of Georgia, Augusta,
thronged with impressive treaty-making Indians, Savannah on its
bluff laying out its first squares, and its port of Sunbury, white
with coastwise sails.

He visited the few English plantations beyond St. Augustine, its
streets deserted, its Castillo neglected, and saw English tobacco
and indigo growing in clearings among old mission fields and groves
of old orange trees. Florida was crammed with birds, fish, alligators,
rattlesnakes, with plants and trees of bewildering variety, sweetgum,
live oak, liquidamber, magnolia. It was empty of people except for
the wonderful life of the Seminoles among the fires of their villages
on the rich Alachua plains. Bartram shared their hunts and dances
and ceremonials, their freedom and their plenty.

He followed on horseback roads overgrown with forests, to St.
Marks and Pensacola, ruined by hurricane and neglect. Mission bells
were silent. He heard only the jingling pack train of some Scots
trader from Carolina coming down to trade with the Florida Indians.
More houses were standing in Mobile because they had been built
with Spanish walls.

Hurricanes had cut everywhere their huge furrows of fallen
timber. Sailing a little boat alone up the empty beautiful St. Johns
River, Bartram camped out under a huge oak tree felled by a hurricane. Then he lived through a hurricane which no one else ever
wrote about. It was probably in 1774. There were two recorded

hurricanes that year, in September in Guadeloupe and in Jamaica in October.

He sailed past grassy swamps and oak-dark bluffs to follow a creek that would open into a lake. It was about noon and still. The air was like hot glass. There was constant thunder under the hazed sky and, nearer, the roaring and echoing voices of crocodiles, as he called them. They were alligators. Ashore, he climbed a bluff to stare around at the varying green of forests, meadows, swampy islands. He was terrified. The clouds flamed up in purple, veined with blue livid lightning. Thunder shook the earth. He heard the forests cracking as he tried to find shelter. Heavy branches were switched overhead like leaves. His small boat was sucked into the lake by the strong current that usually ran out of it. He found shelter underneath the shrubs on a bank. The rain nearly drowned him. After another hour, the hurricane was gone and the light broke over desolation.

A little breeze took his boat across the foam-thickened lake, to the plantation of his friend, who stared at him in a daze. The hurricane had broken down all the heavy log cabins. The house was twisted on its foundations. One hundred acres of indigo, ripe for cutting, and several acres of green cane were beaten into muddy pulp. Enormous live oaks were torn up by the roots. Of the sixty Negro slaves, only a few were uninjured.

But now, in the English colonies of the Atlantic coast a deeper wind was beginning to rise, not weather, but human force.

2 *HAMILTON AND THE REVOLUTION*

The American Revolution was a storm raised over America by the changing forces of men's minds. A West Indian hurricane affected the life and certainly colored the thinking of an extraordinary boy, who would help shape America's later destinies. He was Alexander Hamilton.

The bright world of the Lesser Antilles, of Puerto Rico, Jamaica and faraway Louisiana, in the early fall of 1772, was obliterated by the moving stain of a hurricane curving north, west and northwest, in four unbelievable days and nights. It left an appalling ruin. In Dominica all the ships were wrecked and 2,500,000 pounds of prime muscovado sugar destroyed in unroofed warehouses. Antigua, Nevis and St. Kitts lost more sugar than the last year's shipment to England.

The island of St. Kitts was blotted out on the night of August 31. The hurricane made the fortune of the young Alexander Hamilton.

He was born illegitimate on Nevis, 1757, to a twenty-year-old mother divorced for desertion by an older husband. She was forbidden to marry the father of her two sons, a Scots merchant, James Hamilton. Alexander, the small, fair boy, eyes at once large and piercing under a great forehead, may have been unhappy, lacking schooling, but his long nose was forever in a book. His mouth and jaw must even then have been set proudly tight. He spoke the excellent French of old St. Kitts French families. His figuring amazed everyone. At twelve or fourteen he sailed over to Danish St. Croix to work in Nicholas Crueger's counting house. He was so quick and yet dignified, so ambitious and so intelligent that soon he was writing all Crueger's merchantile letters, in the courtly English of the time. Before Alexander was fifteen, Crueger often went on long trips, leaving the whole business to the boy already considered a financial genius.

There he was then, in the Danish town with its baked white streets and prim houses, no doubt looking out the counting house door, with a quill pen over his ear, at the strange glaring sunset.

After it was all over, Alexander wrote to his father.

Honored Sir— I take up my pen just to give you an imperfect account of the most dreadful hurricane that memory or any records can trace, which happened here on the 31st ultimo at night.

It began about dusk, at north, and raged very violently till ten o'clock. Then ensued a sudden and unexpected interval, which lasted about an hour. Meanwhile the wind was shifting around to the South West point, from whence it returned with redoubled fury and continued so till near three o'clock in the morning. Good God! What horror and destruction—it is impossible for me to describe—or you to form any idea of it. It seemed as if a total dissolution of nature was taking place. The roaring of the sea and wind—fiery meteors flying about in the air—the prodigious glare of almost perpetual lightning—the crash of the falling houses—and the ear-piercing shrieks of the distressed were sufficient to strike astonishment into Angels. A great part of the buildings throughout the island are levelled to the ground—almost all the rest very much shattered—several persons killed and numbers utterly ruined—whole families running about the streets unknowing where to find a place of shelter—the sick exposed to the keeness of water and air —without a bed to lie on—or a dry covering to their bodies—our harbor is entirely bare. In a word, misery in all its most hideous shapes spread over the whole face of the country.—A strong smell of gun powder added somewhat to the terrors of the night, and it was observed that the rain was surprisingly salt. Indeed, the water is so brackish and full of sulphur that there is hardly any drinking it.

My reflections and feelings on this frightful and melancholy occasion are set forth in following self discourse. Where now, Oh! vile worm, in all thy boasted fortitude and resolution. And much more.

This was the letter, admired then as much for its pious remarks as the description of the hurricane, that James Hamilton showed pridefully to many gentlemen of St. Kitts. It was sent to the editor of *The Royal Danish-American Gazette* in St. Croix, who decided "it would not prove uninteresting to the Publick." It was printed in the issue of October 3. It created a sensation. Some planters of St. Kitts, in the midst of ruin, took up a collection to send him to America for better schooling. By 1774 he was a student at King's College, now Columbia University, in New York.

When the American Revolution came, his education was interrupted. But the war, like the hurricane, gave him opportunities he had the genius to seize. He wrote pamphlets fiery for freedom, such as *A Full Vindication of the Measures of the Congress from the Calumnies of their Enemies*. His brilliant reasoning, his mature grasp of the principles of the English constitution, caused him to be chosen as confidential aide to George Washington. That was in 1777, when he was twenty years old.

Hamilton's greatness rests on his Federalist influence on the American Constitution as much as on his financial genius as first Secretary of the Treasury.

The curious thing is that although the hurricane blew him out of his boyhood to become an American patriot, nothing separated him from the basic thinking of those English islands. His great contribution to the Constitution lay precisely there, that he could believe in nothing other than a strong and orderly central government. The tradition of the islands linked him with the Caribbean-going New Englanders, who believed that to survive the sea and its storms requires a strong single command. The New Englanders to a man backed his Federalist principles, his demand for a strong merchant marine and the freedom of the seas.

Those seamanlike beliefs were in complete conflict with the democratic ideals of Thomas Jefferson, to whom Hamilton was always "that foreign bastard." To Hamilton, Jefferson's and Madison's faith in the people, in the separation of the states and a withdrawal from sea commerce, was pure demagoguery. Indeed after the war, the quarreling and confused states would probably have fallen apart into futility, as all Europe expected them to do, if it had not been for Hamilton's rocklike insistence that the Federal government should pay the nation's debts and establish, once and for all, a durable national honor.

Together, the strong opposed beliefs of Hamilton and Jefferson gave the Constitution the magnificent balance of forces without either of which the great ship would long since have been lost.

Hamilton's weakness lay in his total inability to value democratic principles. He lacked the toughening tradition of the American frontier out of which both independence and interdependence among men had been slowly wrought. His indiscreet habit of political intrigue can be blamed on the narrow island snobbishness, its insistence on caste and special privilege, from which he must have suffered. On the other hand, his farsighted ideas on national credit, security and honor certainly sprang from his boyhood knowledge of the miseries inflicted on precarious debt-ridden human lives by such vast, unforeseen catastrophes as hurricanes.

August 14, 1773, the neat villages, salt marshes, rocky pastures and harbors of maritime New England were hurricane invaded.

The cows from the stony common in Boston went home early that night as a slashing rain began. The houses, under gambrel and hip roofs that rose like a pleasant picture above the harbor and the salt rivers, crowding among trees up Capp's and Beacon hills, topped with its beacon over many steeples, were tightly shuttered. Men stumbled home in blowing darkness through crooked streets. The cold salt spray was blown across Salt Pond and the roughened river and the water of the Back Bay.

In harbor, the seagoing fleet of small vessels, built on the banks of nearby tidal rivers of local oak, pine and hatckmatack, bobbed wildly or ran for shelter as the long gray waves surged up the two-thousand-foot length of Boston's Long Wharf, smashing into warehouses and ropewalks. Some ships were torn from under the lee of steep drumlin islands by the winds that drove waves over the wharves of Charlestown, under the rain-scalded knolls of Bunker and Breed's hills, to flood the meadows of Cambridge.

Boston Light, the first in all America, was lost in whistling murk as the seas drove higher. Single-decked sloops from the towns up the north shore, Marblehead topsail schooners, sharp-bowed Essex Chebacco boats, small fast schooners and brigs from Salem and down east, bigger ships from all that trade swarming in from the Carolinas, the Chesapeake, Philadelphia, New York and Europe, that made Boston hum, were scattered and wrecked like drowned hens along the Massachusetts rocks.

Salisbury Point, Amesbury, Haverhill took the violence of small tornadoes at the hurricane's edge. The waves were forced so furiously up the Merrimac River that people on the north shore fled from their farmhouses, sure it was a tidal wave. Apple orchards were stripped and broken, all the cornfields were mud, rail fences were down and panicked cattle dead. It was reported that the terrible winds tore oak planks from the wrecked ships, blew them straight on the level air to crash into roofs, chimneys. One broke an aged lady's leg. Windmills, barns, blacksmith shops were down in piles of debris. At Salisbury Point a child left in bed in a house of which only the walls were standing, was found, bed and all, in the cellar with tons of brick fallen on top, but only slightly injured.

But that sea-worn coast was no out-of-the-way tropic island. Collections of food were taken up in churches. Wagons rumbled in from Roxbury and Dorchester along hastily cleared Boston Neck. Before all the broken windows were repaired, men were working to raise the ships sunken at the wharves, and shipyards rang with hammers. There were codfish on the banks and fallen trees being cut into barrel staves and shingles. The ships must sail with fresh or dried fish to be exchanged in Mediterranean ports for Malaga grapes and Valencia oranges, and wine; salt herring from New Bedford and Taunton for the West Indies trade. Weatherly 100-ton vessels from Salem or Ipswich must not be delayed on the ways, from sailing to Brazil or around the Horn, where 500-tonners were to difficult to handle in those multitudinous seas.

No hurricane must hold up the famous triangular trade; rum from Medford distilleries to be traded for slaves in the barracoons of the Guinea coast of Africa, sold or bartered in the West Indies for sugar and molasses and back to New England again, perhaps with slaves direct for the two great American slaving ports, Newport, Rhode Island, and Charleston, South Carolina.

It was all "free trade" which was another name for smuggling, and not only the codfish aristocracy of Boston, and the rice aristocracy of Carolina, but the fur traders of New York, the butter and cheese merchants of Philadelphia, the tobacco dealers of Norfolk, were growing rich from it. They paid no attention to Great Britain's attempts to restrict them.

But Great Britain was so heavily in debt that, like Spain, she had to look to America for revenue. The Stamp Act and the Molasses Act brought Boston and Sam Adams, Patrick Henry and Virginia, and all history, boiling up in protest. Nobody drank tea. The hurricane of 1773 had no effect on the Tea Party.

People forgot about hurricanes when in June, 1774, George the Third closed the port of Boston for all that world trade and not even a rowboat splashed an oar in Boston harbor. The Continental Congress met in Philadelphia in September before other schooners sneaked down with food to hurricane-struck French Guadeloupe and British Jamaica.

By the summer and fall of 1775 the British who had hurried back to Boston from Lexington and Concord were besieged there by Washington's nondescript army, and hurricanes went unnoticed that destroyed sugar waiting for American vessels in the islands and stopped sugar production in Cuba. The British army could get no food from the devastated islands, which got no help from England.

The American schooner *Hannah* was fitted out under the pine-tree flag to seize any British supply ships bound for Boston. They were hungry and cold there, chopping down for firewood the old North Church, wharves, idle ships, the Liberty Tree and many old houses.

By the first of March the Americans were toiling feverishly to set up breastworks on Dorchester Heights. At dawn the British woke up to find the city and the fleet at the mercy of American guns. Five regiments were ordered to leave the Long Wharf for an island fort and then land on Dorchester peninsula. If the British landed, Washington was ready to send 4,000 men to attack. A bombardment was begun from Roxbury. The British assault was to be joined by two more regiments landed from flatboats, with bayonets. The Loyalists of Boston crowded the hilltops to watch as the Americans sweated all that hot day long to pile up their defenses.

That night about midnight "a Hurrycane or terrible sudden storm," as an American described it, began to blow from the south. Sheds and roofs were blown away. A heavy surf drove many ships on the pebbly shores. The wind blew all that night and the next day, with extraordinary torrents of rain. On March 5 General Howe wrote, "The intended expedition last night was unavoidably put off by the badness of the weather." They had evacuated the city long before the famous Fourth of July.

A few American fur-trappers and traders, slipping down the Ohio, down the great swirling Mississippi, carried the news to New Orleans in the summer, in time to share a hurricane with the friendly French. There was no war yet between the French or Spanish and the British in West Florida. Yankee sloops and schooners, privateers now, slipped back to their favorite islands in the West Indies to intercept British ships or trade their own salt fish, shingles and rice, were caught like so many islanders in the great hurricane of September at Martinique and Guadeloupe, St. Kitts, Antigua and Puerto Rico.

If that hurricane had curved northward up the Atlantic across Long Island, as George Washington was turning the defeat into which he and his army had blundered, into the masterly retreat which took them to New Jersey and the victory at Trenton, the Revolution might have ended then and there.

No hurricane has been noted for the fall of 1777, but there may have been one at sea of which an edge or reaching fierce squall lines

of rain and thunder caught Howe and his regulars with only fence
rails for shelter. On September 11, the day was hot and close for
the British victory at Brandywine but by the fifteenth the heat was
blown away by a sharp northwest wind that shifted violently to the
northeast. Washington's men were drawn across a valley from the
British when rain came down in a cloudburst that savage winds
blew in sheets along the ground, half-drowning men, muskets, ammunition. Washington's barefoot men marched for three days to
get dry powder.

In 1778, after Valley Forge, France allied herself with America
and declared war on England.

By July 26 a French fleet of sixteen ships and frigates, under Admiral Charles Henri Theodat, Comte d'Estaing, high-strung, auto-
cratic, handsome, a great hater of the British, arrived to blockade
Newport by landing on the west side of the island as soon as the
Americans under General John Sullivan could cross over from
Tiverton. Six British vessels were grounded or blown up when the
sea to the south was white with British Admiral Lord Howe's thirty-
five sail of ships.

The French sailed out to meet them on a brisk northeast wind.
Howe refused to engage and sailed off southwest, waiting two days
for the wind to change. That was the twelfth of September. The
wind did change, in a violent storm that came in whistling. All the
ships were damaged, many wrecked.

The wind tore at Newport's roofs, wharves, trees and chimneys
and screamed off inland blowing the sea gulls far away from the
salt-filled cow pastures, flooding Narragansett Bay, Providence
River, the town, pushing high water up the Taunton River, up the
Seaconnet and the small streams, stopping the water mills and spoiling the flour.

Howe took his hurricane-beaten fleet back to New York to re-
fit but returned to unhappy Newport, burned New Bedford and
Dartmouth and all the privateering vessels caught in harbor.

It was a bad autumn for storms. Admiral Byron, called "Foul-
weather Jack," who had sailed from England in July, earned his
name in August when his squadron was scattered by a hurricane.
Some were driven back across the Atlantic. Every port in North
America received one or two of his half-dismantled vessels. He refitted in Halifax from which in October he sailed into even more

frightful weather. One ship foundered. Others were driven across to England on the last of the hurricane that on October 28 churned through Cuba.

There were no other hurricanes that season to interfere with the British and French briskly capturing each other's islands. Late in '78 the British occupied Georgia. By January, 1779, Spain relucantly joined France on the side of the American rebels. It was odd, because she was fighting rebellion in her own South American colonies. All Spain wanted, actually, was to rid west Florida and the Mississippi of the English.

Into the harbor of Fort-Royal in Martinique sailed a fleet of four ships of the line, under the greatest French admiral and seaman of his time, François Joseph Paul de Grasse. He took command of the French Windward Island fleet.

The other French admiral, d'Estaing, arrived off Tybee Island in Georgia with a colorful big fleet, to drive out the British hastily fortifying Savannah. He and the Americans waited too long for pilots, in the blue fall weather. On September 2 scudding clouds darkened the lifting sea. A hurricane moved up the coast. Its center passed between Tybee and the upriver city. The French fleet was scattered.

By the time d'Estaing got upriver, the British were ready for him with one hundred guns. Many men died, including the brave ally, Pulaski. d'Estaing, wounded and unhappy, sailed home to France as the jubilant British looked toward Charleston.

In New York, Clinton was nervous about the French fleet, which he thought was headed for Newport, and about hurricanes. He ordered the British ships back to New York, and Newport, to its delight, evacuated.

This, to the great and furious British admiral, Lord Rodney, was "a most fatal measure. He gave up the best and noblest harbor in America, from whence squadrons in forty-eight hours could blockade Boston, New York or Philadelphia."

D'Estaing's homegoing fleet was overtaken and wrecked by a seagoing hurricane on the twenty-eighth of October. Some ships were captured by the British. It was a heavy blow to the French.

By this time the British were moving on Charelston but so deliberately that Governor Rutledge had time to appeal for a fleet from the Spanish at Havana. They were not interested.

There was one young Spaniard, however, boiling over with military energy, the able young governor of Louisiana, Bernardo de Gálvez. His father was the Viceroy of New Spain and his uncle was the powerful minister for the Indies, but he had made his reputation fighting the Apaches of the Pecos and handling firmly the rebellion of French inhabitants of Spanish New Orleans. He had already showed friendship for the Americans and was deeply concerned about British forts on the Mississippi and their new fortifications at Pensacola.

Under Gálvez, the city of New Orleans, now with a population of 8,381 whites and over 9,000 slaves, was humming with prosperity. The French had been permitted to enter freely with sugar and coffee from the French islands and Negro slaves from Africa, the American trappers down river with furs. Bears' hams, bear oil, venison came south in bateaux from the Spanish forts in Arkansas, the Aux Arcs and St. Louis.

English ships were not permitted to land or go up the river. Yet the courtly Gálvez received with great kindness the English from west Florida frightened by bloody American raids.

Before July when Spain declared war, Gálvez had been secretly getting ready a fleet of small gunboats with oars or sails, Spanish balandras, frigates and a bomb-ketch, because he was sure the British in west Florida had not received the news of war. His War Council advised him to defend the city. But Gálvez knew that the best defense was swift and unexpected attack. He had his supplies and ammunition loaded on his gunboats and announced that he meant to sail on August 23.

He had forgotten the season. On the eighteenth of August, with no warning, a hurricane blew up the dirtied sky, out of the Gulf, over the empty swamps and silvering scrub and the looping bayous, wind-beaten into yellowed froth. Gálvez' fleet was sunk, or banged to kindling wood against the broken docks. People ran gasping out of wrecked houses. Slaves were drowned in ditches. Horses were drowned in lanes turned creeks. City, river, fields, trees, swamps, were beaten and broken in the chaos of water and bitter air.

In three hours Gálvez' expedition was ruined.

But now was the time, he saw, when the British from Mobile and Pensacola, beyond the track of the storm, could attack New

Orleans. He called the people out from their broken houses, their littered streets, to the cleaned-up Place d'Armes.

With all the splendor of flags and drums and marching soldiers, Gálvez made them a thrilling speech. He had been appointed their governor, he told them, but he could not take the oath to defend the province, if they were too poor-spirited with disaster, to follow him. They answered him with a great echoing shout. Within a week his expedition had taken the forts at Manchac and Baton Rouge. Triumphant American flatboat men brought the news that British forts had been taken by George Rogers Clark and the mighty river was free.

For the attack on Mobile Gálvez needed help, in men, money and ships, from Havana. The Council there preferred an attack on Pensacola. Gálvez insisted. Five hundred men in four transports sailed from Havana on February 10, 1780. They were overtaken from the southwest by a wind "of hurricane proportions," as an officer wrote. Gálvez' fleet of twenty assorted vessels was scattered by another violent southwest storm.

He took Mobile in spite of wind, rain, thunder, lightning, the loss of some ships, and others so badly damaged they were abandoned. Out of their wreckage, he made ladders to scale the fort. He became "Governor of Louisiana and Mobile." But Havana would not hear of his attacking Pensacola, so Gálvez returned to New Orleans.

It is possible that Havana officials were worried by the early hurricane of June 13 which wrecked English ships and plantations at St. Vincent and St. Lucia, and caused deaths and losses to Puerto Rico, crowded with 100,000 people in thirty-four towns and villages, the center of all the smuggling trade of all the islands. They measured time in quiet Puerto Rico, it was reported, by the visit of a bishop, or a hurricane.

For months now the British and French had gone through the beautiful and precise naval maneuvers of those days, a spectacular square dance of white-sailed, heavy wooden ships, passing each other, ship to ship, in exact line of battle with opposed rows of guns blaring point-blank flame and destruction. The blood that soaked the gouged and splintered decks could not be seen by watchers on some nearby island, seeing the gun flashes terrible through roiling smoke, against the blue-glittering tropic sea. They saw spars topple, sky holes blossoming in riddled canvas, masts go by the board.

In the smoking reek below decks men served the hot guns shoulder to shoulder, slipping in their own blood, as men in gold lace on the quarterdeck or men desperately cutting away rigging died the same death. There were almost no victories.

In America, Cornwallis tightened his hold on Georgia, South Carolina and Charleston. But in Havana, the War Council was more aware that Sir Hyde Parker's British fleet lay at anchor at St. Lucia and that George Brydges, the great Lord Admiral Baron Rodney, had sailed over with reinforcements from the triumphant relief of the siege of Gibraltar. Sixty-one years old, gouty, bad-tempered, elegant, a consummate seaman, Rodney was a force to be considered.

3 THE GREAT HURRICANE OF 1780

In May of 1780 a great Spanish convoy arrived off Dominica on its way to Havana, seventeen armed vessels and eighty-three transports crammed with 11,500 men, dying by hundreds of the filth below, bad food and ship fever. It was commanded by Admiral Don Joseph Solano who dodged the British and came in at last grandly under the sun-colored rocks of El Morro as the ancient city of Havana burst into festival.

Bernardo de Gálvez was there from New Orleans, arguing with the languid War Council about the attack on Pensacola. Suddenly, Gálvez' plans were approved by Admiral Solano. As soon as the ships could be got ready, he would be given command of 3,800 men with more brought in from hurricane-swept Puerto Rico.

The French were worried by the news of early hurricanes so that de Grasse refused Lafayette's invitation to sail north in a demonstration against the British in North America and ordered the main French fleet back to France, leaving nine ships to patrol the islands.

Rodney thought they had sailed to join Rochambeau, wining and dancing in happy Newport. He dreaded the hurricane season, too, and sent five ships to England under convoy of the *Stirling Castle*. Five sailed to St. Kitts, five joined the ships of Vice-admiral Peter Parker guarding the great harbor of Port Royal and Kingston at Jamaica. Rodney, in his flagship *Sandwich*, took a squadron to New York. Admiral Hotham's *Vengeance*, guarded by five ships, was on the careenage at St. Lucia. The *Albemarle* was at Barbados, three cruised east of Martinique and three more in the northern Antilles. There were, then, some twenty-seven British ships based among the British islands.

It was hot glaring tropic summer in the West Indies. The sun blistered the sands of the green islands and the roofs of the little stone towns tumbling down to the curling surf. In the strong trade winds the palm fronds clattered like metal. Ships' decks burned the hard soles of seamen as heat shimmered over brasswork.

Below, where the fetid bilges reeked, it was an oven. Men slept on deck where the long shadows of masts barred the moon glare. The strokes of bells, the voices of the watch carried to the shore over the moon-colored water, where ships' lanterns plunged their sparks among the wavering stars. Waking men, or admirals, stared as if in a dream, feeling the sweat strickle. Many a sleeper moaned.

On the third of October, about one o'clock in the afternoon blaze, people in the old Spanish-built Jamaican town of Savanna-la-Mar came out of their houses to see a dirty haze creep across the sea up the southern horizon. Even by the courthouse and the old church and the three-storied brick houses with galleries, up the slope, the surf beating on the beach was hoarse. The English houses of flimsy boards, crowded down below tidemarks to the very docks, quivered to the wave shocks.

A sharp gale edged in from the southeast. Men in harbor were frantically anchoring their boats or dragging them ashore. On the three British ships in harbor everything was stowed away. The outlines of the ships were already blurred with blowing rain and sea water. Ashore there was a rising din of crashings and smashings.

The sea was swelling, rising up, coming in, waves out of the mist topping docks, roaring up the land. The whole bay moved in over the lower houses, gray-white, impenetrable.

At eight o'clock at night, almost full dark, the deadening tumult of the wind stopped abruptly. It was still enough to hear water dripping, cries for help, waves smashing debris against walls. Houses swerved from their foundations and broke up in a welter of planks. The terrible undertow sucked the sand away and whole houses were swung out to sea, with people in them who were never seen again.

Ships were being hurled far up the land and dropped keel up or deck up in a marsh. When the wind came back people left alive felt the shocks of an earthquake. It was the sea shaking the earth.

Next morning, with no wind, there were no houses left below the extraordinary high-water mark. The only survivors lived for weeks crowded on board the ships left stranded, upright, in the marsh.

From Savanna-la-Mar, or what was left of it, that great hurricane of October 3, 1780, the fourth that season, surged north to overwhelm Montego Bay, the village, the pretty harbor, the plantations on the green ridges above.

Four ships of the line had been anchored there while the sailors ranged the shore and the gold-laced, high-hearted, ruddy young English officers were banqueted enormously, dancing all night with colonial beauties, carousing over incredible rum punch bowls, battalions of bottles of wine.

The sloops *Victor* and *Barbadoes* had waved their gay farewells and sailed on the twenty-ninth. The *Scarborough* sailed on the first of October for the Spanish main. Not one of the three was ever heard of again. The *Badger* and the *Phoenix* were carried straight north by the hurricane to the coast of Cuba and there on the cliffs of Cabo de la Cruz shipwrecked. The hurricane moved in its terror across the open fields of Cuba, to the vulnerable low Bahamas. Men died there also. It surged on northwestward up the Atlantic and overtook the *Stirling Castle* and its convoy, crippling them badly.

Two ships to the south of Jamaica, and two to the east, near the Caicos on the other side of the hurricane track, felt no more than a still breeze. Sir Peter Parker, commanding that battered squadron, in his report wrote, "The hurricane ran in veins."

The best narrative we have of that great cyclone, called to this day "the Savanna-la-Mar hurricane," was written as a letter to his mother in England by young Lieutenant Archer of the *Phoenix*, commanded by Sir Hyde Parker, known as "Old Vinegar," who had seen typhoons in the Indian Ocean.

Archer wrote:

At eleven at night it began to snuffle, with a monstrous heavy appearance from the eastward. Close-reefed the topsails. Sir Hyde sent for me. "What sort of weather have we, Archer?" "It blows a little, and has a very ugly look." "Don't hoist the topsails till it clears a little, there is no trusting any country." At eight in the morning I came up again, found it blowing hard from the east-northeast with close-reefed topsails upon the ship, and heavy squalls at times. Sir Hyde came upon deck. "Well, Archer, what do you think of it?" "O, Sir, it is only a hurricane in the East Indies, and the beginning of it had much the same appearance as this; so take in the topsails; we have plenty of sea-room."

At twelve, the gale still increasing, wore ship, to keep as near midchannel, between Jamaica and Cuba, as possible; at one the gale increasing still; at two harder yet; it still blows harder. In the evening no sign of the weather taking off, but every appearance of the storm increasing, prepared for a proper gale of wind; secured all the sails with spare gaskets; good rolling tackles upon the yards; squared the booms; saw the boats all made fast; new lashed the guns; double-breeched the lower deckers; saw that the carpenters had the tarpaulins and battens all ready for hatchways; got the top-gallant-mast down upon the deck; jib-boom and spritsailyard fore and aft; in fact, every thing we could think of to make a snug ship.

The poor devils of birds now began to find the uproar in the elements, for numbers, both of sea and land kinds, came on board of us. When they came over the ship they dashed themselves down upon the deck, without attempting to stir till picked up, and when let go again, they would not leave the ship, but endeavoured to hide themselves from the wind.

At eight o'clock a hurricane; the sea roaring, but the wind still steady to a point; did not ship a spoonful of water. . . . Went to supper; bread, cheese, and porter. The purser frightened out of his wits about his bread-bags; the two marine-officers as white as sheets, not understanding the ship's working so much, and the noise of the lower deck guns, which, by this time, made a pretty screeching to people not used to it; it seemed as if the whole ship's side was going at each roll. . . .

At ten o'clock I thought to get a little sleep; my cot was full of water; for every seam had begun to leak. Stretched myself, therefore, upon deck between two chests. At twelve a midshipman came to me. "Mr. Archer, we are just going to wear ship, Sir." "O, very well. What sort of weather have you got?"—"It blows a hurricane." Went upon deck; found Sir Hyde there. "It blows damned hard, Archer." "It does indeed, Sir." ". . . the wind has shifted to the southeast, and we are drawing right upon Cuba; so do you go forward, and have some hands stand by; loose the lee yard-arm of the foresail; and when she is right before the wind, whip the clew-garnet close up, and roll up the sail." "Sir, there is no canvas can stand against this a moment; and we may lose three or four of our people; she'll wear by manning the fore shrouds."—"No, I don't think she will." "I'll answer for it, Sir; I have seen it tried several times on the coast of America with success."—"Well try it." This was a great condescension from such a man as Sir Hyde. However, by sending about two hundred people into the fore-rigging, after a hard struggle, she wore; as the sea began to run across, she had not time to rise from one sea before another lashed against her. My God! to think that the wind could have such force!

Who can attempt to describe the appearance of things upon deck? If I was to write for ever I could not give you an idea of it—a total darkness all above; the sea on fire, running as it were in Alps, or Peaks or Teneriffes (mountains are too common an idea); the wind roaring louder than thunder (absolutely no flight of imagination); the whole made more terrible, if possible, by a very uncommon kind of blue lightning; the poor ship very much pressed, yet doing what she could, shaking her sides, and groaning at every stroke. Sir Hyde upon deck lashed to windward! I soon lashed myself alongside of him, and told him the situation of things below. "Hold fast! that was an ugly sea; we must lower the yards, I believe, Archer; the ship is much pressed."—"If we attempt it, Sir, we shall lose them, for a man aloft can do nothing; the gale cannot last for ever; twill soon be daylight now." Found by the master's watch that it was five o'clock; glad it was so near daylight. Another ugly sea. Back-water from leeward, half-way up the quarter-deck, filled one of the cutters upon the booms, and tore her all to pieces; the ship lying almost on her beam-ends, and not attempting to right again. I said to Sir Hyde, "Shall we cut the mainmast away?"—"Ay! as fast as you can." I accordingly went into the chains with a pole-axe, to cut away the lanyards; when a very violent sea broke right on board of us, carried every thing upon deck away, filled the ship with water, the main and mizen-masts went, the ship righted, but was in the last struggle of sinking under us.

As soon as we could shake our heads above water, Sir Hyde exclaimed: "We are gone at last, Archer! foundered at sea!"—"Yes, Sir, farewell; and the Lord have mercy upon us!"

I thought I heard the ship thump and grinding under our feet; it was

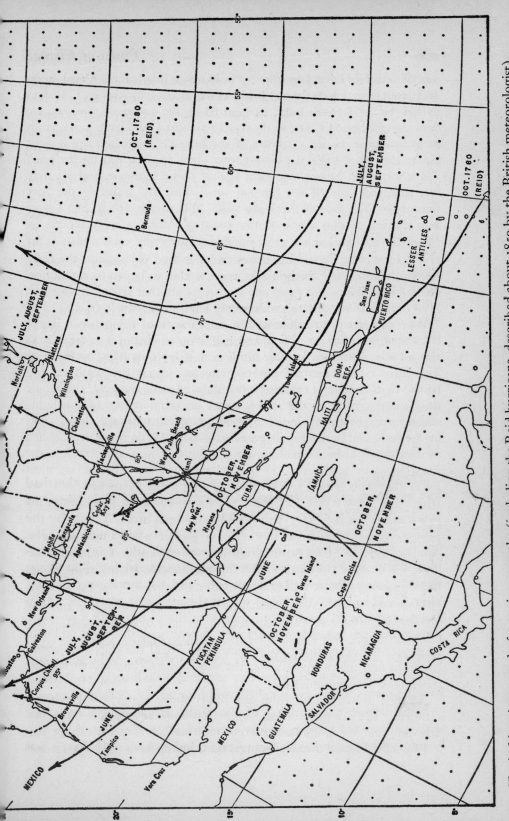

Typical hurricane tracks for various months (including the Reid hurricane, described about 1850 by the British meteorologist).

so. "Sir, the ship is ashore!" . . . every stroke threatened a total dissolution of her whole frame; found she was stern ashore, and the bow broke the sea a good deal. . . . Lost five men cutting away the foremast, by the breaking of a sea on board just as the mast went. That was nothing, every one expected it would be his own fate next: looked for daybreak with the greatest impatience; at last it came, but what a scene did it show us! The ship upon a bed of rocks, mountains of them on one side, and Cordilleras of water on the other; our poor ship grinding and crying out at every stroke between them; going away by piecemeal. However, that unmerciful sea lifted and beat us up so high among the rocks, that at last the ship scarcely moved. . . .

Two got safe; by which means, with a line, we got a hawser on shore, and made fast to the rocks, upon which many ventured and arrived safe. . . .

By twelve it was pretty moderate; got some nails on shore and made tents; found great quantities of fish driven up by the sea into holes of the rocks; knocked up a fire, and had a most comfortable dinner. In the evening, I proposed to Sir Hyde to repair the remains of the only boat left, and to venture in her to Jamaica myself. It was, next day, agreed to, therefore got the cutter on shore. In two days she was ready, and at four o'clock in the afternoon I embarked with four volunteers and a fortnight's provision; . . . Steered her myself the whole night by the stars, and in the morning saw the coast of Jamaica, distant twelve leagues. At eight in the evening arrived at Montego Bay.

These were the only men alive of the four lost ships that had lain in Montego Bay. Sir Hyde Parker was tried and acquitted of negligence in the loss of the *Phoenix*.

Still that was not the last of the Savanna-la-Mar hurricane. Far up the Atlantic H.M.S. *Shrewsbury* was patiently if ineffectually blockading the French off Newport and Rhode Island, while Narragansett and Buzzards Bay swarmed with sloops bringing in supplies. On the eighth of October the *Shewsbury*, and many another smaller sail, was bumped and tossed by rough seas, that pushed the tides far up the salt rivers with strong gales that veered from east-northeast all the way around to west-northwest. Windmills and windows, apple boughs, loose shutters and washlines, were broken in what many an old-timer called, nodding wisely, "the line storm."

Long before the morning of the tenth of October a fifth and more monstrous cyclone began to whirl somewhere south of the Cape Verde Islands and move in its masking arms of rain squalls and

violent winds westward across the Atlantic. Before it and to all
sides rolled the slow batteries of the increasing swells. When it approached Barbados, its outermost winds touched Trinidad and in
the north reached the Virgins.

When it moved away from Barbados, there was nothing left but
mud, debris, dead cattle and corpses. Some people were left alive.
Lord Rodney hastened to raise the unprecedented sum of 80,000
pounds for relief.

The center passed over St. Lucia, beating it flat, but at least
drowning a plague of ants that had been eating the cane. Of the
British ships, the *Vengeance* was wrecked on the shore, the *Deal
Castle* was blown to Puerto Rico and smashed, the *Thunderer*, just
arrived from England, sailed and disappeared forever. Ships were
dismasted as far south as ruined St. Vincent and Grenada where
fifteen Dutch ships were smashed on the rocks.

The ships east of Martinique were broken on the roaring Atlantic
rocks. The twenty-five surviving Englishmen, dazed and dripping,
were taken prisoner by a gang of French slaves, but the Marquis
de Bouillé, Governor of Martinique, sent them back to St. Lucia,
writing that he would not keep as prisoners men who had suffered
the same horror and misery that had overtaken them all.

On the other hand, Lord Rodney hurried to seize St. Vincent,
hearing that it had been wrecked. But the French drove him away.

Ships, towns, churches, houses, a hospital had been demolished
in Martinique, and nine thousand people died. Five thousand were
drowned at Dutch St. Eustatius and every building was smashed
and washed into the sea.

In North Carolina, on October 14, where Lord Cornwallis was
retreating, after the American victory at King's Mountain, a heavy
rain was falling. His soldiers, as hungry as the Americans had been,
plodded for days under cold gray sheets of rain, through swamps
and mudholes. They huddled at night on the wet ground, for fifteen days of wretchedness.

It was raining heavily in Havana, gray over the harbor, soaking
the furled canvas and glistening decks of the Spanish fleet that had
been promised Bernardo de Gálvez for the attack on Pensacola.

On the morning of the fifteenth the center of the great hurricane
was moving up the Mona Passage with its rain squalls extending to
Puerto Rico and to Santo Domingo on the east side. The island of

Mona was swallowed up, and a convoy of British ships with the *Ulysses* and *Pomona*, that had been battered by the first hurricane. Now they were disabled. But the logs of two other ships on each side of the center, the *Couvert* and the *Venus* on the east and the *Diamond* and the *Pelican* to the west, show that the huge winds were blowing in opposite directions.

On the sixteenth the sun was brilliant over Havana and Bernardo de Gálvez sailed at last with ships and men west out of the harbor to the sparkling dancing sea. He was sailing toward Veracruz.

By the eighteenth Bermuda was lost in the dark tumult and wrath of the ocean, where on the rocks below the uprooted cedars fifty vessels of all nations were splintered.

On the nineteenth, at nine o'clock at night, under stars, the *Stirling Castle*, that had suffered so much already and now sailed, badly crippled in the old channel north of Santo Domingo, was drawn by the boiling, vicious currents to strike, as so many galleons and great ships had done, on the Silver Shoals. There she broke and was sucked down among the dim spines and turrets of coral to slide into the muffled deeps. Of her whole crew, one midshipman and four seamen were saved.

Although the undiminished cyclone curved to the northeast Atlantic, its long reaching gales were felt off the Delaware where Lord Rodney had stationed a squadron which was so crippled and dismantled that they had to return to New York. At Sandy Hook, Lord Rodney himself, pacing the quarterdeck of the *Sandwich*, his elegant high nose sniffing the bright October day, felt nothing of the hurricane at all.

Off Long Island, however, H.M.S. *Shrewsbury*, that had been damaged off Newport in the earlier hurricane, and was now refitted, and H.M.S. *Resolution*, bowling along on a sunlit ocean, in one day of sudden dirty squalls were forced to strike their topgallant masts. The *Shrewsbury* split a topsail. But that wind knifed down from the north. Northeast of Bermuda the hurricane was observed only by H.M.S. *Berwick* to be curving toward the Azores. It reached at least the latitude of Great Britain. Its winds were less strong but at one moment its width apparently covered the distance from Newfoundland all the way across the Atlantic.

It has been considered to have been the greatest Atlantic hurricane of the eighteenth century. It is also extraordinary that this is the first hurricane in history which may today be traced in the painstaking day-to-day logbooks of those unhappy British ships which felt it to their shuddering oaken hearts. By masts lost, men lost, sails ripped to rags, rudders gone, deck houses and boats stove in, rigging parted, leaks, strains and breakages, the hurricane left a track thousands and thousands of sea miles long.

British sea power in the Caribbean was so weakened by it that they could not carry out a project to capture Puerto Rico. English woodcutters and fishermen had for years tried to live on Crab and Vieques Islands, near Puerto Rico, which were also a haven for deserting British slaves. The possession of Puerto Rico would have enhanced British prosperity as well as her control of the West Indies. The great hurricane put a stop to that. In fact, until the naval victories of two years later, there was practically no strength left in the British navy, as the course of the American Revolution would show.

It was not, however, the last hurricane of that terrible year of 1780.

Field Marshal Don Bernardo de Gálvez should have been more wary of the perfect day of the sixteenth of October, on which he sailed with seventy-four ships and nearly 4,000 men for his longed-for attack on Pensacola. The fleet was commanded by his staunch friend, Admiral Don Jose Solano, in his flagship *San Juan*, who could not have been expected to know about hurricanes.

The fleet was all day streaming out of Havana harbor toward Veracruz, where the horizon lay like a taut crystal line. By dawn the Admiral counted fifty-eight ships. A kind of haze hid the rest.

By the eighteenth the northeast winds of the hurricane of which they had no idea, that had howled north of the Grand Cayman Islands and over Cape Antonio, were sending a low scud over the Spanish ships' lowered foresails. By night the Admiral could see only the nearest ship, as the winds flung waves over his rolling decks.

The *San Juan* struggled in seething rain for two days, alone. The winds increased. The pumps worked but the rudder broke. The wind came around. The sea came up. The ship pitched away her bowsprit and all her masts. The wind blew a little less hard. They got pieces of sails on the stumps of the masts. They rejoined a few more ships.

Bernardo de Gálvez' ship lived through it although it was blown to New Orleans. Admiral Solano shifted his flag to another slightly less battered vessel, cruised to Pensacola, saw no Spanish ships there or at the Tortugas rendezvous, and returned to Havana where Bernardo de Gálvez ruefully joined him.

As for Pensacola, the English under General Campbell, always fearful of a Spanish attack, did not know until much later how the hurricane had saved them.

"Have we so little constancy and tenacity that a single tropical storm suffices to halt us?" Gálvez wrote in hot argument with the War Council in Havana, about another expedition against Pensacola. He fought off a British attack on Mobile. The cautious War Council had to admit that the British were too weak to attack Havana.

The next May, therefore, after great labor, Gálvez drove at Pensacola again. The first fleet commander, Calbo, refused to cooperate and it was not until Solano came up with a fleet which he put at Gálvez' orders that Pensacola fell and the British lost all West Florida.

This has always been called "Solano's storm" because an English ambassador at Madrid copied Solano's log from the Spanish records. But Solano was only a latecomer. It should be called "the last hurricane of Bernardo de Gálvez," who had endured so many. It was the last of the great hurricanes of 1780, the first ever to be so completely traced and reported.

4 THE REVOLUTION AND AFTER

The American Revolution was in a very bad way. Cornwallis in the south was moving fretfully into Virginia to Yorktown, beyond the head of Chesapeake Bay. But Washington, with his gloomy, unpaid inadequate troops could not attack New York or march south to stop Cornwallis. Rochambeau in Newport had no money to help him. Then the news came that Gálvez, stopped by no more hurricanes, had taken Pensacola from the British.

The French went into action. Their greatest admiral, de Grasse, who on July 16 arrived at Cap Haitien leading the fleet in the great flagship *Ville de Paris,* had raised one million livres to aid the Americans by an appeal to the enthusiastic Spanish people of Havana. He replied to Rochambeau's letter quoting a desperate General Washington, by stating that he would sail north from Santo Domingo on August 13, with twenty-six war vessels, 3,300 men, field cannon, siege guns and mortars, for Chesapeake Bay. He would land and fight until October 15, precisely.

He was as good as his word. He ignored a hurricane that on the first of August laid waste Kingston in Jamaica and another on August 10 that curved up and into North Carolina. He sailed on August 13, for secrecy slipping along the dangerous old Bahama channel and capturing some light British vessels that might have fled north with the news, in the silky blue after-hurricane weather.

Washington ordered Lafayette to surround Cornwallis and moved around New York to plunge his army hastily southward.

Lord Rodney in the West Indies was ill and nervous about hurricanes. He believed de Grasse had sailed to attack New York. So he gave up his command to Hood and ordered him to sail to New York by way of the Chesapeake and Delaware capes. Hood was to return to the West Indies "after the full moon in October" when the hurricane season was considered over.

A hurricane hit New Orleans on the twenty-third, but Hood, on the twenty-fifth, at the Capes, found the weather still sparkling blue and the sweet sea empty of French. He clapped on sail for New York.

On August 30, de Grasse arrived at the Chesapeake, anchored inside Cape Henry to blockade the James and York rivers and landed soldiers to join Lafayette in bottling up Cornwallis.

The news was a thunder stroke to the British in New York. Admiral Barras had sailed with his fleet from Newport.

Off the Capes twenty-seven sail of ships were reported to Admiral de Grasse, British under Admiral Graves. De Grasse moved out of Lynnhaven Bay, through the narrow channel of the Middleground, and fought a murderous engagement, 1,410 British guns, to 1,794 French ones. All the British ships were damaged. De

Grasse edged them northward. When Barras arrived there were only French sails off the Chesapeake, in weather still bright blue, although fall winds were roughening.

The British decided that "the position of the enemy, the present condition of the British fleet, the season of the year so near the Equinox and the impracticability of giving any effective succor to General Earl Cornwallis," was reason enough for the British fleet to get to New York and stay there.

Without de Grasse or with a hurricane Cornwallis would not have had to surrender. With firing of cannon, clanging of bells, the news swept north to Maine and south to New Orleans. The American Revolution was ended.

In the West Indies, war was still going on, France and Spain against England. All along the Atlantic coast a depression began. Ports were crowded with sailors, ex-privateers and one-time smugglers. Now that they were neutrals, they were all out of work. From the army, impoverished officers and men struggling home with nothing but worthless scrip for their seven years' endurance, found no work in farms, fields and villages and no money, nothing but mortgages. It was the beginning of the first postwar depression.

The end of fighting seemed suddenly to untie the knot that with varying success had held the new states together. The planters of Virginia began to look with doubt and suspicion on the traders and seamen of New England. The tidewater gentry of South Carolina refused to consider they lived in the same world as the scattered hill farmers of North Carolina or the boisterous individualists of Georgia making their own wars on the southeastern, French-loving Indians.

Each state insisted on making its own laws, tariffs and agreements with foreign governments. All refused to pay taxes to any central government whatever. There was no money for an army or navy. No one wanted any more law and many cared very little for order.

They were not linked by roads, of which there were only local paths and a post road no better than a long, muddy, rocky trail that wandered north and south through forests and swamps and crossed rivers by ferries or fords. Ice, snow, sleet, spring freshets, autumn hurricanes blocked everything. Wagons and coaches bogged down in mud. Horseback was the common way of travel and there were very few inns. The great common highway was the sea, accessible by rivers, island-sheltered sound and bays, where small sailing craft, cut off from the West Indies, went crowding up and down to barter homemade goods and badly needed cloth for farm products, shoes for tobacco, oysters for hay, all the way from Boston to Charleston and back.

The edges of a hurricane in 1783 that beat up the sandy beaches of North Carolina and half-drowned the village of Ocracoke, had increased the tides at Charleston, delaying the last ships of departing Royalists.

Planters, former British officers and soldiers, well-to-do merchants and cotton brokers, with their families and slaves and goods, left to take abandoned plantations or Crown lands in Jamaica and Dominica. They found only ruin. Another colony from British Florida, now Spanish again, arrived in Dominica just at the beginning of the hurricane season. Food shipped for their relief was already rotten. They had only flimsy temporary shelters and were forced to live on the charity of the already distressed islanders.

In the new American states, jobless and landless men shoved across mountain gaps and rivers westward to the Ohio and the legendary majesty of the Mississippi. Indians from the bluffs looked down on their flatboats drifting south in the great silence at the heart of the continent. Gálvez' booming city of New Orleans clamored to buy their furs and bear meat, barrel staves and honey. The very boats were broken up for building material. That August the winds like long knives slicing off tiles and trees and masts to the sound of driving rain taught many a backwoods American what tropical cyclones were like.

From Canada to Savannah in the American states there were only a few hundred more than five million people and only six important cities, Boston, Newport, New York, Philadelphia, Baltimore and Charleston, and none with more than 6,000 inhabitants. Times had been bad everywhere except in the rice and tobacco states of Virginia and Carolina, still allowed to trade with England. So that it was a double shock to Charleston, battered by the hurricane of 1783 that destroyed rice in the warehouses that could have been sold in the West Indies where the same hurricane had worked havoc. Island taxes, that in those years were the chief source of British revenues, were not paid that year and England suffered.

Misery in Jamaica and Santo Domingo was dreadfully increased by the great Cape Verde hurricane of '84. But in the United States it was recognized only by the first poem ever written by an American about a hurricane and, let us hope, the worst.

If Philip Freneau had not written so much verse, on every subject in the world from honeysuckle to British prison ships, or if there had been any others writing in the time of the American Revolution, perhaps he would not be so well remembered in American anthologies. His verse, certainly not poetry, was stilted, unoriginal and imitative. He was himself a very modern type, unsuccessful, unsure, at once rebellious and ineffective. He wrote voluminously for newspapers, but was forced to take to the sea to make a living. In June, 1784, he sailed as supercargo on the brig *Dromelly* for Jamaica. The brig was hit by the great hurricane of July 30 and just escaped being wrecked.

Freneau, depressed and frightened, later wrote, "Verses, made at Sea, In a Heavy Gale," of which the outstanding stanzas are:

> *Happy the man who, safe on shore,*
> *Now trims, at home, his evening fire;*
> *Unmoved, he hears the tempest roar,*
> *That on the tufted groves expire.*
> *Alas! on us they doubly fall,*
> *Our feeble barque must bear them all.*

> [Three stanzas omitted]

> *While death and darkness both surround,*
> *And tempests rage wtih lawless power,*
> *Of friendship's voice I hear no sound,*
> *No comfort in this dreadful hour—*
> *What friendship can in tempests be,*
> *What comforts on this raging sea?*

> *The barque, accustomed to obey,*
> *No more the trembling pilots guide.*
> *Alone she gropes her trackless way,*
> *While mountains burst on either side—*
> *Thus, skill and science both must fall;*
> *And ruin is the lot of all.*

No one in the West Indies could remember such bad times; seven hurricanes in 1785, six in '86.

Of the nine in '87, two swung west to overpower a small ancient settlement, persistently British, on the coast of Honduras, where the Belize River carries mud between mangrove swamps into a bay sheltered by islands from the wild seas. Sailors from wrecked ships, logwood cutters, escaped Negro slaves, helped by Mosquito Indians of the coast, helped fight off the attacking Spanish. It was to this colony that many Charleston and Savannah Royalists had come to settle, just in time to be blasted out by the two hurricanes.

There were six hurricanes in the islands in '88.

In Jamaica alone 15,000 slaves died of starvation and disease. Of 775 sugar estates, 177 were sold for debt and 92 held by mortgage owners. In the Leeward Islands, salt works were closed down by the shutting out of American vessels. In Antigua, houses stood empty or ruined. In Dominica where the town of Roseau was burned and many plantations abandoned, rioting slaves escaped to live with the free Caribs in the mountains.

Even such islands as Jamaica, opened to American schooners bringing in food and building supplies, could not get enough to do much good.

For all that, in the year 1789, there were no recorded hurricanes at all. Peace had brought such a glut of hoarded sugars to England that the bottom had dropped out of the market. So able a sugar planter as Mr. John Pinney of Nevis, whose family had always made money by hard work and good judgment, wrote complainingly to his agent, "The sugar market does not get up. We sadly want to report of a war, a hurricane, or something to give it a lift."

He was always prepared for hurricanes. His entire year's schedule was always planned around the threat of them. He had refused to plant the new popular Otaheite cane, with its high sugar content, because it matured too late in the season. He never had his fields plowed, but hoed by hand, because hurricane rains leeched off the rich, deep-plowed earth. He always raised his own slave food, chiefly rooty vegetables, with plenty stored for hurricane time because the prices of smuggled herring were too high. By July, and no later, he had his sugar all ground and curing in his hogsheads, his heavy and costly sugar machinery, beams, rollers, pipes and coppers dismantled and snugged away. It was easier to let his flimsy farm buildings blow away, and rebuild, than strengthen them. He shipped to England only a few hogsheads in each ship, to prevent greater losses in possible hurricanes.

The next year, 1790, Pinney's early brown sugar was fetching better prices in Bristol because a hurricane kept Jamaica sugars from reaching England. But his wish came home to him like a black hurricane bird in a blood-red sunset later, although he was ready for the hurricane. When it was all over and his slaves were hard at work cleaning up, he must have heard the story that would become a classic hurricane story up and down those islands, told of a Mr. Hamilton who had just built a new house set up finely on pillars, in the beautiful small island of Tobago, to which, although at the moment French, many English planters had clung.

When the hurricane lifted out of the Atlantic over Tobago that wrecked twenty vessels and flattened plantations. Mr. Hamilton left his wife and two other ladies, children and servants in the house to go and see about his properties. He was able to struggle home only after the torment of winds had gone over, in pitch darkness. He groped up the littered path to his front door. There was nothing behind it but a hole into which he fell. The house, his wife, ladies, children and servants had blown completely away and were all found undamaged in a field. Mr. Hamilton was confined to his bed for a week.

In August of 1791 a hurricane killed three thousand people. A revolution exploded in fire and bloodshed in the rich French island of Haiti. Two thousand white people were killed brutally in the north and thousands of Negroes killed and tortured by French authorities in the south. The English sugar market soared so high that a Jamaica hurricane in October had no effect on it.

As white men fled from Haiti the French revolution hung on the horizon like a vast threat. They executed Louis XVI in 1793, England declared war on France, and there was a profound depression in the sugar islands, except perhaps in Tobago that the English suddenly recaptured.

War flared in the Caribbean. British Admiral Rodney and General Vaughan high-handedly took the free port of St. Eustatius and three million pounds' worth of supplies, especially American naval stores which were taken to rebuild and stock the harbor at Antigua for use by the British Navy. It had been shattered by a hurricane.

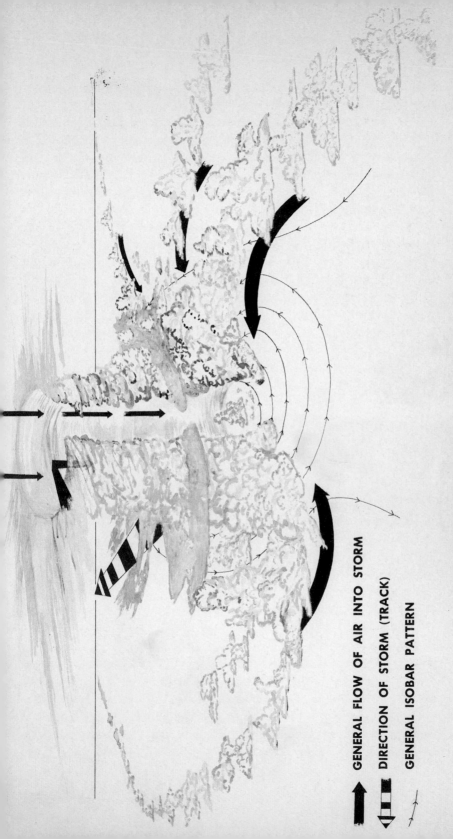

GENERAL FLOW OF AIR INTO STORM

DIRECTION OF STORM (TRACK)

GENERAL ISOBAR PATTERN

Three-dimensional drawing of hurricane, showing comparatively clear opening of the eye and the small "hub cloud" at the bottom of the eye.

This picture, taken in 1945, is typical of what has happened to ships off Florida in hurricanes since Columbus's time. (Wide World Photos)

Hurricane winds lashing trees and forcing heavy breakers over land. (Wide World Photos)

The terrible 1928 hurricane killed hundreds at Lake Okeechobee, Florida. This is the unroofed schoolhouse, showing bell and seats still standing. (Wide World Photos)

National Guard rescue workers collecting dead bodies (mostly from World War I veterans' camps) on the Florida Keys after the September, 1935, hurricane. (Wide World Photos)

A boat awash at Montauk, Long Island. (Photographed by *The New York Times*)

A Long Island town after hurricane waves came over the beach and flooded streets. (Photographed by *The New York Times*)

This happens to be Gravesend Bay, Brooklyn, but it could be almost any hurricane-beaten beach. (Wide World Photos)

Peterboro, New Hampshire, in 1938, when fire added to usual hurricane damage and the flooding Contoocook River barred attempts at fire fighting. (Wide World Photos)

Above, a fishing ves·
is adrift and other bo·
are piled up at the M·
nemsha section of Ma·
tha's Vineyard. *Le·*
the steeple of Bosto·
historic Old Nor·
Church is toppled f·
the second time sin·
1804.

(Wide World Photos

Market Square, Providence, Rhode Island, after Hurricane Carol, August, 1954. (Wide World Photos)

Hurricane Hazel, October, 1954, struck from the Caribbean to Canada. Unroofed and shattered houses in Jeremie, Haiti. (Wide World Photos)

A boat flung into the street at **Morehead City, North Carolina.**
(Wide World Photos)

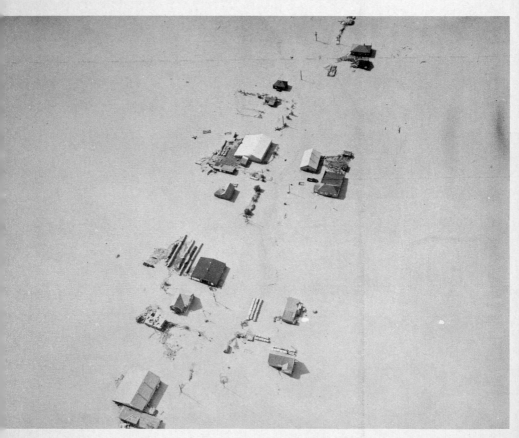

Hazel does damage in Canada. Farms at the Holland Marsh area north of Toronto
after the Humber River flooded from hurricane rains. (Wide World Photos)

The guillotine of the French Terror was set up in Point-a-Pitre, Guadeloupe, by a rough-and-ready terrorist named Victor Hugues, who cut off the heads of French Royalists, and fought off Admiral Sir John Jervis, taking over St. Lucia, St. Vincent and Grenada. Guadeloupe at once became the home port for a swarm of French privateers called "picaroons." Smuggling Americans dodged everywhere thereabouts in their neat fast vessels. Times were so distressed in the West Indies now, as hurricanes continued almost unnoticed, that the Americans were allowed free entry in the English islands and the ports of Spanish Santo Domingo, sparsely settled by Negroes and only a few whites, desolate with hurricanes and now ceded to French Haiti.

The Americans were tough traders. Rice from the Carolinas had never been so dear, over forty pounds a hundredweight. For their lumber, wheat flour, barreled beef and pork, Indian corn and salt herring, they demanded in barter huge amounts of sugar, molasses, cocoa and coffee from the planters of impoverished Jamaica, who for the first time had been promised loans from the British government, to keep them alive. But before the money arrived, a hurricane of August, 1795, reduced them to complete destitution.

The desperate British had been beaten by France in the Low Countries but they had more troops now for the war in the West Indies. A fleet of eight ships of the line under Admiral Christian, with 16,000 troops under Sir Ralph Abercromby making a delayed sailing on the fifteenth of November, were so overwhelmed in the channel by a late Atlantic hurricane that all but one was either sunk or badly damaged.

British luck was still bad in the next hurricane season.

BOOK FIVE

WAR IN THE WEST INDIES

1 *HAITI AND BOSTON*

Stranger things than hurricanes were happening in the West Indies, too strange to be much affected by them.

The hurricane of 1796 interrupted only briefly the prosperity of Charleston, South Carolina, basking in high prices for its rice. Sea-minded President John Adams, incensed by the capture of American trading vessels by French picaroons, sent down a re-organized American Navy that fought late in the hurricane season but was touched by none. The British had been forced by yellow fever to give up their ill-fated invasion of Haiti's south coast as the dramatic ex-slave Toussaint L'Ouverture, fast friend of America, dominated a free and strange Haiti.

No one would have a clear picture of that island then, if a hurricane in the fall of 1799 had not wrecked a small Danish bark making its way up the Windward Passage. It drifted by the fort at the bay of the present Cap Haitien, then Cap François. The half-drowned crew and an English officer, for safety calling himself an American, were allowed ashore.

He was Captain Marcus Rainsford, sailing to join his regiment in Martinique. At Cap Haitien he mingled in fascination with the crowds in the half-wrecked French city, among rejoicing Negroes in rags or scarlet uniforms or satin knee pants, barefooted and with elaborate high headdresses. And American captains and merchants were doing excellent business. His long striped pantaloons and curls and short blue jacket over a fine cambric shirt were heartily approved and he was invited everywhere in that society with its fine French manners, half-delirious with freedom, to concerts, balls and banquets. He played billiards with Toussaint L'Ouverture himself, among his courtly black officers, a superb figure in scarlet, with gold braid and gold epaulettes, a feather in his hat and a huge sword. Rainsford admired enormously his kindness, his wisdom and his genius. He set it all down, Toussaint's brooding words and the massed review of thousands of his precisely trained Haitian troops.

It may be that Napoleon Bonaparte, who would soon attempt to regain control of Haiti and capture his black rival, learned many things about the state of the island from the book that Rainsford published on his return to England.

As it continued its voyage along that rocky coast, the badly repaired vessel, with Rainsford aboard again, was forced to put in, leaking, at Fort Egalité. Rainsford was promptly arrested as an English spy and condemned to death by a huge black officer called Henri Christophe, who would later be emperor. Rainsford managed to send an appeal back to L'Ouverture, who ordered that he be released at once to resume his voyage but "must never return without the proper passports."

There was an early hurricane in May, 1800, which did not prevent the American Navy from capturing a number of French privateers and scattering a British fleet under Lord St. Vincent. Three other hurricanes overran Cuba and New Orleans and roughed up the faraway British Channel where on the French coast Napoleon was training a superb army for his passionately held project of the invasion of Britain.

The British had been blockading the seas off Brest and the Channel ports under Admiral Sir John Jervis until he was given an earldom and called Lord St. Vincent. His successor was elderly Sir Hyde Parker, "Old Vinegar" whose ship had been wrecked in the West Indies in the great hurricane of 1780. It was as if Sir Hyde could not stand any more bad weather, with the fleet off Brest in the heavy fall gales, and went home to bed. Still he was sent as fleet commander to the Baltic against the Russian fleet. Timid and weatherworn Sir Hyde was not equal to the action planned for him by the brilliant captain and fleet strategist, Horatio Nelson. Sir Hyde was recalled and Nelson, not previously considered socially eligible, was given the supreme command.

News of a July hurricane had delayed Napoleon's fleet under Victor Leclerc, husband to lush young Pauline Bonaparte, so that they did not sail until December to subdue the black revolutionaries in Haiti.

In August of 1802 a hurricane came tearing over the bayous to

New Orleans. It upset the French royalist refugees crowded in from Haiti and the loaded bateaux of American rafters and boatmen coming downriver, which the Spanish government had allowed to enter free under a "Right of Deposit." The engineer supervising the erection of a fort in Plaquemines Parish was drowned in his house as the flood water rose two or three feet above the top of the fort where workmen stood up to their waists and so survived.

A greater excitement came to New Orleans with the news that Spain had ceded Louisiana, "nothing but swampland," to France. The only other hurricane that year howled in from the Atlantic to explode in rain and surf high up the abandoned pearl islands off the coast of Venezuela, a disaster almost unremarked on the continent seething with hidden rebellion against Spain.

By that time, Leclerc's French invasion of Haiti was a wretched failure. Toussaint L'Ouverture was taken by treachery to die in a French prison. General Leclerc died of yellow fever that killed thousands of French soldiers. The victorious bloodthirsty Negro General Dessalines besieged the starving French in Cap François, under Captain General Rochambeau, while a British squadron hovered in deep water outside.

Rochambeau was the son of the great general who had served so well in the American Revolution. He was not of his father's stamp. By signing false articles of capitulation he tried to trick Dessalines into allowing him ten days to evacuate his army and at the same time tried to prevail on the British to take him and five hundred men back to France not as prisoners. The British refused. Weather had the last word.

A hurricane moving northwestward along the difficult Old Bahama Channel overwhelmed the British blockaders who struggled to hold their place. The Bahamas had had a hurricane in July and another in September. The waters had been foaming, disturbed, rain-swept, wind-harried all that season. There had never been a moment's peace, when Rochambeau could slip out of harbor.

Dessalines, who had threatened to destroy the French ships with red-hot shot from the forts, grudgingly accepted the British claim to a French surrender. The wind dropped. Rochambeau sailed out on the land breeze with eight thousand men left alive out of forty thousand, and struck his colors.

In the United States, wages were rising. Quiet Robert Livingston, in Paris, bought Louisiana and nobody knew how far west, for fifteen million dollars.

Great Britain declared war on France before Napoleon was ready for it, thereby driving French commerce from the seas and giving a new chance to American West Indian trade. Napoleon planned to hurt the British by developing French manufactures, especially by producing sugar from Rhineland beets, and kept his army ready to cross the Channel.

The American Navy in the Mediterranean, under Preble, Bainbridge, Decatur and the others, recalled the United States to its old sea pride by disrupting the pirate navy of Tripoli. Even Thomas Jefferson, who had previously ordered the Army disbanded and the Navy broken up, designed a new gunboat, of which Congress ordered twenty-five as coast defenders.

They were small, not over fifty feet, cheap to build, variously rigged and with oars. In time the country afforded fifty in 1806, and 188 in 1807. Each was to carry one cannon, in rare cases two. Unfortunately the cannon was so heavy it could not be fired unless the boat was anchored, or it would sink itself by its own recoil. Jefferson felt there would be no temptation to send them dashing out recklessly in seas beyond their depths, that could lead to nothing but foreign wars.

Gunboat No. 3 was finished and launched on July 18, 1804. On the fourteenth of August it anchored among the rakish trading craft off the Battery of the city of Charleston. On the third of September it sailed upriver to Savannah, Georgia, to cast anchor under the bluff and wait orders on coastal defense from the Governor.

The first of six hurricanes in 1804 left the depressed planters in Jamaica despairing, then Antigua, St. Christopher, Nassau and Charleston on September 3, 6, and 7. The long sandy beaches northward past Cape Fear were assaulted by waves raging up along Hatteras and the outer banks to Norfolk, Virginia. There, at least, there were no longer any navy vessels or navy yard to be damaged. Thence the hurricane curved out to sea and was lost. It was reported that in the balmy days that followed, fruit trees still standing blossomed again.

Puerto Rico's hurricane of September 21 was remembered for years as the terrible storm of San Mateo that struck Jamaica the next day.

In October a great Atlantic storm bore northward for the incurving coast of Georgia. The tide and hurricane wave surged half over Tybee Island and swelled upriver beyond the pine barrens. The winds swept across Savannah on her height, lashing her streets with rain like lead, blowing off roofs and chimneys, smashing slave cabins and ships. There, also, high if not dry, stuck in the gluey mud of a cornfield, lay Mr. Jefferson's favorite gunboat, No. 3.

"It was the best navy on earth," to the huge merriment of Virginia planters and the bitter laughter of New England seamen.

In October the last cyclone of that season boomed up the Atlantic, curving northeastward, leaving a trail of debris on the southeastern New England coast. On the ninth it was heaving blackly over prosperous Federalist Boston.

When its violence had passed, Boston was in bad shape. The rocky islands were fringed with wrecks. The Long Wharf and the old India Wharf, that ran far out to deep water, where between them forty-eight sail had been counted, were wet masses of wreckage. The narrow streets paved with beach stones were crowded with battered buildings right down to the wharves. Houses, warehouses, sail lofts, rum shops, ship fitters, were a mash of broken wood. Up the three hills roofs and windows were frowsy with blown stuff, cracks, holes, gaps. Half the chimneys were like broken teeth. Copley's pasture was knee deep in wet refuse.

With the first light of the quiet day after, crowds of men and boys clambered through the streets, blocked with fallen trees, fences, overturned wagons and refuse, to see the damage. Not one of them marked everything with such concentrated energy as tall, elegant Charles Bulfinch, Boston's thirty-one-year-old "great selectman." He was also the superintendent of police and had already ordered out his deputies.

At least half young Bulfinch's anxiety that morning was for the buildings he had built, the architect who was making Boston beautiful, dignified and elegant. He rejoiced that his great dome on the Massachusetts State House, heavier than he had really liked, and not yet gilded, rose like a rock. The new brick column of his design, sixty feet high, was safe, on the top of Beacon Hill, that had taken the place of the old beacon blown down in the high gales of '89.

Bulfinch hurried along, often in the middle of the littered streets, to take a look at Franklin Place. It was the first group of connected buildings in the United States, the Tontine Crescent. Across a little park, he had designed a straight line of harmonious residences on his return from his studies in Europe. It had taken his concentrated genius to push, prod, argue, connive, and take risks. He pledged his own and his family's money to get them built. He had lost every cent. But there they stood now, tested, unshaken and untouched but for a litter of trees.

The steeples and churches he had designed were all right, Holy Cross in Franklin Place, the new North Church in Hanover Street. But he had to push his way over debris and a milling crowd of sight-seers to get a view up the narrow street to Christ Church. The steeple had blown down and its ruin blocked both streets. It was a tragic sight to him then but in 1807 he was to build there a much more beautiful steeple, white and pinnacled, one of the lovely Bulfinch spires that crown many a New England village or hill with enduring graciousness.

Most of all he must have stared with regret at the splintered stump of the steeple which he had not built, of the old South Church, long since historic.

Then as chairman of the Board of Selectmen he had to struggle through the wreckage downhill to the ruined wharves where his family's and all Boston's fortunes had most truly begun, in the long trading voyages to Oregon and to China. Now India Wharf, with its ropewalks and warehouses, was a wooden mountain of ruin.

The next year, Bulfinch was chosen to draw a plan to open up a seventy-foot street from State Street to Battery March Street, which would be widened and named Broad Street. He rebuilt the India Wharf itself in brick, thirty-two stores of three stories with counting rooms and warehouses under its graceful arch and dormered slate roof. For many years it was the finest harbor development on the coast, handsome, solidly impressive, looking out on the forests of masts of Boston's global seafaring. It had a profound effect on the design of business buildings throughout the United States. It stood many another storm until Atlantic Avenue was cut through at the arch, leaving something of the stately old building still overlooking the harbor.

The hurricane left Boston eager for recovery and new building. Charles Bulfinch, devoted public servant, who seems not to have made a cent out of all his superb architecture, was the creator, thereafter head and shoulders above his imitators, of the Federalist charm, the dignity and elegance of innumerable Boston mansions, public buildings and institutions. His renown in New England led to his employment in Washington as the architect who embellished and completed Latrobe's ambitious plan for the Capitol of the United States.

Napoleon's Army of the Coasts of the Ocean had been waiting all this time in high spirits along the English Channel, ready to invade frightened England if the English fleet blockading the Channel ports could be drawn away for even six hours. Spain declared war on England in December and Napoleon crowned himself Emperor of the French, and Josephine, Empress.

The hurricane that overcame Jamaica on July 27, 1805, and the one that hurled out of the Atlantic to ruin Barbados in two terrible nights, were too late to flutter even a sail of the French fleet under Villeneuve, trying to entice the English from the Channel by sailing as if to capture the English West Indies. Or of Horatio Nelson's fleet from the Mediterranean which early in July followed them there, and never found them.

It would not have affected the result if a hurricane had overtaken the French fleet. But if Nelson's ships had been scattered Napoleon would have invaded England. Nelson understood perfectly the risk he took. As it was, immediately after the battle of Trafalgar, where Nelson overtook and defeated Villeneuve, and even as he lay dead on his own quarterdeck, Napoleon was wheeling his vast army for the attack on Russia.

2 *PIRATES OFF FLORIDA*

Although there were seven hurricanes in 1806 and three in 1807, trailing their destruction chiefly over the British Islands, the sailing in May of the last British slave ship from Africa, was to the planters a more dreadful calamity.

The protests of English and American Quakers had roused the conscience of Great Britain. Over the frantic protests of sugar planters and merchants the bill was passed that made slave dealing in the West Indies punishable as a felony and, for a second offense, hanging for piracy.

Sugar prices had been falling steadily. Now the price of slaves rose extravagantly. To breed them in the islands, the planters complained, was expensive. Care now had to be taken to decrease the high mortality of Negro babies and adults by better food, housing and doctoring. The suppression of the slave trade was blamed for all the losses of the one-crop system, waste, debts, graft and inefficiency.

Now ruined island estates found few buyers. In Jamaica suits were pending against more than a hundred estates. At least sixty-five were abandoned. For the lack of able slaves new colonies could not be developed.

Americans might have grown rich smuggling slaves, except that Thomas Jefferson and the American Congress clapped shut all the Atlantic ports with an embargo. Jefferson was sure it would turn Americans from seagoing to farming, and keep the country out of European wars. Boston was furious. It was the end of seagoing commerce for small ports such as Newburyport, Massachusetts, and New Haven, Connecticut. Even Boston shippers, more able than others to put up heavy export bonds, were driven to despair. Thousands of men were idle.

The south coast of now Spanish Florida, Key Biscayne to the Caloosahatchee and Tampa, gave harborage to ships landing slaves from Cuba for the march to Georgia. In the Bay of Barataria, southwest of New Orleans, on islands beyond bayous and trembling swamps, the masts of pirate schooners were concealed behind live oaks and palmettos.

The privateers sailed under letters of marque from the republics of Venezuela and Colombia, now free of Spain, and took to the summary court at Barataria every ship they could lay their rapacious hands on. Goods and slaves were sold to shouting bidders and the money spent in the coffeehouses, shops, brothels of New Orleans. The Place d'Armes, the markets and levees of the old city were crowded with new adventurers.

The leader of the whole smuggling business was a Frenchman named Jean Laffite.

The hurricanes of 1809, the five in 1810, brought ruin to many a West Indian island ruined already by the lack of supply ships. By 1811, Wellington was fighting the French in Portugal and Spain and no help of any kind could be sent to the Leeward Islands, devastated by a September hurricane that may have been the same one that whirled over Charleston, South Carolina, sinking ships idle in harbor and spoiling rice in the waterfront warehouses. A tornado followed the eye of the hurricane that cut a swath one hundred yards through the city, killing many people.

Next year, after all the confusion and anger of British attacks on American ships, British Orders in Council restricting American trade, with James Madison President, the United States declared war on Great Britain.

Those were dark days of unemployment and stagnant commerce not only in the states and in England, but in France. Napoleon's army was still invading Russia. The weather was bad in June and July, thick fog west of the Grand Banks and violent gusts of wind over the whole ocean. But American frigates sailed out to an amazing list of victories over British ships, that revived pride in American breasts, after the failures of war in the Great Lakes. The British blockaded American ports with ships, cruisers and frigates based at Jamaica and Barbados, Newfoundland, Halifax and Bermuda.

The American sloop-of-war *Wasp*, eighteen guns, under Master Commandant Jacob Jones, got under way but ran square into an enormous hurricane, the fourth that season, that had ravaged the ancient city of Trinidad in Cuba, after damaging some of the British squadron in Kingston Harbor, Jamaica. Before the eighteenth of October it had overtaken a convoy of British merchant vessels bound from Honduras to England and wrecked many including the British brig-of-war *Frolic*. Both the *Wasp* and the *Frolic* were in bad shape when they met.

The Britisher attacked at once, to protect his distressed ships. The *Wasp* came up rolling to within sixty yards. Canvas creaking full, bows spouting spray like snow over the dark waves, they sailed side by side and their guns shot point-blank in flame and smoke. The *Wasp's* main and mizzen topmasts crashed down in a tangle of

rigging and blasted canvas. The *Frolic's* boom-mainsail was shot
away. She became unmanageable. Jones just managed steerage way,
working his sloshing, bucking *Wasp* near enough to close with
grappling irons and rake the *Frolic's* decks with a couple of broadsides. "Although so near," he wrote afterward, "while loading the
last broadside our rammers were shoved against the side of the
enemy."

A seaman on the *Wasp*, Jack Lang, hating the British who had
once impressed him, leaped with his cutlass at the *Frolic's* bowsprit
which had been rammed over the *Wasp's* deck, and hand-over-hand
swung himself to the *Frolic's* deck. Lieutenant Biddle, with his
boarding party, found the British decks filled with dead and
wounded.

The British flag was down in forty-five minutes. The British ship
of the line *Poitiers*, coming up after the hurricane had moved north,
captured the *Wasp* and its captured vessels.

By the end of 1813 the British had blockaded all American ports
from the Mississippi to Long Island Sound. Boston alone, which
had been against the war, had been left free for the important
traffic with British Halifax. That fall, twelve hurricanes were reported, that added to the losses and discomforts of the blockade
and the misery of the islands. American vessels that had been permitted to anchor and, by free deposit, exchange grain, fish, meat
and lumber for sugar and coffee, were sunk and wrecked. In the
Leeward Islands people were in such distress that it was forbidden
for any island to send help even to its nearest neighbor. In November, Boston ships were destroyed in Nova Scotia's bleak harbors.

Between the war and this most dreadful hurricane year, prices
in the West Indies were unbelievable. No one could repair damaged
houses, in sugar islands cleared of forests, with pitch pine lumber
smuggled from America at forty pounds a thousand feet. Irish beef
cost over sixteen pounds a barrel, and salt fish, if an American
merchant ship were captured, brought four pounds ten a hundredweight.

In thrice-hurricaned Dominica, Negro slaves escaped bondage
from poverty-stricken masters to the rain forests and cloud-fogs
of those mountains. Only the three or four exquisite notes of the
bird called "solitaire" followed them across valleys filled with
bloomy space or by the lake-filled craters of volcanoes, among rain-

brilliant leaves. The chilled Negroes hid in caves behind the sprays of threadlike waterfalls, or ate and were warmed at the remote fires of the free Caribs.

Still their hate of white men drew them back to isolated estate houses with bloodshed and fiery horror. So, as it was done before in St. Vincent, the British sent troops, country boys and boys from London slums in scarlet woolen tunics, to hunt out and shoot at the darting black figures that climbed and clung and dropped down a cliff face like heavy fruit. This went on for a whole year until, after the ruin of another hurricane, the English gave up Dominica, leaving the last blacks alive.

In the United States there was much depression, no commerce except for smugglers. In Europe, Napoleon had fled over the snows from Moscow and lost the Peninsular War to the British, who were in a bad way financially. Still they had troops now to send to burn Washington, take away thousands of slaves and work ruin as bad as hurricanes along New England coasts.

The next year when Charleston, South Carolina, and Puerto Rico knew the only two hurricanes, there were great sea victories at Lake Champlain, and at the end, white-crested Andrew Jackson taking Pensacola, taking Mobile, and, with the help of Laffite's loyal pirates of Barataria, taking New Orleans. The states were united at last in the common pride of being Americans.

American vessels put out to sea at once with rice, lumber, tobacco, salt fish, that had been straining the warehouses to the amount of fifty-three million dollars' worth. Goods from England and the replanted sugar islands flowed in. The Navy finally settled the Mediterranean pirates and things were booming.

Some of the eight hurricanes of the violent season of 1815 caught pirate craft dodging among the islands, along with a lot of over-eager merchantmen. The New Orleans authorities finally broke up the pirate stronghold at Barataria. The greatest hurricane of September surged up from wrecking St. Bart's and lonely Turks Island and the whole coast suffered.

The great "September equinoctial gale" was felt most terribly up the pleasant shores and islands of Narragansett Bay. The height came in the morning between ten and eleven-thirty when the tide rose twelve feet above normal at Providence. The bridge connecting the two parts of the town over the river was swept away. Thirty-five vessels were wrecked at the head of the basin or among the wrecked wharves.

On the west side the water came to the tops of windows and many buildings crumbled, from which people were rescued in boats. On the east side, water flooded Weybosset Street, and on Westminster Street the water was eight feet above the pavements and the Second Baptist Church was demolished. In the river, men from a wrecked brig crawled over the rolling and tumbling debris and people watching from nearby roofs pulled them to safety with ropes.

In Connecticut, New London, Groton, Norwich, Stonington were damaged. Point Judith light was destroyed. All along the Massachusetts shores villages and towns were battered. Salt water was blown more than forty miles inland so that everything was scalded and white with salt.

In Boston Harbor sixty vessels went down in one awful blast that knocked down trees ashore. It was bad at Abington, where a sailor familiar with the West Indies said there would be a terrific wind before day had passed for there was a crackling in the air and the sky haze loomed up as he had noticed in the tropics. Houses were unroofed and damage everywhere up the coast, Cambridgeport, Marblehead, Salem, Gloucester, Reading, Newburyport, Danvers, Saugus, and as far as Wells in Maine. No one ever listed the people killed.

But when it was over there was a wave of rebuilding throughout New England, especially in Providence where the wrecks of dilapidated wooden warehouses were burned to make way for brick buildings and more elegant houses. Charles Bulfinch of Boston, the famous architect, was asked to design the beautiful First Congregational Church in Providence. His finest spire of all, the New South Church of Boston, finished in 1814, had not been damaged. ⟩

The toll of hurricanes went on remorselessly in the West Indies, three in 1816, four in 1817, nine violent ones in 1818, especially the hurricane of September that swept over the low Cayman Islands, peopled with a few heroic fishermen and turtle hunters.

In 1819, the great blank coastline that curved from Louisiana to the Rio Grande was as it always had been, a waste of sand and endless barren islands cut with inlets from inner bays, lagoons, and drowned river mouths to the tinted expanse of the Gulf of Mexico. There were islands covered with snakes or thousands of white nesting birds, white pelicans, snowy terns, white herons, white and blue least herons, crisscrossing the sky with the whiteness of their tens of thousands of wings.

Within the salt lagoons the tawny land went off into sun haze and unimaginable vastness, shadowed in pools by clumps of live oaks and the twisty trunks of mesquite, misted with leaves. Some of the hot sand was salt where hurricanes had overflowed or shifted the island passes.

None of it had been included in Napoleon's sale of Louisiana to the United States. Spain had done no more than claim it, with a royal governor in the old mud-and-sun-colored city of San Antonio, where already Mexican revolutionaries had been fighting. At crossings of the Great River there were Laredo and a few forts. There was nothing else but wandering wild cattle, wandering Indians, desperadoes, traders, outlaws and North Americans. It was called Texas.

When Jean Laffite, the dark Frenchman, lean as a bone, suave as a grandee, the dominant force in all that whooping privateering smuggling trade of the Gulf of Mexico, had had to leave Barataria, he cruised the sun-dried coast of Texas for a harbor. He liked a long island with a narrow shell ridge blown up by northers, even if it was looping with rattlesnakes. Sand dunes by the Gulf shore offered protection from the hurricanes, it was said. On the lee side a bay reached up the mouth of the Trinity River, across bars and shallows darkened with fish and among islands alive with wild duck.

There at a settlement of revolutionary Mexicans, Jean Laffite, traveling as a buyer of prize goods, organized a sort of colonial government and prize court, ostensibly Spanish. It was first called "Campeachy." Goods of all kinds, chests of spices, bales of silk, tobacco, minted silver, diamonds and New England wooden ware, overflowed the warehouses. Ships were burned and sunk. Their charred timbers lie below there now. After that, Laffite gave the ships back to their shipmasters to be captured again. He renamed the riotous pirate town, for that vigorous young Spanish governor who had built Louisiana, Bernardo de Gálvez, for Bernardo's father, who had been the energetic governor of New Spain, and for Bernardo's famous uncle, the head of the Council of the Indies. It was "Gálvez-town" or Galveston.

The town had more than two hundred buildings, stores, dram shops and auctions of goods. His most valuable trade goods were slaves from captured slave ships, who, when doctored, rested and well-fed, were smuggled into Louisiana at top prices.

Laffite lived like a lord in money-drunk Galveston in his fine mansion, "The Red House." There were cannon on the roof to repel boarders. He inspected every prize from his handsome sailing yacht, *Le Ciel Bleu.*

One of the nine hurricanes of 1818 loomed over Galveston, with no warning from any ship captain. What the people saw first was the bar of the hurricane black on the south horizon, and moving up fast. The air was full of fine sand blown from the dunes as the dark waves rolled in, white-topped.

Laffite and many of his men rowed out to his anchored yacht, leaving the Red House as refuge to all the women and children. The wind and rain came in faster and the dunes melted before the wild rising Gulf water.

In the black night, Laffite's yacht rolled over on its beam ends and stuck there. He and his men managed to get ashore. No one heard in the tumult the Red House collapse and the women screaming and drowning who were not killed by the roof cannon falling in on them. Everything was washed away but wreckage.

With the first calm light Laffite began to clean up and rebuild, shanties out of broken boards, stockades for more slaves. They ate pelican and fish blown ashore. The winter was hard and there were few prizes.

Both American and Spanish governments, agreeing about their boundaries, were sick and tired of Laffite and his pirates. In New Orleans, some of his men were hanged. In 1821, the United States sent Lieutenant Lawrence Kearny to tell Laffite, over whom he had no jurisdiction, that he must get out of Galveston in three months.

Laffite had fire set to everything. The town and the wharves and the shanties burned all night with a flame that lighted the island and the bay and the Gulf. By morning, Laffite was gone. No one really knows what became of him.

Hordes of vicious small-time pirates were still haunting the coasts and islands of Cuba. There were more than three thousand acts of aggression against American vessels trading in island ports after three years of hurricane destruction, the Virgins in 1819, St. Kitts in '20 and the third of five in '21 that stripped Montserrat of all trees, so that there was no lumber for coffins and the dead were buried in old trunks and boxes.

Florida, by purchase from Spain, was at last American, and General Andrew Jackson, the new territorial governor and his troops, stood at salute in Pensacola while the Spanish flag floated down and old Spanish ladies cried. The new flag soared up in a burst of band music and cheering. Tallahasseee on its oak-and-pine-clad hills became the capital, with a steady drift of new citizens from Georgia and Virginia. At the Cow Ford or ferry crossing at the King's Road across the St. Johns, a few more shacks were built and called Jacksonville. American winter visitors drifted along the bay front of almost deserted St. Augustine.

But the chief value of Florida was as an outpost against pirate activity southward. At the end of the long chain of Florida Keys, always hurricane haunted, Lieutenant M. C. Perry, of the U.S. schooner *Shark*, took formal possession of the largest sun-blasted island known to pirates and Cuban charcoal burners as "Cayo Hueso" from a great mound of bones that had been found there, or "Key West."

Here a naval station of sorts was established, houses scattered among the yellow-green scrub beyond the salt pond and the warehouse and a small Navy hospital. Commodore David Porter, of the heroic *Essex*, and a number of young officers who would be heard from later, notably his ward, David Farragut, commanded there in 1823. Every week now as many as thirty American vessels sailed to and from Havana and twenty from Matanzas while increasing numbers came by from New Orleans and Galveston. Porter could sit under his deck awning and look around at the frigates, sloops, brigs, schooners, gunboats, the old square-rigged *Macedonian* that Decatur had taken from the British.

His flagship was the improbable-looking steam galliot *Sea Gull*, with round paddle wheels amidships and sails. He had no confidence in it nor in the future of steam, unless there was no wind. But what he needed, he wrote angrily to Washington, was a lot of rowboats that could be sailed by armed men around Cuba. He got them, and began his war.

Meantime, the new city grew prosperous as the circuit judge

came from Jacksonville to try salvage cases that meant money for
Key West salvors with every hurricane that swept northward to
hit Mobile once, and Charleston and the Carolina coast twice in
1822. By the next hurricane season, in which Porter took his ships
and men north for safety, they had raided the Cuban coast and
the islands so successfully that the pirates were all out of business.

Porter's own private invasion of Puerto Rico in pursuit of pirates
got him court-martialed. He resigned from the Navy, to his later
regret. He died many years later in Constantinople as head of the
American Foreign Service, but he had lived as long as he could in
Key West, even after he was commissioned to organize, briefly,
the Mexican navy.

Hurricanes were hitting Georgia and the West Indies, while all
this was going on, in 1825, '26 and '27. By that time the fear of
them which in that time had not once touched Key West, and of
yellow fever, which ravaged it again and again, was being made
capital of by political pressure from west Florida. The Naval Station was moved from Key West to Pensacola. Key West was almost forgotten except for its wreckers.

Pensacola was beginning to thrive as a port for cotton from Alabama and Mississippi. The unverified story that is told in Key West
is that a hurricane promptly blew over Pensacola and destroyed
what there was of the Naval Station, not much more than officers'
quarters, walled to keep pigs out.

President Adams had prohibited American trade with the British
West Indies. But the terrific hurricane of August 17 that blew
until the twenty-eighth of August, 1827, reduced the islands of
St. Kitts, Nevis, the Virgins and especially Anguilla and its salt-
rakers, to such wretchedness that for three months those ports were
opened to free trade with vessels of all nations. Andrew Jackson
was then running for President. He protested so loudly against West
Indian ports being closed to American ships again that he won the
support of powerful merchant and shipping interests, and the election. American ships were thereafter allowed to trade in British
colonial ports amounts equal to goods that British ships carried
from American ports.

The Cape Verde hurricane that remotely helped Andrew Jackson
to the presidency had headed for Cape Hatteras where the first
lighthouse had been set not long after the great hurricane of 1804

had battered New England. In June of 1824 the first lightship was anchored fourteen miles south over the hidden tip of the Shoals. She was a small dumpy vessel pointed at bow and stern, heavy above water, thick below and with only enough speed to give her steerage way. She bore two lights.

Her captain in 1827 was a Navy veteran, Captain Life Holden, who had his wife and three daughters aboard, as well as the crew, keeping the warning beacons safely lighted. It was home to the Holdens until the hurricane of August 27.

The lights went out on the small lightship, as the hurricane surge covered all that sea. There was too much wind and rain to see the extraordinary height and wild tumult of the waves. They could only feel the ship jarring, bucking, rolling. The ship was tossed stern down, and bow straight up. When she was dropped back on even keel she was hit broadside by a sea that with the boom of cannon threw her over on her side. Again she bobbed back. The strain parted the cable.

For fourteen hours Captain Holden, his wife and those three girls and the crew lived in total darkness in the hollow of that howling storm. The next morning they were aground on Ocracoke Island, and safe. But it was years before there was another lightship on the Diamond Shoals.

3 EMANCIPATION AND STEAM

The abolition of slavery was a menace more grave even than hurricanes, or so thought the British planters of the sugar islands. The slave trade had been abolished but the conscience of England and "The Society for the Mitigation and Gradual Abolition of Slavery Throughout the British Dominions" insisted that no actual progress had been made.

Against it, "The Society of West Indian Planters and Merchants" raged. They were deathly afraid the slaves would hear of the agitation in England. They did. There was unrest and rebellion everywhere, which in Jamaica was put down with wholesale floggings, shootings and hangings. Chapels of nonconformist ministers preaching the end of slavery were burned and some were attacked.

East Indian planters, raising sugar with free labor, added political pressure to break the West Indian sugar monopoly.

Every hurricane that overran the islands therefore exaggerated the conditions of unrest. The hurricane that overwhelmed Boston on July 29, 1829, on the contrary, did not halt the thrust of her commerce into all the oceans. In September, a hurricane that fiercely blew salt water over the marshes and sandy barrens at the mouth of the Rio Grande flattened a few settlers' huts and killed fish, and that was all.

In Trinidad, Crown slaves were liberated. By '33, the British government was planning a twenty million pound indemnity to be paid to owners for the release of their slaves after six years of apprenticeship. There were laws for the welfare of freed slaves.

On August 1, 1834, Great Britain abolished slavery.

The whole way of life in the British islands was forever changed. Many a bankrupt planter took his indemnity money and went home to England. Slaves from abandoned estates ranged the mountains, settling on unclaimed land. Many had little or nothing to eat until they raised a crop. It was a time of bitter confusion.

Hurricanes struck miserable Dominica, south Texas, French Martinique, Spanish Santo Domingo; in '35, Barbados twice, and Antigua once, where one of the first barometers fell one inch in an hour and twenty-seven minutes. The now unpiratical city of Galveston in the struggling Republic of Texas only slowly recovered from a hurricane.

Thirty-seven was terrible, with ten hurricanes. The eighth, that surged over the Gulf of Mexico from September 27 to October 10, known as "Racer's Storm" because it dismasted a British sloop-of-war of that name in the Yucatán Channel, curved into the Mexican coast south of Matamoras and out again across the town of Galveston on its sand island. The excitement of the revolution had crammed it with adventurers who were badly battered, especially in the wreck of the new Hotel Tremont. Then the hurricane boiled off cross-country to Carolina.

Just then, the fine new paddle-wheel steamer, *Home*, was coming

south on her third trip from New York to Charleston, crowded
with more than ninety passengers. Water was already sloshing from
the roughening sea in her hold. She was bucking tremendous waves
off Hatteras the morning of the ninth, rolling and pitching so
desperately the paddle wheels thrashed out of water. All the crew
worked the pump, all the passengers bailed. Sea water put out the
fires. She groped under sail. The captain thought he had passed Cape
Hatteras and headed her west. At 10 P.M. she struck on the beach
six miles from Ocracoke. There were only two life preservers. Almost all the women and children, herded together on the forecastle,
drowned when the vessel began to break up. Only forty people
from the ship survived. That was the hurricane wreck that caused
Congress to pass the law that requires every vessel to carry a life
preserver for every passenger.

The small liberal island of Antigua was the first to emancipate all
its slaves at once, with no period of apprenticeship. What happened
in Antigua was an example of how emancipation worked, not for
the planters, whose sugar economy was already dying of beet-sugar
competition from France, but for the freed slaves themselves. What
happened to them in hurricanes pointed up the difference between
slavery and freedom.

In thirty years, to 1864, Antigua suffered at least seven hurricanes
in '35, two in '37, in '38, '39, '48 and '51. There was also a bad earthquake in '43. Yet in those thirty years, Antigua's economy was
made over to an unpretentious prosperity for the people themselves.

The small dry island, low fields in the north sloping to not very
high mountains in the south, boasted three excellent harbors, Falmouth, Parham—the port of St. John—and Nelson's favorite, English
Harbour. When not ruined by hurricanes, they gave work to many
men, refitting merchant ships, as well as the British navy. Of the
island's 70,000 acres, 58,000 had long been exhausted by ruthless
sugar production and eroded by hurricane rains. The mountains
were unfit for cane growing.

Yet after emancipation, Antigua produced more sugar than it
had for years, with one record crop of 20,000 hogsheads. Many
more things were raised, especially food crops, and some were
exported.

The reason for this was the new condition of the ex-slaves. They
were said to have been taken from some of the most advanced, independent and warlike tribes of the African slave coast, such as the

Ashantis. They were tall, well-muscled people whom only the English and Americans bought, because they were hard workers. Unlike the practice on any other island, long before emancipation these people were allowed to attend church schools. After it, a large proportion of their children went to day schools. Marriages became the custom. Acres of mountain land were set aside for their private holdings. They built themselves wattle-thatched huts, African fashion, and slept on dirt floors.

The swept earth before their doors, by their cooking fires, where they ate by day and sat about in the starlit early evenings, became the common ground for a village. In a few years there over sixty-seven villages in the hills, housing over nine thousand free people, living on their own food, cassava, yams, eddoes, peas, tropical fruits, chickens, sugar cane, and some cattle.

For ready money the people could hire out as day labor on some old sugar estate; but everywhere, on every island, all Negroes hated gang labor. Antigua proved first the old truth, that a man works better free on his own land, than any slave. In Antigua ex-slaves soon bought better land at fifty dollars an acre from some discouraged white planter who could not bring himself to work and live as the Negro could. In Antigua, a man owning ten acres of land, or five acres and good buildings or paying good rent, could vote. With a larger income, he could be elected to the Assembly. He could be a carpenter, mason, cobbler, merchant, or anything else. He was free to learn and teach and preach.

When those seven hurricanes in thirty years barreled down on Antigua, it was badly battered. But it was not ruined. Cane fields and fruit trees were blown down but the rooty vegetables were not all lost. There was a little money or beeswax to trade for salt fish from some Yankee schooner. If a man's wattle hut lay in the mud he went out with his neighbors to cut new poles and thatch in the hills. Work was shared. Root crops were replanted at once. Nobody died of starvation. Courage and energy set Antigua going again.

It was not like that in Barbados, which took the brunt of nine savage Atlantic hurricanes in that thirty years. Every inch had been cultivated by the great sugar estates. After emancipation, only a few estates were broken up for Negro owners. The mass of people worked as they always had but now for very little pay. White planters were energetic. They introduced plows and steam mills, got good prices for sugar. But when the hurricanes struck, although the estates could afford devastation, the people suffered dreadfully. Two and one-half years after the hurricane of 1831, Lt. Col. Reid was still working to rebuild the island and help the distressed people with government aid.

In those thirty years not a single hurricane struck St. Vincent and the lovely little Grenadines. Yet roads were impassable, estate houses falling in, the cities dilapidated. It was all the fault of emancipation, according to what was left of "the plantocracy." They paid only a shilling a day and complained that the Negroes, to whom they had never given any education, were lazy. Yet even there small Negro farms increased in the hills. Men worked all day long in their patches of cane and provisions, putting in coffee and cocoa trees and clearing more land for pasture.

In Dominica, a hurricane struck in the chaotic year of emancipation, September, 1834. Two hundred people died. Cane-field soil was washed down the long slopes into the gullies and the sea, and under the apprentice system not enough work was done to get the cane fields going again, so that it was a long time before the island recovered.

In 1837, St. Lucia, with her great harbor under the mountain, was struck, and again in '41, but its progress under free labor had been immediate, because the planters uniquely paid well for work or allowed the Negroes to work on profitable shares. By '41 there were over two thousand men owning their own farms and over four thousand paying taxes. Hurricanes, no matter how bad, were worse when endured by slaves than met by free men.

Jamaica, on the other hand, that in those thirty years suffered not one hurricane, looked to be in worse state than any other island. The cities and estates were falling to pieces with neglect. There was hardly any export trade. The production of sugar was reduced almost to nothing. The few planters left were apathetic and despondent, and still in debt.

The freed slaves got nothing of the indemnity paid their owners. They had never been allowed schools or any training. The only land they got was up in the mountains. But they built huts, scratched out gardens, bartered produce. Somehow they lived. The planters with cane fields complained the Negro was too lazy to work without the whip. The Negroes said, "Buckra no pay." Indeed a labor gang was often cheated even of its one shilling a day per man. It was better for a man who had known slavery to work on his own rocky clearing, to sleep, cold and damp, in his own thatched hut, pick up money for the shouting Christmas excitement by breaking stones for government roads.

Twenty years after emancipation in Jamaica there were little Negro farms and flowery villages up mountain slopes and jungles never before cleared. The merchant women made their own paths, striding down with headloads of things to sell at crossroads markets. Men raised a little sugar, coffee, indigo, pimento, beeswax to barter for Yankee salt fish, cloth and tools. With no hurricanes for a while, only white men did badly in Jamaica.

Back in 1835, the fourth hurricane swung westward like a pointer to a new course in history, pushing rains and savage tides up the Rio Grande to Matamoras, where the old fort was now a customs house. The hurricane crumbled old Spanish houses and broke off trees and spoiled gardens where Stephen Austin had dreamed of the province of Texas. Mexican soldiers had plodded through dust that was now mud on their way to besiege Americans in the old yellow mission in San Antonio known as "The Alamo."

The first hurricane of '38 churned over that coast again and ruined Austin's town, San Felipe de Austin, on the Brazos. Americans' log huts chinked with mud and a stick chimney were soaked and pounded, the one or two stores that sold liquor and food were flattened, and the low plain was turned into a running swamp. Veracruz, the old city of Cortes, was blown over by two hurricanes late in November.

But now a new thing was changing the ways of mankind on sea as well as on land. Everywhere now among fleets of sail, paddle wheels thrashing, their sails dirtied with their own wood smoke, went the new steamboats. They would in time, with warnings, be able to get clean away from all hurricane danger. But at first they were the hurricanes' special prey.

They carried their machinery so high that they were capsized in the first gales. Their boilers blew up with the first slap of sea water. The paddle-wheel shaft was disabled at once and in deep troughs the paddles threshed helplessly in air. Contemptuous sea captains said they were useful only in calms or for entering or leaving harbors. They could never get very far from shore where they had to cut wood for fuel.

Steamships steadily increased in use in the Gulf of Mexico, where

Sam Houston was for the second time President of the independent Republic of Texas, and Mexico raided the river towns. Steamships carried supplies from New Orleans to Galveston for a Texas army invading Mexico and brought back infuriating rumors of Texas soldiers starving and dying in Mexican jails.

Steam railroads were changing the face of the land, especially in west Florida, where there was a rush to open Florida Gulf ports to the good business of shipping Georgia and Alabama cotton. The railroad pushed down to old St. Marks on the St. Marks River. A mile south, Port St. Leon was being boosted. The town of Apalachicola on the Apalachicola River had already dredged a deep channel and a hundred ships were loading. The most exciting town, loud with speculators, was St. Jo, shoving eight miles of railroad down to a deep-water bayou. Life in St. Jo was gayer even than the territorial capital, with race meetings and balls and overflowing hotels and taverns, as well as the soberer meetings of the Constitutional Convention, trying to figure how to make Florida a state.

In 1840, St. Jo's population was about 4,000. Apalachicola could hardly keep up with it until the summer of '41, when an epidemic of yellow fever drove the gay crowds from St. Jo and in September an enormous Gulf hurricane blacked it out with furious waves and winds. There was nothing much left of St. Jo after that. Only three gravestones now mark the place about which Florida circuit riders preached that the hurricane, or what was then called a tidal wave, was a judgment for the town's wickedness.

4 *SHIPS AT SEA*

The fall of 1841 on the North American seacoast was one long spell of broken and uncomfortable weather. Charleston was howled and blown over and knocked down and rained out by a hurricane in September. By the end of the month, in northern New England there was over five inches of rain and snow. Winds were violent. Yet men from Cape Cod went out fishing, because south, on the Georges Bank, the cod were moving in great schools.

By midnight of Saturday, the second of October, the wind from the north freshened into a hard gale. It was raining in Massachusetts. The fishing boats had sailed from the Cape to be on the fishing grounds the next day. The sun rose clear but there were black clouds coming over. By eleven o'clock a heavy sea was running. There were vessels that had not looked for such weather already on rocks and beaches. It blew hard all day. By 2 A.M. Monday the wind came faster, faster, incredibly veering a little northeast.

People had wakened the night before and listened uneasily to the bump and scrape of boughs against the house. Men who watched the sky anxiously worked to put out stern lines on their plunging boats and house the gear and the farm tools, as old chimneys fell. Women, who shooed the chickens into the barn and scolded the children for running out between stinging rains, that howling shattering night got no sleep at all.

After that the wind began to let go, like a relaxing fist.

By 10 A.M. Tuesday the light of Indian summer fell on a land blasted with winter. The trees were stripped or lying in windrows on the salt-scalded and seered meadows. Every village, every farm looked frowsy, the streets piled with broken stuff, dead chickens, mud.

There had been no warning. At Siasconset, they said, when the wind slid over with that high scream, every building trembled. Boats were under water at the docks. The dark sea had carried away ropewalks, houses, barns.

At Cape Cod the beaches from Chatham to the Highlands were dark with debris out of the white foaming waves, forty or fifty vessels, and dead men rolling like logs in the wash. Hyannisport lost the schooner *Franklin*, the schooner *Tangent*. Dennis lost the *Bride of Dennis* and twenty-six men. The *Forest*, of Gloucester, was broken up there, the *Ellis* of Plymouth, the schooners *Industry* and *Spitfire* of Halifax. At Truro—but wait. That story was not known when the hurricane darkened the sky northward, with that night-in-day of rain and wind—such wind. They could never forget how the wind screamed at Cohasset, at Cape Ann; at Portsmouth, New Hampshire; at Portland, Maine.

Every place had its wrecks. A vessel from Maine at Portsmouth parted its cable in the filthy sea and was driven ashore on Cohasset rocks, seven passengers, four crew, all choking and dying deep in the green tossing salt. At Cape Ann the lifeboat they had been proud of since '39 was stove in and useless. Fourteen of the fishing fleet were ashore at Pigeon Cove. Fish houses, fish flakes, 60 barrels of mackerel, 200 barrels of salt, 300 empty barrels—all gone, that would have brought to those hard-working, dangerous-living, poor fisherfolk something like $50,000. Afterward there were public meetings to help the fishermen. But many with their children went cold and hungry that winter.

That was the hurricane about which Oliver Wendell Holmes wrote:

> *Lord how the ponds and rivers boiled*
> *And how the shingles rattled*
> *And oaks were scattered on the ground*
> *As if the Titans battled*
> *And all above was in a howl,*
> *And all below a clatter,—*
> *The earth was like a frying pan*
> *Or some such hissing matter.*

People chuckled over his last lines,

> *I lost—oh, bitterly I wept*
> *I lost my Sunday britches.*

It had a curious poverty of emotion in the face of what happened, especially in Truro.

There was no warning that the men of Truro could read in the thin scud or uneasy seas. The stout boats of the fishing fleets carried no barometers. The mackerel had been running fine and fat, and the men on or near the southwest part of the Georges Bank were hauling them in by the washbarrelfuls, shining like sound money. There are no more dangerous shoals off New England than the Georges, where the strong currents that clamor under the elbow of Cape Cod make an eternal riot of sand below the glittering surface.

The *Vesper* of Truro, well loaded and already bound home by sunset Saturday night, spoke Captain Joshua Knowles of Truro, master of the *Garnet*, and he shaped his course for the good fishing.

Captain Mathias Rich of the *Water Witch* caught up with the fleet at sunset and started hauling in the fish. At four o'clock Sunday morning Captain Rich woke to find the weather bad. He wore ship at once and started for the Cape. The sea was fast and heavy although the sun rose clear except for the wild clouds. The fleet saw him running under full sail and some loosed jibs and followed him. At the same time, Captain Knowles of the *Garnet* was in the teeth of a gale which had already torn his foresail. At ten a great comber washed away the boat and davits. They were drifting fast, with shoals under their lee. In the face of the tearing wind they carried close-reefed sail and would have gone clear, if the foresail and mainsail both had not exploded into ghostly ribbons.

The *Water Witch* was in trouble now. Captain Rich had made up his mind to run her on the bold shore, when a squall struck her and a great livid sea went completely over her. They lay under double-reefed topsails, shaking off water. All the crew were below but the captain, because they could not cling on the wild deck. Through his smarting eyes the captain saw land under her lee and to windward. He called all hands to set the jib, which they did. But when they tried to hoist the double-reefed mainsail the vessel lay over on her broadside, the sail blew to pieces. The boom went over. They fought wreckage, the sea, the wind, the bucking deck, rigged a tackle, fought the boom and part of the mainsail out of the water, righted the ship, came up into the wind, and began to crawl off. The capain steered, lashed to the helm.

The *Garnet* had been drifting into shoal water, six fathoms. The sea was breaking white over her bow and stern. Captain Knowles ordered all below but his brother Zack. They tried to put up the bucking helm, to swing her off before the wind, their only chance. Just as she began to answer in that wicked wind, an enormous fretted sea rose up, higher than houses over the little ship, hung, crashed down, covered her. She went over on her beam ends as brother Zack was washed off. Somehow he got his fist locked on the blowing mainsheet and came aboard hand over fist, wild-eyed, blowing water, streaming water. The foremast had gone fifteen feet above deck, the unstepped mainmast lay in a welter of rigging on the smashed planks, where everything else had been swept clean off. The ballast had shifted, holding her over, rolling.

Captain Knowles remembered the sharp hatchet under his berth.

His bellow brought the men up. Zack, a lanyard on the hatchet and a line around him, hung to leeward. When she rolled out of water, he cut away the rigging. The captain was chopping away at the mess forward, cut away everything.

The men got into the hold and threw the ballast back so she righted. But she was a logy helpless wreck.

After the great breaker the sea was more regular. They patched holes with canvas, put out the anchor for a drag, and drifted. They drifted through the afternoon, until the sea was green under them.

The *Water Witch*, by now, had weathered the breakers and let go her anchor in Herring Cove. Captain Rich left the helm where he had been lashed for twelve hours.

But the *Garnet* drifted all night. By Tuesday morning although the wind was moderate, she lay lower and lower in the water. They rigged some canvas on the stump of the foremast and could just steer. At ten o'clock the day was fine. They opened the hatches and found some potatoes floating in the salt water; found, luckily, the teakettle in the cabin although the galley had gone overboard; built a fire on the ballast and had boiled potatoes, their first food since Sunday. Tasted good.

At sunset, the crack Liverpool packet ship, the *Roscius*, hailed them and took them aboard. But before he went aboard Captain Knowles with the same hatchet let the blue water into the *Garnet's* strakes and saw the sea begin to take her.

The *Water Witch* and one other were the only vessels to get home. The other was the *Reform*, Isaac S. Levi, master. With a dragline, she was lying under bare poles, with all hands holding tight below thinking long thoughts about drowning. Elisha Paine, Jr., crawled out on deck. In that moment a stupendous sea went over her and took her down. The men within felt themselves tumbling head down in the blackness with water shooting into the cabin. She was completely bottom up. A minute later she turned over again and bobbed up. When the shaking men crawled on deck, there was the rushing air and the sky, but no masts on the ship and the hawser wound around the bowsprit to prove she had turned completely over. But Elisha Paine was never seen again.

Now there is a monument in Truro to her losses by what they called "The October Gale." It was Truro's greatest tragedy. The men who went down were the town's youngest and ablest, all under thirty, and many sons, brothers and cousins of the same family.

The vessels of that lost fleet were "*Dalmatia*, David Snow, master, aged 27, and nine men; *Cincinnatus*, John Wheeler, master, aged 28, nine men; *Poncona*, Solomon H. Dyer, master, aged 23, six men, the youngest 14; *Altair*, Elisha Rich, master, age 26, two brothers, and three other men; *Prince Albert*, Noah Smith, master, aged 28, with nine men, aged 30, 23, 19, 16, 14, 12 and 11."

When the *Dalmatia* sailed, Gamaliel S. Paine, a crewman, had been left in Truro. He walked to Provincetown the Sunday before the gale, went out in another vessel, found and boarded the *Dalmatia* and went down with her. Another man who had refused to take the walk lived to a ripe old age.

In 1842, both Texan and American coasts were invaded by hurricanes.

On July 12, the first of seven terrible hurricanes blew up to Lookout Shoals and Pamlico and Albemarle sounds, and the long sea-worn line of the Outer Banks of Hatteras.

The little village of Ocracoke seems to have caught the smoking, screaming, crashing winds about its center, and the center's silence. The savage ocean loomed over the Back Beach to the frame houses in deep sand under the live oaks. The people saved themselves as they could. William Howard's small store exploded into loose boards and was washed away with planks from the boats. Only one house was left standing at Portsmouth as the sea water obliterated it. Two ships went down in smother over the Diamond Shoals and no one ever knew their names, or the names of the men who drowned.

Fourteen vessels went ashore between New Inlet and Ocracoke. Six wrecks were swept out to sea again by the undertow. Dead horses and cattle drifted in the calming Sound. Immediately afterward, another hurricane struck and Hatteras earned her title all over again, as "The Graveyard of the Atlantic." The cyclone that on August 30 battered Havana, where the barometer dropped to a record 28.93 inches, plowed into Tampico and flooded the Rio Grande. It stopped for a while the hot talk of war in Texas river towns.

There were records of human tragedy everywhere, notably in a bottle picked up in October in a Bermuda bay. The scrawled note inside read:

Schooner *Lexington*, off Cape Hatteras, July 15. This morning at half past two o'clock a.m. it commenced blowing a strong North Wester, which increased to such a degree that it was certain my vessel could not stand it. At 5 I tried the pumps and found she made eleven inches. She being an old vessel, worked in her joints. At half-past eleven, I determined to leave her with my crew (three men and myself) in our launch; but before leaving sounded the pumps and found she had increased the water in her hold three feet. I write this and enclose it in a bottle, so that if we should not be saved and the bottle be found it may be known what became of us. At 1 p.m. got into the boat with provisions and water sufficient for six days, having beforehand offered up our prayers to God to protect and save us. Signed Wm. H. Morgan, Captain; John Rider, Mate.

In September of 1843, Port Leon on the St. Marks River in Florida was destroyed once and for all by a hurricane. In '44, another crashed over the Mexican Customs House at "the arms of the St. James," drowning more than seventy men but not touching the village of driftwood huts built by adventurous Americans on Padre Island, the longest sand island on that coast. The boundary dispute between Texas and Mexico went on unabated.

Another hurricane in October started up just south of lonely Swan Island, off Honduras, destroyed all the fishing villages on the Cuban coast between Havana and Matanzas and passed eastward of small Key West, dousing its ships and sandy streets with furious rains.

Galveston, Texas, was rebuilding with vigor its Hotel Tremont, shattered in '42, so that it would hold fast for one hundred years. Things were stirring in Texas.

The wreckers of Key West in their fast boats followed storms up the Florida Keys, to get to wrecks before the men from the Bahamas or Jacob Houseman from Indian Key. Key West was prosperous with the rich returns from salvage courts as the cargoes were auctioned off on the sands. The wooden houses were crammed with furniture and goods from the wreckers, and the whole island, haunted by yellow fever and mosquitoes, lived through hurricanes with the resilience of a good small ship.

Florida became a state in 1845 and the United States Army pulled out of the unresolved Indian War for the Mexican border, where "Old Rough and Ready," Zachary Taylor, set his camps on the long white sand islands off the Brazos de Santiago. After his victories at Palo Alto and Resaca de la Palma his wounded men died in huts on the hot sands, for the moment untroubled by hurricanes.

The most noteworthy blow of '46 crashed up along South Carolina to Hatteras and opened a new inlet in the long beaches between the sound and the ocean. It is still called "Oregon Inlet" from the first ship to go through it. And that is curious, too, because there is a story, perhaps hard to verify, that the state of Oregon was named by French voyageurs down the long river to the stormy Pacific who learned from the French West Indies to call any hurricane or tempest, "ouragan."

Unsinkable Key West was wrecked by the last hurricane that year, that flattened its new lighthouse and the light on Sand Key and wrecked the wrecking fleet. It laid violent hands on the U.S. brig-of-war *Perry*, that had blockaded Mexican ports until the war was over. She was struck off Havana and her masts gone, blown helplessly up on a Florida reef and over. In sunlight next morning she was safely afloat in the calm waters of Florida Bay. This was the brig that in '44 had sailed out to China and back with the treaty that opened Chinese ports to American traders.

Thirty-nine more hurricanes had roared everywhere by 1864, with their inconceivable burdens of human adventure and suffering. The most famous was the hurricane of '56 that overwhelmed a huge lighted resort hotel on a low island off the delta of the Mississippi, Isle Dernière. Brilliantly lighted, crowded with dancing guests, it was destroyed utterly, without warning. It was made famous by one of Lafcadio Hearn's first articles for a New Orleans paper.

But the human storm then rising in the United States, that engulfed the country with the bloody drama of the Civil War, left little thought for weather.

BOOK SIX

THE BEGINNING
OF KNOWLEDGE

1 *THE STORM BREEDERS*

The weather of the thirteen United States lay behind all the facts of their histories, and worked an electric change in the varied lots of Englishmen and Europeans who settled here. It made them American.

In one year of their lives people almost everywhere knew the strong prevailing westerlies from unimaginable far lands, the steely Atlantic nor'easters, the golden serenities of Indian summer, thunderstorms, blizzards, salt fogs, the long freezing winters that taxed their endurance and their ingenuity and the gales, as they called them, that here and there climaxed the falls.

Weather was their first concern. Would wind and tide serve so that the ship could sail? Would the well run dry with no rain? When would the first snow fall? How hard would the winter be? When should the oats be planted, the apples picked, the hay raked? Would the fish bite, the corn grow, the woodpile last the winter?

No houses were adequately heated. Children cried with chilblains. Snow and rain blew down the chimney and ashes into the room. Women grew bent carrying water from the well and helping with harvests before thunderstorms. Ice formed on the water jug. The barn was struck by lightning and the hay burned. The mill stream dried up and rats got into the unground corn. The roof blew off. When there was no rain in summer there were neither apples nor turnips for winter. With too much rain the hay spoiled and the potatoes rotted in the ground.

Everyone was sure weather made them ill or healthy, tubercular, malarial, sanguine, or strong. It was the first thing they talked about.

Weather signs and portents were handed down for generations, even from the Indians. Farmers planted and harvested by the waning and waxing moons, whose brightness quivered up tidal creeks and brimmed salt meadows with fine etched silver. There were harvest moons and hunters' moons. Lonely horsemen in frosty forest trails heard the howling of wolves if winters were hard. The deep Atlantic ebb and flow of tides moving on their vast courses about the watery world were vital.

What tomorrow's weather would be like was part guesswork, part superstition, part minute, if little understood, observation. People made out what was to come by the shape of goose bones, groundhog shadows, the aching of once broken bones, the thickness of squirrel fur, a plague of woolly bear caterpillars, and the high honking of wild geese flying south at night over frosted rustling cornfields. To kick a cat in the dark meant rain. Everybody knew that Groundhog Day was February 2, when if the groundhog comes out and sees his shadow, there'll be six more weeks of winter.

Almost no practical scientific instruments were in use. Ships at sea depended upon the sun, the stars and the compass. Torricelli's barometer which was invented in Italy in 1643 was hardly used at all. The first weather instruments—a barometer, thermometer, hydrometer and rain guage—were introduced in America in 1731 at Charleston, that most hurricaned city of the mainland, by a Scottish physician, Dr. John Lining. He was sure the weather was the cause of epidemics.

Dr. Lining must have read eagerly a book published in London in 1738 called *A Rational Account of the Weather*, in which was included "The Signs and Forerunners of the Plague . . . , as follows: 1. If Spring and Summer have been too moist; if Winter and Autumn too Wet, and not Cold enough. 2. If the South-Winds have blown without Tempests or Hurricanes." There were many more.

As to the barometer itself, then called "the Baroscope," the same work quotes the learned Dr. Halley's observations. "Hence I conceive that the Principal Cause of the Rise and Fall of the Mercury, is from the variable winds which are found in the Temperate Zones."

As a sure guide, the early colonists had *Poor Richard's Almanac*.

A thin paper pamphlet, smearily printed and illustrated with woodcuts, dirty and torn from constant use, it hung by a string to a nail in kitchens of Boston mansions or cabins in newly cleared wildernesses over the mountains. It was the only calendar. Often it was the only book. Children learned to read from it. Its gusty, shrewd, American proverbs, anecdotes, jingles; its tables of weights and measures; household hints; cures for ringworm, warts, rheumatism, colic in horses and gapes in hens was almost their only written source of knowledge. The phases of the moon, planets rising, tides, prophecies of rain or drought, were there in believable print. On the margins of almanacs men scrawled the events of their hard days, births, deaths, storms, travelers, Indians, or ships bespoken, cows fresh, hay spoiled or harvested. Its place was unique.

William Bradford of Philadelphia had printed the first American almanac in 1687. In France they had been common earlier, in England and Scotland later, but nowhere else were they so important as in America. Here, three or four printers of almanacs made money supplying bookshops and the peddlers who penetrated the farthest trails on horseback. In Newport, James Franklin printed a pamphlet which had been developed not long before in France, an almanac called *Poor Robin's*.

It was James's younger brother Benjamin who wrote and printed in 1732 the almanac called *Poor Richard's*. In no time at all Franklin was printing ten thousand copies. In it, wit and weather lore of the whole country was distilled through Franklin's wonderfully sane common sense to become a penetrating American wisdom. Many other almanacs followed his. None so quickly took its place in American literature and history.

This was the time, mind you, when even the literate public, teachers, lawyers and above all, ministers, were sure that to inquire into natural causes in the world about them was to fly in the face of an all-wise Providence. No science was taught in any existing schools.

Benjamin Franklin soon began to gather together in Philadelphia, the most liberal city of its day, a series of small groups of men interested in chemistry, astronomy, biology, botany, every phase of what was called "natural philosophy," to discuss ideas and exchange observations. In thirty years these meetings were joined together in the American Philosophical Society, the first truly scientific group in this country and now the oldest, that helped push back the narrow American borders of the unknown and the misapprehended.

Thomas Jefferson, whose interest in weather, like his interest in plants, rocks and explorations, was that of a gifted eighteenth-century country gentleman, was later a vice-president of this society. He thought that weather observations should be exchanged all over the country. "By seizing the days when the winds centered in any part of the United States, we might, in time, have come to some of the causes which determine the direction of the winds, which I suspect to be very various," he wrote long afterward. It would have been the first weather service.

It was Benjamin Franklin's effective practical genius, however, his constant curiosity about nature, which led America toward the modern world.

He made the first acute observation about hurricanes in the fall of 1743, when he was about to sail for Boston to observe an eclipse of the moon. His ship could not sail because of a terrific northeast storm which he took for granted would be felt in Boston. To his amazement they wrote that Boston had had an absolutely clear night which was followed by a severe storm.

That was the Atlantic hurricane of 1743, which Franklin did not recognize as such but from which he deduced that storms did not occur in single spots but surged from south to north, with winds curving from some unknown center. It would be years before that theory was tested.

Sailing home from France on the fifth of September, 1789, after his great years as ambassador, Benjamin Franklin experienced a storm which may have been the last lash of the hurricane which battered Dominica. He was eighty years old and suffering from "the stone" but was busy observing the temperatures of the sea water, which would lead to his discovery of the Gulf Stream.

The report of his marine observations included other ideas to which people paid little attention then. He was sure that paddles driven by some engine might take the place of sails in ships and that lives might be saved in storms at sea by watertight compartments and adequate lifeboats. He argued also that an office should be established to insure farms against weather damage, as well as from blight, insects and drought. It was the basis of the present windstorm insurance.

Still neither Franklin nor many other people knew enough about hurricanes to name them correctly. Men along the Atlantic coast called them "September gales." Or "line storms," or just "the equinoctials." Not even seagoing Americans, who had experienced them in the Caribbean or lived through typhoons in the Pacific and Indian oceans, believed they were hurricanes.

Thomas Jefferson, as wise about weather as any scholarly country gentleman, ambassador to France after Franklin, making arrangements for his daughter Maria to join him in France, wrote, "I must now repeat my wish to have Polly sent to me next summer. This, however, must depend on the circumstances of a good vessel sailing from Virginia in the months of April, May, June or July. I would not have her set out sooner on account of the equinoxes."

Later, planning his return from Europe, Jefferson cautiously delayed his sailing for three weeks. "By advice of those skilled in sea voyages" he chose to sail "between the autumnal equinox and winter." He considered it extremely dangerous to be at sea in March and September, "the boisterous equinoctial months."

Since 1814 the Army Medical Corps had shared the general interest in weather as affecting health. John C. Calhoun, as Secretary of War, had ordered a study of weather in the Middle West and the Louisiana Purchase. The rudimentary weather service went west with the frontier.

American shipmasters had sailed around the world by dead reckoning, measuring latitude, which is distance, by compass, log and lead. But they had been unable to figure longitude, which is time, because they had no dependable sea clocks or chronometers. A Salem mathematician, Nathaniel Bowditch, at sea as a ship's clerk, taught all the crew to work lunar observations, which was a way of finding longitude without proper timepieces. In a standard English work on navigation he found 8,000 errors. So after several more voyages as captain of his own ship he published, in 1802, *The New American Practical Navigator* at Newburyport, Massachusetts. It was the first edition of hundreds of that great work that always, in all the seas, is called simply *Bowditch*, and always kept up-to-date.

In his first edition Bowditch presented a chapter on "Winds" that made no mention of hurricanes, only of tornadoes, that were "sudden gusts of winds, blowing from all points of the horizon."

It was not until the great hurricane of 1821 that a keen young Connecticut saddler began the first real study of such storms.

It came roaring across the Atlantic to Turks Island in the Bahamas on the first of September that year. By 3 A.M. on the third of September, ships thirty miles off Cape Fear were laboring in its gale-driven seas, although up the Cape Fear River no wind blew. Spray blew over Ocracoke on the Outer Banks, from seas booming on the back beaches. Off Roanoke, Virginia, the wind streamed with incredible violence from the east, then from southwest and then northwest. A Bermuda vessel on the western edge of the Gulf Stream logged heavy seas and whipping winds.

The dark majesty of the storm moved across the James River to Norfolk, wrecking everything. It was reported forty miles off Cape Henry and off Chincoteague. Baltimore felt nothing. But Cape Henlopen in Delaware had furious winds coming up from the east-southeast that in twenty minutes blew from east-northeast. In an hour in a dead calm, the center passed. It crossed Cape May, New Jersey. It raged at Philadelphia and at Trenton.

In two hours at New York, it was reported, the bustling growing city between the rising rivers was more heavily damaged than ever before in its history. The howling rainy winds pushed up the incoming tide thirteen feet in one hour. Wharves were submerged in racing waves, and ships were smashed against warehouses and crashed on cobbled streets.

Hurricane winds at Bridgeport, Connecticut, veered in three hours from southeast to southwest. New London and Middletown, Connecticut; Springfield, Northampton and Worcester, Massachusetts; lay in the storm's path. Portland, Maine, felt its last impact as it blew out to sea. There was not enough disturbance in Boston to prevent a balloon ascension.

It was not a greater storm than many, although the damage and deaths were bad enough. The point was that there were people everywhere who noted it, in ships' logs, in newspapers, in church and town records, on the margins of kitchen almanacs.

At this time William Redfield was about thirty-two years old, a saddler. When he was thirteen his father, a sailor, had died and William had to leave school and help support his mother and the five younger children, by becoming an apprentice to a saddler and harness maker. His mother married again and took the family west, leaving William alone in Middletown, Connecticut.

He had a friend, Dr. William Tully, from whose library he borrowed such books as there were then about science, especially physics. He remembered with avid interest his father's stories of the sea and storms. His constant reading made up for his lack of ordinary schooling.

In 1810, when he was twenty-one, he walked to Ohio and back, to see his mother. Everything he saw in that frontier world interested him. In Middletown he went into business as a saddler and harness maker and walked long distances among the Connecticut villages to drum up trade. His observations had been so wide and so keen that he was never satisfied with the books he read.

The center of that hurricane of 1821 crossed the eastern part of Connecticut on its way northeast. Shortly after, as William Redfield rode up into Massachusetts, he followed the wide swath cut by the cyclone and saw to his surprise that the trees blown down in the eastern part of Connecticut and Massachusetts lay with their tops to the northwest but those blown over in the western parts lay with their heads to the southeast.

Later, he heard about the sailing vessel *Illinois*, which was overtaken by the hurricane swell from the south but, with a fair wind and the Gulf Stream, outran it, as the hurricane itself moved toward Charleston. In two days more the hurricane overtook her from the south at the same time its northeast winds were blowing off roofs and chimneys in New York.

To William Redfield all this was positive proof of what he had begun to believe, that a hurricane was an enormous whirl of winds blowing in all directions from a center moving slowly on a long curving course. It was entirely his own idea. He had never read a book by a German, H. W. Dove, published in 1828, suggesting, as evidently other Europeans had done, that a tropical cyclone was a whirlwind. With them it was theory. Redfield's contribution was revolutionizing because he could prove it. He called them "rotatory storms."

He was the first man to discover and state that the movement up and down of mercury in a barometer is caused by the varying weight of the atmosphere.

It would still be many years before the barometer would come into use on even government vessels. Most naval officers until as late as 1850 refused to believe in or pay attention to any theories regarding storms at sea. The barometer was only a nuisance. A distinguished Civil War officer said, "When I was in the Gulf and at Veracruz, that damned thing nearly drove me crazy."

He continued to think about storms and collect reports of them while working himself into a good job superintending boats on the Hudson River. He talked to a deeply interested passenger, Professor Denison Olmstead of Yale, who insisted that Redfield write his hurricane theories for the *American Journal of Sciences*. His first article, called "The Nature of Hurricanes," was published ten years after the storm he had first observed.

Redfield also charted some of the seven hurricanes of 1831 but particularly the great hurricane that overwhelmed Barbados with almost complete disaster, passed terribly over Cuba, and destroyed everything at the mouth of the Mississippi at Louisiana.

His writings had a most important effect on Lieutenant Colonel William Reid, of the Royal Engineers, who two years and a half later was sent out from London to try to rebuild the government buildings in Barbados that had been wasted by the storm. Reid was horrified by the condition of the island and of the people.

He began to collect ships' logs and make his own charts. He wrote to Redfield and their correspondence and exchange of data led Reid to write and publish in 1838 his excellent book, *An Attempt to Develop the Law of Storms by Means of Facts Arranged According to Time and Place*. It was for this book that he collected the ships' logs in the great hurricanes of 1780.

Lieutenant Colonel, later Brigadier General, Reid had become so interested in studying hurricanes, that he was instrumental in having sent to India, by the East India Company, an Englishman, Henry Piddington, who, as curator of the Calcutta Museum and later president of the Marine Courts of Inquiry, charted the terrible circular storms of the Indian Ocean.

It was Piddington who coined the phrase by which all such storms are now known, "cyclone," meaning "the coils of a snake," "tropical," of course, for the warm seas in which only they are born. Piddington published it in his now forgotten work, *A Sailor's Hornbook*.

The Pennsylvania legislature took a great step forward in 1834 by voting $4,000 to equip one weather observer with a barometer, thermometer and wind gauge. In '42 the Franklin Institute was founded by the American Philosophical Society to which James Pollard Espy contributed papers on weather. It was unfortunate that he did not agree with William Redfield, or with the great mathematician Heinrich Brandes of Leipzig who agreed with Redfield that cyclones were "rotatory."

Espy was assigned to duty as meteorologist, first with the Army, then with the Navy, and finally with the Smithsonian Institution for which he drew the first weather maps. Mr. Espy argued passionately with everyone in Washington for the establishment of a national weather service. Ex-president, now congressman, John Quincy Adams very well expressed the general American attitude toward weather studies.

"Mr. Espy, the storm breeder," he said, "left with me a paper exposing his three wishes of appropriations by Congress for his benefit. The man is methodically monomaniac and the dimensions of his organ of self-esteem have been swollen to the size of a goiter by a report of a Committee of the Franklin Institute endorsing all his crack-brained discoveries in meteorology. He said that he had thought of addressing the Senate and asked if they should pass a bill in his favor whether I would support it. I said . . . that I would do all I could for him in the House."

Mr. Adams was not interested in Espy's proposal that meteorological observations should be made throughout the Union, with a national station in Washington. Adams in a later speech said, "Mr. Espy, the storm breeder, came with a communication that the Committee on Ways and Means were about to retract the appropriation for some small interloping office under the War Department with which to pursue a study of storms." Mr. Adams' heavy sarcasm prevented any more money being appropriated at that time.

Scientists everywhere were taking an interest in weather and hurricanes. A French physicist, G. G. Coriolis of the Ecole Polytechnique in Paris proved that the rondure of the earth and its rotation deflected the course of cyclones north and south of the equator toward the east. To this day weathermen call it "the Coriolis Effect."

As William Redfield said it would, the widespread use of the electric telegraph in 1844 enormously increased the quick exchange of local weather news. In Europe a great advance was made after the Crimean War when a fleet of French supply ships were sunk by an unexpected storm in the Black Sea. Napoleon III, shocked, ordered the French physicist Leverrier to begin a thorough study of the weather with the new "magnetic" instruments.

But it was the direct and keen young American, Redfield, who changed the study of hurricanes from the theoretic to the directly observed and began the slow upward march of weather knowledge from superstition to science.

2 *PROGRESS IN PEACE*

From 1851 to 1865, before and during the Civil War, by some strange freak of weather, there were only eleven authenticated hurricanes. But with peace, there were not only more hurricanes but an increasing interest on the part of scientists to learn about them.

Mobile was knocked flat twice in 1860, Louisiana plowed across twice in '65, Galveston flooded in '66. The others curved and smashed about the Caribbean, bringing only local losses and local griefs. None affected the harbors of Bermuda or Nassau in the Bahamas, packed with the Confederate craft that ran the Federal blockade with bales of cotton, worth its weight in gold, and slipped back war materials and supplies.

The Weather Bureau makes no mention of the hurricane of October, 1862, when twenty-five Federal vessels left Hampton Roads with coal for the fleet about to attack Port Royal in South Carolina. The next day, fifty more vessels sailed. On the thirtieth of October, off Cape Hatteras, they were swallowed up and spewed everywhere by appalling winds and seas. Two steamers were lost. The attack on Port Royal was abandoned.

It must have been this storm, as the Cape Fear people tell it, that cut a new inlet across one of those sand islands at the mouth of the river, just in time to let a blockade runner from Wilmington, North Carolina, elude a Federal blockader.

There was no doubt at all that there was a hurricane in October, 1863, because the narrative of the extraordinary Confederate steamship *Alabama* that lived through it, is one of the great stories of the war.

After Fort Sumter fell, the United States Navy began the blockade of 3,500 miles of Confederate seacoast with exactly twenty-four wooden paddle-wheel steamers and sixty already obsolete sailing vessels. But until 1862, the Confederacy had no naval vessels at all nor the equipment, materials or skill with which to build them. A counterblockade was impossible. Their only chance was to cripple the huge Northern sea commerce with light and fast cruisers which could keep the sea on long aggressive voyages.

They asked Raphael Semmes to command their first propeller steamer, the *Sumter*. He was the chief of the Lighthouse Service at Montgomery, Alabama, and became one of the most remarkable officers in the Confederacy.

Semmes sailed at once for the West Indies and across to Spain. He had to burn many ships he took because all neutral ports were closed to him and his prizes. In Cadiz, where he was not allowed to coal, the *Sumter* was laid up and sold. The Confederacy had contracted from England for a ship of 900 tons, 230 feet in length, a barkentine with large fore-and-aft sails and an engine of 300 horse-power, not only graceful but efficient. In only fifteen minutes, Semmes boasted, her propeller could be detached from the shaft and lifted high out of water. With her sails set, to convert her to a steamer again all he had to do was to start the fires, lower the propeller, brace her yards and signal full speed ahead. She made, one way or the other, about ten knots. Once, under sail and steam, she logged thirteen. She carried eight guns, twenty-four officers and 120 men. She cost $250,000.

There is no single exploit of the Civil War, on either side, more daring, dramatic, effective, or more piratical than the lonely career of the *Alabama*, under Raphael Semmes. Sailing almost every sea, she captured, sank, burned, converted, at a low estimate, over seventy Northern vessels, until the *Kearsarge* took her.

The *Alabama* alone, it has been calculated, drove from the sea the carrying trade of the United States. Insurance rates went to prohibitive heights. The American carrying trade was taken over by British and every other foreign kind of ship. The United States won the Civil War, but its merchant shipping has not yet recovered from the beating it took from the *Alabama*.

This was the ship, then, and this the man, which early in their career met a hurricane. Raphael Semmes wrote its story, in his *Memoirs of Service Afloat*.

The cyclone, of which I am writing, must have travelled a couple of thousand miles, before it reached the *Alabama*. Its approach had been heralded . . . by several days of bad weather; and, on the morning of the gale, which was on the 16th of October, the barometer began to settle very rapidly. We had been under short sail before, but we now took the close reefs in the topsails, which tied them down to about one third of their original size, got up, and bent the main storm-staysail, swung in the quarter-boats, and passed additional lashings around them. The ship had her head to the eastward, her yards were braced up on the starboard tack, and she took the wind, from S. to S.S.E.

The ship is lying still. The storm travelling to the northeast, is approaching her. The winds, running around the circle, howled, and whistled, and screeched like a thousand demons. She was thrown over, several streaks, and the waves began to assault her with sledgehammer blows, and occasionally to leap on board of her, flooding her decks, and compelling us to stand knee-deep in water. By this time, we had furled the fore-topsail; the fore-staysail had been split into ribbons; . . . We were now under nothing but the small storm-staysail, the topgallant yards had been sent down from aloft, there was very little top-hamper exposed to the wind, and yet the ship was pressed over and over. . . .

But she behaved nobly, and I breathed easier after the first half hour of the storm. . . . It was almost as much as each man could do, to look out for his own personal safety.

The storm raged thus violently for two hours, the barometer settling all the while, until it reached 28.64. It then fell suddenly calm, almost like the fiat of death. We were in the terrible vortex of a cyclone, from which so few mariners have ever escaped to tell the tale! . . . I pulled out my watch, and noted the time of the occurrence of the calm. The barometer was reported to stand at 28.64. The *Alabama's* head now lies to the southeast—she having "come up" gradually to the wind, as it hauled—and she is in the southeastern hemisphere of the vortex.

The scene was the most remarkable I had ever witnessed. The ship, which had been pressed over, only a moment before, by the fury of the gale as described, had now righted. . . . The aspect of the heavens was appalling. The clouds were writhing and twisting, like so many huge serpents engaged in combat, and hung so low, in the thin air of the vortex, as almost to touch our mast-heads. The best description I can give of the sea, is that of a number of huge watery cones,—for the waves seemed now in the diminished perssure of the atmosphere in the vortex to jut up into the sky, and assume a conical shape. . . . They were not running in any given direction, there being no longer any wind to drive them, but were jostling each other, like drunken men in a crowd, and threatening, every moment, to topple, one upon the other.

The vortex was just thirty minutes in passing. The gale had left us, with the wind from the northwest. We could see it coming upon the waters. The disorderly seas were now no longer jostling each other; they felt the renewed pressure of the atmosphere, and were being driven, like so many obedient slaves, before the raging blast. The tops of the waves were literally cut off by force of the wind, and dashed hundreds of yards, in blinding spray. The wind now struck us 'butt and foremost,' throwing the ship over in an instant, as before, . . . The gale raged, now, precisely as long as it had done before we entered the vortex—two hours—showing how accurately Nature had drawn her circle. . . .

In four hours and a half, from the commencement of the gale, the *Alabama* was left rolling, and tumbling about in the confused sea, which the gale had left behind it, with scarcely wind enough to fill the sails, which, by this time, we had gotten upon her, to keep her steady. The wind had travelled around the circle. The *Alabama* lay still during the whole gale, not changing her position, perhaps, half a mile. As the circle touched her, she took the wind from S. to S.S.E., and when it had passed over her, she had the wind at northwest, yet it had not changed a hair's breadth.

The master of the *Alabama* handled her entirely as a sailing ship. In those seas he could not have kept steam up for a second. And the war was long over and the screw propeller developed, before both shipowners and the U.S. Navy in their passion to save fuel, failed to censure severely any captain who used steam except in emergencies.

When the age of steam was fully established, however, the then greatest edition of *Bowditch* included rules for maneuvering steamships in cyclones. They consisted chiefly, for the right or dangerous semicircle, in keeping the wind on the starboard bow, making as much way as possible and, if obliged to heave to, keeping her head to the sea. Caught in the storm track in front, the rule was to run like hell for the left navigable semicircle and keep going. If in the rear avoid it in any way practicable, "having due regard for the storm's recurving to the northward and eastward."

There was no question that a screw-propelled steamship had a better chance than a sailing ship to get away from danger. As warning services improved, few steamships were caught. There were actually fewer ships to give warnings. The great need was for more exact knowledge of the hurricanes themselves.

The first detailed studies of the nature of hurricanes in this hemisphere were begun before the American Civil War by a group of poverty-stricken Jesuit scientists in Havana, Cuba. Science-loving Jesuit fathers at Manila in the Philippines, had already begun to record the fierce typhoons of the western Pacific and the China Sea. Jesuits maintained observatories in England and on the continent. It had not been quite a century since they were expelled from the Spanish empire in America. In 1853 when they were allowed to return to Havana, they opened a college in an abandoned monastery for about four hundred boys who were educated for nothing, including some poor boys.

The director of "The Royal College of Belén," Father Antonio Cobre, a mathematician and physicist, gave his classes in practical science training in daily weather observations.

The College was a poor place, bare but clean. The boys ate the plainest of food. The fathers ate even less, flapping about in worn soutanes and cheaply cobbled shoes in order to afford a few scientific instruments.

They aroused an overwhelming demand for weather information from the hurricane-conscious people of Havana. When Father Cobre took his report back to the head of his Order in Spain, the Belén Observatory was given a set of the most up-to-date scientific instruments, telescopes, theodolites, sextants, a fine chronometer, barometers, thermometers, rain gauges, hygrometers and anemometers.

The hurricane service was not set up until the observatory obtained a full-time director, a trained physicist, Father Benito Viñes. He had finished his studies in Paris after escaping, with other Jesuits, the Spanish revolution of '68. In Havana he learned in how few years of its recorded history Cuba had not been assaulted by hurricanes, its people, fields, villages, cities and sea-borne commerce

destroyed. It was as if the long island, rising athwart the long tra-
jectories of the trade winds, were the very heartland of the hurricane world.

There had been no one at all to help them before this small, dry
scientist-priest, Father Benito Viñes, S.J. For twenty-three years
he led a life of single-minded devotion to his religion and to hurricanes, up a narrow staircase from the great weed-grown courtyard
where the boys clattered all the way to the roof where he lived
and worked in his observatory. The table and a few plain chairs
in his office were piled with books and papers. Around the walls
were the instruments, their paper barrels unrolling as the pencils
marked temperature, barometric pressure, humidity. Clocks ticked.
Outside under a shed among the roof tiles under the blazing or
cloud-piled sky were his telescope and other instruments and the
workshop in which, as a practical mechanic and optician, he kept
them in order. This, with the library, his own bare sleeping room
with a hard cot and a crucifix, and the plain chapel of his Order,
was his life.

Not a hurricane invaded the coasts of Cuba but Father Viñes was
there as soon as possible, scrambling in his rusty robe among the
piles of debris and the odor of many deaths. He asked questions
of innumerable survivors, stammering out what they could remember about the way the sky looked beforehand, how the rain came
and the terrible voices of wind. His careful notes would record
dryly the figure below which lay the cumulative history of loss and
suffering.

There was no training in weather in those days but schoolbook
physics. It was true with Father Viñes, as it had been with the
American pioneer William C. Redfield, as indeed it is true still
for this most mysterious of all sciences, that a great weatherman
is not made. He is born.

During the hurricane season Father Viñes, with his watchful
single vision forever on the sky and his instruments, often did not
sleep for two or three days or eat unless someone put food in his
hand. His ascetic mouth folded more deeply over silence as he grew
bent with years, more gaunt, and his habit more threadbare. Often
he was ill, but the deep eyes behind his spectacles never lost their
sparks from July to November.

All year long he wrote pamphlets and articles for scientific journals in America and Europe, and carried on an enormous correspondence with learned societies and individuals. For the Havana newspapers he produced weather bulletins and forecasts. But if any newspaper, in those anticlerical days, said anything disparaging about the Catholic Church or the Jesuits, he refused implacably to send them any weather reports at all. He consoled himself by saying that all the other newspapers carried his forecasts anyway. He plunged with the same boldness into scientific controversy, disagreeing hotly with some of the theories of wind circulation in hurricanes stated by Redfield, or qualifying them.

That he received medals and recognition and honors abroad and at home probably did not please him so deeply as that in the time of hurricanes the staircase to his roof was jam-packed with people hurrying to ask his advice, sea captains depending on his word whether to sail or not, city and government officials asking what precautions to take, merchants, interested schoolboys, delegations from the Academy of Science, travelers undecided about taking passage for America or Europe, cane planters from the country, and distinguished European visitors.

In his first year, however, Father Viñes could only study reports of what hurricanes there had been immediately before his day; 1866, the October hurricane that engulfed the Bahamas, wrecking innumerable ships, in which the vortex over the storm-bedraggled islands had taken from 7:30 to 8:50 P.M. to pass. No doubt Father Viñes had to shove up his spectacles to take a careful look on the map to find Galveston, Texas, where another hurricane that October foamed over the low sands and the city.

He must have been aware, as many Americans were, of a slight westerly shift of hurricane courses for '67, in October, along the Rio Grande. Veterans of the Mexican War thought of endless hot days and graves in the sand on Pedro Island, old Civil War blockade runners, of cotton bales piled up in Brownsville to be hauled to the Clarksville ferry for Mexican Bagdad. Now both downriver places were obliterated in the same winds and raging water and mud, so that there is not a trace of them left.

Galveston was flooded next and a few weeks later the Danish Virgin Islands and Puerto Rico were ravaged by the most violent Cape Verde hurricane in a hundred years. In St. Thomas alone, 600 people were drowned. It was said that the islands looked as if fire had raged over them or that all the housetops had exploded. The hurricane was remembered for many years as "San Narciso" because it hit on that saint's day in October. It did not change the popular belief in the islands that there was never any hurricane danger after the first full moon in October, which that year rose on the thirteenth. Father Viñes paid careful attention to all those reports.

The only recorded hurricane for 1869 (none was recorded in '68) went surging up out of the Atlantic to hit the southeastern New England coast on September 8. There were violent gales early in the morning that flatted out by afternoon when the weather turned blue and golden as the leaves beginning to turn. By 3:30 P.M. a sharp southeast wind rattled rain on wharves, sails, innumerable rooftops, trees, as the sun went in. Along the rocky or eelgrassy shores the hissing waves mounted and rain crashed. The steely whining wind tore fast and faster. Leaves, boats, spray, late apples, sand, loose boards, elm boughs, stacks of swamp hay, all flew. At five the gray hurricane light moved across Narragansett Bay, straight across to Maine. The path of damage was not fifty miles wide. Trees, the new telegraph wires, factory chimneys were down, roads blocked.

In Boston the Coliseum building was wrecked over its organ, wooden sidewalks were smashed, the spire of the Hanover Street Church crashed down. The First Baptist Church of Lynn was wrecked. Homes were down and people hurt all the way to Marblehead Neck, Salem, Beverly. Vessels were smashed on the rocks at Kennebunk, Boothbay, Portland, Orr's Island. At Gloucester, crews were saved by the new lifeboat. A man was swept off the sloop *Helen Eliza* by a lifting grayback, swept back on board where he clung until he found an empty barrel, cast himself into the angry surf and drew himself up at last on the rocks. The others were all lost.

In the next ten years, something like fifty-six hurricanes struck many of the same places within the American coast line and what Father Viñes was one of the first to call "the great Bay of America."

Father Viñes had only begun his work in 1870 when Matanzas was struck in October, the old city east of Havana, rising above its two rivers and the fine harborlike roadstead. Great hurricane waves, under clouds that seemed to howl at the level of the rooftops, backed up the rivers, surged and crashed over ships, houses, streets, and plazas. Over eight hundred people died. "Those who were not killed under falling roofs and walls met a more dreadful death in the waters of the bay," a Havana newspaper reported. They could not clear all the streets or find all the bodies to bury them before the air was polluted and the city given over to pestilence.

The nineteenth of October, Father Viñes saw one from the south that struck to the west of Havana. "October hurricanes," he wrote later, "are the most disastrous of all to the rich southwest coast of Cuba. These hurricanes come over with such rapidly increasing speed there is hardly time to take the proper precautions if there is no warning well in advance."

In 1870 he saw the first of seven hurricanes that would devastate parts of Cuba in nine years. In '73, the small Florida village of Punta Rassa was completely demolished, an unimportant place except to Father Viñes, who regretted that especially because at Punta Rassa the first cable from Cuba came ashore, of which, for carrying weather information, he had had high hopes. The cable house was completely blown away.

The hurricane problem on which Father Viñes spent his life, he saw as twofold. The nature of the hurricane itself must be better understood, and the signs and laws, direction, velocity, intensity, wind speed, and the rest by which its position and future course may be determined. He wanted to set up throughout the Caribbean a network of trained observers who would wire or cable him constant reports in the hurricane season, through whom also advice and warnings could be sent to people in time for them to protect themselves. His other problem was that, as Belén had no money, he had to find men or governments who would share the expense.

That year, 1870, was also the date when the United States Weather Service was organized. It was part of the Army Signal Corps. At 7:45 A.M., November 1, 1870, as ordered by Brigadier General Albert J. Myer, the first simultaneous weather observations were collected by telegraph from twenty-four stations. The petition to Congress, pushed through by General Halbert E. Paine, had been drawn up by a Milwaukee naturalist concerned with Great Lakes storms, Increase A. Lapham. By 1871, General H. A. Hazen, Chief Signal Officer, was writing to college presidents for the names of good students interested in weather service training. In wartime, they would be commissioned officers.

By this time, although there were no hurricane studies, as such, except that a few observers were stationed in Cuba and the West Indies, a system of observers had been set up, who cabled local weather figures three times a day to the central office. But in '73, because of a panic in the United States, the weather service was curtailed as an economy measure and hurricane observers were recalled. The Washington office had found Father Viñes' regular hurricane information much more dependable.

The story goes that Father Viñes had established in many towns along the remote eastern and southern coasts of Cuba, in hurricane season, a system by which men were ready with horses to gallop to the next town, from which other horsemen galloped, carrying the dread word of hurricanes coming. He heard by telegraph from every city in Cuba, especially Santiago where the English consul, Mr. F. W. Ramsden, gave him years of accurate and enthusiastic support. Spanish consuls and officers of the Spanish Royal Navy in a few years cabled him from St. Thomas, Barbados, St. Vincent, and French islands, Puerto Rico and Jamaica. Spanish ship captains were ordered to cable him from the nearest port any indications of approaching hurricanes.

That was the way Father Viñes was able, in September, 1873, to plot and report accurately the hurricane that came up south of Jamaica, moved west to the Gulf coast and so turned its raking winds through the southern states to the Atlantic. The chief of the Washington Hydrographic Bureau wrote in that year's supplement to the *Pilot Chart*, "Yesterday the weather men at Havana, nine hundred miles away, gave us an accurate account of the movements of the cyclone, judging by the high clouds."

By '74, the American Smithsonian had transferred its meteorological studies to the Medical Department of the Army, under the current idea that the most important thing about the weather was its effect upon health.

No one was able to make such thorough studies of hurricanes as Father Viñes, who traveled in '74 and '75 through the Spanish islands and discussed his observations with Father Gangoite at the Observatory of Cienfuegos and Mr. Ramsden, the British consul at Santiago de Cuba. He wrote a very important paper for the

Washington Signal Office, translated as *Practical Hints in Regard to West Indian Hurricanes*, the first of many reprinted in German and French scientific journals and by the Royal Meteorological Society in London.

It was his studies of the fine high veils of clouds that precede many hurricanes which was his great contribution. In Cuba they are called "rabos de gallo" or "cocks' tails." He described them as fine glittering particles of ice in that freezing high air, and named them "cirro-stratus plumiforms," wind feathers. They were like streamers from mastheads, he wrote, that show the divergent lines of air streams running high above and at the margins of hurricanes. Their direction should show the direction of the median line of the vortex. He described the movements of all the clouds at every level of altitude in relation to a hurricane.

In 1877, he was able to announce a hurricane near Barbados and through fifty observers follow it for fourteen days up the islands to Cuba.

The government still gave him no support. But Havana newspapers like *La Voz de Cuba* campaigned for support for him. Telegraph and cable companies cut their rates in half for all hurricane messages and supplied him with an economical weather code. In time the Chambers of Commerce, Industry and Navigation, shipping companies, merchants' associations, insurance companies and agents of the New York Board of Underwriters in Trinidad, Martinique, Antigua and Puerto Rico, all contributed toward the increasing expenses of his service in the hurricane season.

So there he sat among his wind gauges, barometers and anemometers like a vigilant spider at the center of a network of observers. He waited many a tireless night for the first sign of the dark enemy that would agitate all those far-stretched threads.

3 *BRAVE MEN ALL*

Ten years after the American Weather Service had been organized as part of the Army Signal Corps, a dashing young man of twenty, born and raised in Tennessee hill country, already a college graduate, enlisted to become a weather observer.

He was Isaac Monroe Cline. Until his death at over ninety, with his piercing eyes under his broad Panama hat, neat goatee and mustache, quick, imperious manner, the dress and figure of a dandy, no more romantic figure was ever a meteorologist. At that, he was not a weatherman right away.

Young Mr. Cline reported for duty in July, 1882, outside Washington at Fort Myer, named for Brigadier General Albert J. Myer, organizer of the Weather Service. He was much excited by his new uniform, and by the necessity he was immediately under of commanding a squad for drill, inspection, meals and classes when he had not the foggiest idea of military procedures. The Signal Corps was a cavalry outfit. He and his thirty classmates were put to constant training in infantry and cavalry tactics.

Obviously he enjoyed most the chance to display his dashing horsemanship. They were issued carbines and sabers to drill with, carry around and constantly polish. They had regular guard duty, took turns as waiters, learned military signaling with flags, torches and heliographs, and practiced operating and overhauling telegraph equipment and the new thing that Alexander Graham Bell had developed six years before, the telephone. They made weather observations and attended some lectures by mathematicians and physicists like William Ferrel and Cleveland Abbe. They took rigid examinations for the sixteen vacant posts of assistant weather observers. Isaac Cline passed sixteenth. In spite of that rather odd training a number of men in his class became distinguished, like

Alexander McAdie, later director of the Blue Hill Observatory
and Harvard Professor of Meteorology, and Austin L. McRae,
professor of physics at the University of Missouri.

Cline was assigned to Little Rock, Arkansas, to study the effects
of climate on the development of Rocky Mountain locusts. There
were no locusts in Little Rock. After the 5 A.M. and 11 P.M. daily
weather observations were recorded, reports logged of temperature
and rainfall, as telegraphed by railroad agents, special weather bulletins issued during the crop-growing season and reports for commercial interests, time hung on his hands. With that interest in the
effect of climate on health still so common, Cline enrolled in a
three-year course in the medical department of the University, carried on hospital work along with his weather service, and was
graduated as an M.D. in '85.

After a chance to observe hot summer winds, and hailstones
as big as ostrich eggs in West Texas, which he reported, to the
total unbelief of the *Monthly Weather Review*, he married at
twenty-five, had one child, and for fun edited a weekly newspaper.
Then he was ordered to organize a section of the Weather Service
in Texas. He moved there in March, 1889, settled his family, edited
the *Texas Weather Bulletin* for the Galveston Cotton Exchange,
studied the effect of weather changes on sickness and death, was
registered as a medical practitioner, and was instructor in a unique
course called "Medical Climatology" in the Medical School of the
University of Texas. It is not recorded that he took any interest in
hurricanes.

But in the years between 1880 and 1889, there were, more or less,
seventy hurricanes. There is no earthly way of adding up the damage to houses, ships, cities, harvests, livestock, wildernesses or
plowed lands, coastal islands and forests, above all to people, injured, or killed, in those vast catastrophes.

Congress voted no funds for any hurricane warning service.
Doubt was cast on the legality of spending any part of the appropri-
ation for a weather service in maintaining a station outside the
United States. Later, the Signal Corps obtained a few reports from
English Barbados and Jamaica, French Guadeloupe, Danish St.
Thomas. But they depended most of all on Father Viñes' regular,
accurate and reliable hurricane plotting.

Hurricanes of those ten years swung from Yucatán and Matamoras in '80, from the Leeward Islands, Savannah, Georgia, with a loss of 335 lives, South Carolina, and with effects as far inland as Iowa and Minnesota, in August, 1881. Eighty-one saw Jacksonville hit, and later Manzanillo, Mexico. In 1882, a hurricane was recorded that swept from Turks Island through western Cuba with great damage, but with lighter winds through Florida to Hatteras. It was one of the first hurricanes in which the Signal Corps warnings were effective, in that over six million dollars' worth of shipping was prevented from sailing to probable severe loss. September 4–11, 1883, was a great hurricane, striking Haiti, Nassau, with one hundred vessels lost and fifty lives, and so to Charleston. Texas caught four hurricanes in '86 in one of which the town of Indianola was wiped out, and San Antonio affected.

An incredible fourteen in '87 hit, it seems, everywhere, in the Atlantic, the Islands, Cuba, Yucatán, and Brownsville, Texas. There were ten in '88, two in Texas, two off Florida, one devastatingly great that wiped out Turks Island and Great Inagua. For all his warning service, Father Viñes was unable to prevent over one thousand deaths.

He could know nothing of an extraordinary hurricane met by five very courageous men in an extraordinary place in September, that year of 1888. It had swept up the Florida Straits and gone howling off into the North Atlantic and disappeared, as far as everyone but those five men were concerned.

Swedish Fridtjof Nansen, huge, bearded curator of the Bergen Museum, and four other men in August had begun the great venture that would be the first east to west crossing of the inland ice of Greenland. It was unknown to any European and regarded by Eskimos with superstitious awe as fearfully peopled with demons.

With three Finns and a fellow Swede, all strong skiers, Nansen left Iceland in June. It was the middle of August before they were able to work their way to the coast through the Polar current that swept them southward in a sea black against the broken, white and glittering hummocks of floating ice. They landed and struggled upward on waves of snow among hill-like outcrops of rock and crevasses fringing the inner plateau, to 3,000 feet above sea-level. The sun grew hot at noon, 85° F. while the air was 25° F. The nights were amazing with northern lights more brilliant than the moon. The cold at midnight was −40° F. The snow, as hard as iron, went before them like a dead frozen desert. They moved across at 6,000 feet like toiling black dots on the great shield-shape of the inland ice.

Their sledges grated through snow like heavy sand. The sun shone gloriously on snow with the blinding glitter of diamonds. Then a misty ring gathered about the sun. By afternoon of the fourth of September a biting wind got up from the northwest that whirled the snow before it. The sky cleared. It grew colder and colder. There was so much ice on their beards and hair it was hard to open their lips to speak. Their noses and hands began to freeze.

By the next afternoon and all night as the storm swept from the southwest, they huddled in their sleeping bags, in the tiny tent. By the seventh they could not see outside. They could cook nothing because the tent was full of fine snow. All night the east wind blew with screaming violence. The guy ropes broke. They expected the tent to blow away. One man crawled out the tent door through a snow drift. As far as he could see through blinded eyes the world was a sea of drifting snow. The wind took his breath. There was no going on.

Yet they had to get food from the sledges before they were snowed up. They roped themselves together because after two steps a man vanished in the snow. The man who went out to put storm guys on the weather side had to go on all fours. They braced the inside of the tent with ski poles. They had less and less space as the drifts collected within. At least, the drifts kept the wind out. Nansen wrote:

A little after midday the wind dropped all at once as abruptly as if the current had been cut off short with a knife. There was a desolate calm outside and an uncomfortable silence came upon us, too, for we all knew that the wind would presently fall on us with still greater violence from the opposite quarter. We sat listening intently but the attack did not come at once and some of us thought the storm was possibly over. But presently there came a gentle gust from the northwest, the door side of our tent, and this was soon followed by blast upon blast, each more furious than its predecessor. The storm overwhelmed us with greater fury than before and the inside of the tent even was a mist of falling snow.

Balto had taken advantage of the interval of calm to go out to fill the cooking tins and it was all he could do to find his way back again.

We were now in great straits, as the door side, against which the storm now blew, was the weakest part of the tent and we always made a point of turning it away from the wind. By the help of ski poles, snowshoes, and articles of clothing we managed to strengthen this side just sufficiently as to make the doorway tolerably snow tight. But we were now caged as fast as mice in a trap and there was no getting out for us, however much we wished to.

When we woke next morning, the wind had dropped so much that we found we could move on again. But it was no easy matter to get out of our prison; the tent was buried so deep that only the ridge of the roof remained above the snow and we had to dig our way. Of the sledges there was nothing to be seen.

It had been —40° F. inside. They had reached the very middle of the island ice when the hurricane stopped them. No passing of a hurricane's center has ever been recorded so far north.

Back in the hot countries, it was to Havana still and the small shabby figure of Father Viñes that men looked for knowledge of hurricanes.

The choleric and observant Englishman, James Anthony Froude, was taken by a marquis who had studied at Belén to call on Father Viñes, as one of the most famous sights in Havana. Up among the incomprehensible instruments of the laboratory-shed on the roof tiles, Froude was tremendously impressed by the diplomas and medals but especially by the quiet man himself, and the respect shown as the young marquis, on leaving, kissed his old master's brown hand.

Americans from the Weather Service complimented him more acceptably. Everett Hayden, of the Hydrographic Office, editor of the *Pilot Chart of the North Atlantic Ocean,* and later in October, 1900, Willis L. Moore, a rising American meteorologist, made trips to Havana to consult him, as the leading hurricane authority.

Father Viñes was probably unaware of the storm of revolt brewing among the people of Cuba against the despotism of Spain. A royal order to the Governor General established a weather observatory in Havana, for which Viñes was asked to be a member of the commission. He insisted that it must be the center of a Weather Service organized throughout the West Indies, such as he had struggled to maintain. An observatory was set up at Marine Headquarters and Mr. A. W. Greely, head of the American Signal Service, who had always recognized the necessity of West Indian stations, arranged to exchange West Indian weather information through Key West, from Galveston, Charleston and New York.

Unfortunately, the first enthusiasm did not last and Mr. Greely complained that the information from the Marine Observatory and its promised stations was not regular, and at critical times failed altogether. Only Father Viñes, as Mr. Greely wrote, "has continued freely to place his valuable services at the disposition of this office."

If the weather service of the Signal Corps in those days, ignored by Congress and the public, was inadequate, incomplete and easily confused, the other service which had begun in 1870 was carried to heroic effectiveness. That was the Federal government's Lifesaving Service.

It began in the winter of '74 and '75 along the sands of North Carolina, from Frying Pan Shoals off Cape Fear up along the Outer Banks to Virginia. No section of the coast was in greater need of help. It was inevitable that the men who joined the Lifesaving Service and maintained its heroic tradition, should come from those small villages of survivors from shipwreck. Portsmouth on its sand spit, Ocracoke, Hatteras, Buxton with its tropic woods, Avon, Salvo, Chicomacomico only recently named Rodanthe, all the way up to Kitty Hawk by the high dunes, Duck in its pine woods, Corolla, Wash Woods, all the way to Currituck.

They were all fishermen and seamen, making their little gardens between voyages, with a long history of smuggling in the West Indies, blockade running in the Civil War but, chiefly, rescuing men and goods from wrecked ships.

By 1879 hundreds of men of the Outer Banks were employed as lighthouse tenders, crewmen on wrecking schooners, wreck commissioners and salvage men. In time, like the men of that other ship's graveyard, Cape Cod, Bankers, especially the Midgett family, made up the entire crew of more than one Coast Guard vessel. So in those days, they did the work of more than twenty lifesaving stations from Cape Fear to Currituck, each one with its long record of incredible endurance and daring.

From those stations regularly by night and day men made their patrols of the long miles of sand and thundering ocean under their watch and ward, in blue summer weather, with the white surf forever folding and unfolding, in blackness, in winds that blew salt and sand like abrasives, in snow, in thick fog with only the hollow shaking booming of the sea to guide them. At first their equipment was the simplest, boats and oars and their own arms, lanterns and rockets, a horse to move the boats. Hot stoves and plain hot food, blankets and medical aids were about all the stations offered. So they saved lives. Gradually, better lifesaving equipment was provided, breeches buoys, Coston lights, horses for patrols. It would all have been useless in the hands of lesser men.

The last of the hurricanes of '89, that flattened the Isles of Pines on October 5, marked Cuba with destruction, and whirled up the Atlantic northeastward. The hurricane winds that drove ships on the long beaches occurred on October 23, with raging winds from the northeast. Perhaps that was not the same hurricane. But the wrecks were there.

The *Henry P. Simmons*, a three-masted schooner from Philadelphia, sailed from Charleston for Baltimore on October 17. She had a crew of eight men, including Robert Lee Garnett. Five days later near the entrance to Chesapeake Bay a black hurricane wind hit them, in enormous rushing seas. The crew could do nothing against that steely air but lash themselves to the rigging. That night the helpless vessel was driven ashore on Pebble Shoals. She sank, with only her three masts above the wild water, where the men hung, in the wind and the icy rain. They were a thousand yards from shore in an expanse all foaming surf. One fell off and was lost.

Lifesavers on the sand by the first light tried to fire a line aboard the wreck. It fell short. The seven men hanging there could see them. The second mate and another man dropped. All that day the lifesavers could not reach the ship. At twilight, with the wind still raging, another man was swept off. Four men somehow lived through the freezing night. At dawn, the lifesavers could not launch the surfboat. They telegraphed to Norfolk for a tug. Off Cape Henry, the tug could make no headway against the sea. Another man fell from the rigging.

Along that same stretch of beach the *Lizzie S. Haynes* went ashore, only two men saved with a breeches buoy; the *Busiris* of New Brunswick lost north of Payner's Hill Station; the *Francis E. Waters*, keel up among the breakers at Nag's Head, and only two bodies of her crew in the sand. Three miles off New Inlet the *Annie E. Blackman* of New Jersey was thrown on her beam ends and sunk. Only her captain lived, who got to shore with a life jacket, crawled up the beach to a telegraph pole to which he tied himself and was found next morning tramping round and around it as he had all night, to keep his blood circulating.

The United States Weather Bureau was reorganized in 1891, a year of eleven hurricanes, under the Department of Agriculture, since it had proved its value to farmers. No actual forecasting was done then, more than a kind of listing of probabilities of rain or frost or storm.

In 1893, in July, just at the beginning of the hurricane season, Father Benito Viñes died, not of old age but of overwork, not enough sleep, too much devotion to the study of hurricanes. He was frustrated and disappointed because his high hopes for a great weather service and network of warning stations, supported by the government, were never fulfilled.

In his place, as head of the Belén Observatory, the other weather-minded Jesuit was appointed, from his smaller observatory at the College of Cienfuegos—Father Lorenzo Gangoite, S.J. In 1893, as if to spare him in his difficult task of taking Father Viñes' place in the confidence of all the people, not a single hurricane troubled Cuba, of the eleven listed that year.

Of that number, two were "great hurricanes," surging with increasing force all the way from the Cape Verde Islands. The first, on August 22 to 30, was terrible on the coasts of Georgia and South Carolina, with huge smashing hurricane waves that washed over islands and houses and beaches crowded with vacationing people. A thousand lives were lost. There were corpses in the mud of rice fields. Whole families were killed, damage to property was reckoned up to ten million dollars. The city of Charleston was a wreck.

Northward, that August, at the mouth of the Cape Fear River, Dunbar Davis, the keeper of the Oak Island Lifesaving Station, and his family had summered there alone without the winter crew. There was no warning for them in the hurricane that beat at Charleston. The schooner *Roger Moore* was caught on her way south by the whistling fringes of the central whirl, lost her sails, her deck cargo of lumber and a crewman. The schooners *Mary J. Cook* and the *L. A. Burnham* were sailing north to Boston, the

A. R. Weeks to New Jersey, the *Oliver H. Booth* to Washington, the *Gertie M. Rickerson* to Cuba, the *John S. Case* to Santo Domingo, the *Lizzie May* to Fernandina, Florida. Ships, fifty-five crewmen, and all their cargoes were never seen again.

There were more. At midnight on the twenty-seventh the *Three Sisters* of Philadelphia was caught by the hurricane winds off Frying Pan Shoals lightship, dismasted, the captain and mate drowned. The roaring waves shoved the helpless vessel and six helpless men toward the Carolina coast. Dunbar Davis at Oak Island Station and J. L. Watts of the Cape Fear Station saw her driving in with the surf. Davis, in a small boat against the wind and spray, tried to get to the island. Watts, rowing, met him, and they shouted it would be better for Davis to go back to get his surfboat ready while Watts went to Southport for volunteers. By 8:30 that night against wind and tide the surfboat and its crew struggled to the beach. The ship was riding easily in the tearing surf, too far out for the breeches buoy. Watts and Davis therefore walked back to Cape Fear Station for Watts's surfboat. They had to wait until daylight. Not long after sunrise they had the men safe in Southport.

From there Davis saw a distress signal on the pole of his station and rounded up more volunteers. The German brig *Wustrow* had beached nine miles away and had gone to pieces. But from his watchtower Davis saw another vessel in danger nearer in. They put off in the Cape Fear surfboat but on the bar the wind and the breakers were too much for them. There was nothing for him to do but go back to his station for his apparatus cart and pull it down the beach.

It was slow going against wind and tide rips cut across the smoking sands. They met a man who said the crew of the *Kate E. Gifford* were safe ashore. But Davis pushed on and found the schooner had grounded. He had to go back for gear he had dumped, with a mule he hired and then a team of oxen. It was pitch black night by then and still blowing. Watts and his men joined Davis and at 2:00 A.M., with the hurricane winds letting up a little but with the surf smashing all the way across the beach, fired their Lyle gun to the schooner. The line was aboard but the crew of the schooner, already breaking up, never saw it until dawn. All seven were saved.

Dunbar Davis stayed with the mate to watch over the cargo

coming in from the wreck. It was late afternoon and he was fifty years old. They built a fire and he was getting a wink of sleep when a yawl came driving in from the sea with seven beaten men, from two schooners, the *Jennie E. Thomas* and the *Enchantress*, both damaged and drifting and many of the crews gone. Then men in the yawl had not had food for four days. Davis sent them to the station with the oxen. But even the oxen were too tired to go back for him. So he walked. The station was crowded with eighteen rescued men who had eaten all the food, taken all the beds. Davis probably did not mind sleeping on the floor.

BOOK SEVEN

MODERN TIMES

1 *FROM WAR TO GALVESTON*

Dr. Isaac M. Cline, by order of the brilliant and dynamic head of the U.S. Weather Bureau, Willis L. Moore, was sent from the tree-shaded city of Galveston, where for some time he had been living with his family, to establish a chain of hurricane observation posts around the Gulf of Mexico. Moore was certain that war would soon explode between Spain and the United States over the rebellion in Cuba, and the American Navy must be protected.

Moore had learned about hurricanes from Father Viñes at Havana. He had already cleaned out from the Weather Bureau many men he considered incompetent and "not of good character." He had made many political enemies, importuned Congress for more money for the service and was not liked, but respected, by many men like Cline.

But Cline in Mexico got permission to set up weather observation stations in Tampico, Veracruz and Coatzcoalcos and Mérida and Progreso in Yucatán, to which he traveled carrying new instruments. He was seasick on the small coastal steamers on those green and uneasy waters, and fought off yellow fever in the old sun-bleached cities. He laid the groundwork for an exchange of weather information between Mexico and his Galveston office.

Father Gangoite in Havana was delighted to exchange weather news with the newly organized weather service of the Central Observatory in Mexico. The five hurricanes of 1896, with the one that crashed over the District of Columbia, and the U.S. Weather Bureau's office, and the five more in '97 that seemed to blow everywhere, were variously reported.

The Spanish government not only had taken no interest in the hurricane service of Father Gangoite, but had charged a 30 per cent duty on all imported scientific instruments. But at the insistence of the Royal Academy of Science and others a bill was

249

passed by both chambers of the Spanish government for an annual subvention of the Belén Observatory of 15,950 pesos.

Then, the *Maine* was sunk in Havana Harbor and in April, 1898, the United States leaped enthusiastically into war with the creaking old Spanish empire. All scientific appropriations were canceled in order that the Spanish fleet might be made ready for the sea. It was an unprepared fleet of ships, some obsolete, some without guns, manned heroically by sick, ill-fed and badly trained crews under able Admiral Cervera, who accepted his orders to sail as if they were all doomed.

As they disappeared into the Atlantic, panic fear ran up and down the American coast. Congressmen arranged that cruisers of the United States smart but small new fleet be detached to guard beaches and seaside hotels against the ravages of Spanish attack. Admiral Sampson and Captain Schley were ordered to find Cervera. The Spanish fleet was safe in the harbor of Santiago de Cuba when the American ships, after independently dashing here and there, blockaded them there.

Meantime, the Isle of Pines was occupied by Americans, so that the shallow-draft vessels necessary for those waters could find shelter there in time of hurricanes.

What Cervera might have been doing while the Americans were looking for him was something that only the U.S. Navy Board and especially the great strategist and historian, Admiral Alfred Thayer Mahan, had thought about. Mahan wrote that if the Spanish admiral could have spent more time dodging about the islands, he would have divided the small American Navy and drawn part of it after him. In that case the first hurricane would have reduced the American fleet to numbers the Spanish fleet might have handled. Or, Mahan wrote, if Cervera had waited longer in Santiago Harbor perhaps the American fleet might have scattered before a hurricane, and he could have escaped.

As it was, the Weather Bureau played an important and secret part in Sampson's final victory. Even in wartime the Spanish government in Havana had allowed Father Gangoite to continue to receive and send out hurricane warnings and weather reports in code which the Key West cable station was allowed to be opened once a day to receive. Somebody loyal to the Americans at Havana

Some notable hurricanes, West Gulf of Mexico.

took advantage of the father's weather code to cable military intelligence.

Several officers in the United States Army applied to Willis L. Moore for positions in the Weather Bureau at Key West, like the man whose brother-in-law was an officer in the Spanish Army in Cuba. Moore sent him to a station in Alaska. And was hated for it.

The news that Cervera had entered Santiago Harbor was received along with the coded daily weather reports in Key West roaring with war correspondents like Richard Harding Davis and Stephen Crane, waiting until the blundering, incredible invasion of Cuba on troop ships from Tampa should have landed.

The Spanish government ordered Cervera out to engage the enemy. The American ships saw them leaving the harbor and gunfire echoed and re-echoed from the hills. Men died. The old ships grounded or burned. It was the end of Spain in the New World.

A month later, the first of seven hurricanes delivered their slow vast rockets about the now American Caribbean. One had a comic effect not unlike many facets of that war. When fear of the Spanish Navy sent the Atlantic coast into a panic and warships were detached to guard it, the Navy installed lookout stations, such as the one at Carolina Beach, North Carolina, which were closed after Cervera's defeat. The Weather Bureau took over the Carolina Beach station. The property, when checked, was found to be complete except for one very attractive navy outhouse. A local citizen admired it as too fine to be abandoned and moved it to his adjoining beach property. The government made such a to-do about this, that the citizen returned it, if reluctantly. The heavy surf of the hurricane of October 2 washed completely over the lookout station and destroyed the outhouse, thus earning its title, "The Privy Hurricane."

Now for eleven years, Dr. Isaac M. Cline had found the city of Galveston a pleasant place in which to bring up his three little girls, and enhance the usefulness of the Weather Bureau. With war and the increase of shipping down the rivers it had become a prosperous port and a gay and interesting city. Broadway, its main boulevard, crossed the island over the eight-foot central ridge from which its residential streets, with square frame houses and huge mansions, went off. Ladies in elaborate costumes and elegant gentlemen drove out in the afternoons in a glittering procession of carriages along the beach like a boulevard facing the Gulf, to the races or to Laffite's Grove. There were smart concerts at the Pavilion on the beach and marching military companies with loud brass bands.

Such gaiety meant nothing to Dr. Cline, expanding the Weather Bureau services to growers with forecasts of floods from heavy rains to the westward. He was making it the central exchange for weather information between Mexico and the United States, although he had no direct exchange with Havana or the West Indies because, as he wrote later, "Under orders then strictly enforced no one except the forecaster in the Central Office of the Weather Bureau in Washington had authority to issue emergency or hurricane warnings."

He was not concerned with the bitter disappointment of Father Gangoite that the American occupation of Cuba refused to recognize the long service of the Belén fathers. The American occupation in the Philippines had also superseded the typhoon-wise Jesuit fathers of the Observatory at Manila, but a storm of protest from as far as Japan and China had forced the fathers' official reinstatement. The Americans in Cuba established a public institution which was to become the present excellent National Observatory and Weather Bureau. The Belén fathers, with the support of the Cuban people, continued their hurricane warning services on notices from the British and French of the island. The results were a conflict of forecasts, confusion if not panic in remote cities and villages, and much bitterness.

The climax came in September, 1900.

From the first of September a hurricane of small intensity had been observed in the eastern Caribbean. It crossed the central provinces of Cuba and curving normally west-northwest moved along south of Florida and in the Gulf of Mexico reformed with increased intensity toward the Texas coast.

In Galveston, on the fourth of September, Isaac Cline's office received the same advisory storm warnings from the American observer in Havana, sent to all southern coastal stations by the Central Office in Washington. On the fifth, at 11:20 A.M. Cline received the message, "Disturbance central near Key West moving northwest. Vessels bound for Florida and Cuban waters should exercise caution as storm is likely to become dangerous." On the fifth, when the Belén Observatory announced it, the hurricane was indeed dragging heavy winds along the lower east coast of Florida. High waves washed across Biscayne Bay, smashed small docks and boats and boathouses and surged up the limestone sea-worn ridge along Coconut Grove, knocking down fruit trees and pines.

On the sixth, Father Gangoite issued warnings in the Havana press that the hurricane was moving west-southwest. On the seventh, Dr. Cline at Galveston received notice from Washington to hoist northwest storm warnings.

It was a beautiful day, brilliant and blue and calm, but from the beach sounded a long shuddering booming as swells broke in thunder and flashing foam. The incoming tide pushed higher than high water mark up the slope of the sands.

At 5 A.M. on September 8, Mr. J. L. Cline, Dr. Cline's brother, who had been on duty all night at the Weather Bureau, telephoned him to say the waves were sweeping into the low parts of the city four feet higher than high tide. A north wind came over yet the tide burst up against it. The barometer fell only slowly. Water went on rising.

Dr. Cline was profoundly disturbed. He wired Washington that he had never before observed such high water with opposing winds. He harnessed his horse to a two-wheeled cart and drove fast up and down the beach from one end of the city to the other, where curious crowds and thousands of summer visitors were gathering to watch the wild white smoking seas. He shouted to them all to get to safety, and to people living near the Gulf shore to move to the ridge before their houses were washed away. Hundreds of people were warned by telephone that worse was coming. Hundreds crowded to the Weather Bureau and were told they must seek higher grounds. Thousands moved their families to the center of the city.

Dr. Cline had been sending wires to Washington every two hours about the rising water. At 11:15 Washington ordered him to change the storm warnings from northwest to northeast. Against regulations he wired hurricane warnings up and down the coast. He wrote later, ". . . neither emergency nor hurricane warnings for the disaster were received from the forecaster in the Washington office."

That same morning, Father Gangoite of the Belén Observatory,

having charted correctly the course the storm would take across
the Gulf of Mexico, notified the papers that the center of the hurricane would reach Texas so as to bring the north and east coasts
within the vortex. The American observer at Havana was quoted
as saying the storm was not worth mentioning. It is quite evident
that Father Gangoite's warnings were never sent to Washington.

At Galveston all afternoon the light darkened and the wind increased, with biting gusts of rain. The storm tide, as Dr. Cline and
his brother Joseph found, had covered half the city. All the telegraph wires were down but one, over which Joseph Cline sent the
last message that the disaster was upon them. Two bridges to the
mainland were down and a causeway was covered with racing
water. The city was cut off.

Now the wind came harshly from the east slicing off roofs and
hurling timbers that killed hundreds of people trying to flounder to
safety through the flooded streets. Sea water drove against walls and
spurted through house floors. At 6:15 P.M. the winds slid level at
84 miles an hour. When the anemometer blew away they knew the
gusts had increased to more than 120 miles per hour.

There was nothing left for Dr. Cline to do but go home to the
strong house he had built not far from the beach. He found fifty
people huddled there besides his wife, his three little girls and his
brother Joseph. He stood in the door watching the water race by
in the street until suddenly it was as if the whole Gulf had lifted
and was moving into the city. He was up to his armpits in swirling
water by the time everyone was upstairs, with waves tossing wreckage against the shuddering house.

His brother cried out and broke a window, grabbing the two
older girls as part of a railway trestle loomed over the house and
smashed down. Joseph Cline got out on the trestle with the two
children as the house broke apart and wild water swallowed up
people. Dr. Cline saw his wife and baby daughter sink, and was
sucked down into blackness and unconsciousness. When he
breathed again, he was hanging over a timber. Lightning flashes
showed his baby on a timber which he clutched until his brother
dragged them both, with the little girls, to a tossing frame of
boards, on which they seemed to be swept out to open sea. Unseen
houses crashed into them. The wind and the drowning screamed.

Once they saw by lightning a little girl swirling by them on a door and rescued her.

At midnight their timbers crashed into other timbers on drying ground. The winds were less. They crawled into a standing house.

In clear morning light the city was nothing but an endless jumble of boards, trees, broken furniture, soaked lumber, and endless dead bodies. Only a few buildings were left standing on the ridge, such as the Ursuline Convent and Academy and the railway station. A large ocean steamer had been driven miles into the low wrecked mainland. Twenty per cent of the inhabitants of the city were gone. The body of Dr. Cline's wife was found caught and carried along under the same pieces of his own wall which had rescued them.

The city had bad times to go through after that, even after men arrived from the mainland with help. Martial law was declared and hundreds of men were shot for robbing the living and the dead. There were too many bodies for complete identification. Barge loads were taken out and buried in the Gulf depths. There was no food, no water, no electricity. One half the taxable property was gone, a loss of over twenty millions of dollars, with 6,000 people dead.

A million dollars poured in, in gifts from the rest of the country. Clara Barton arrived for the Red Cross. But at once the citizens began to organize to clean up the city. They decided to build an enormous sea wall more than eight miles long and four feet higher than any known hurricane wave.

The people's driving determination was so great that in one year, one month and sixteen days the concrete base was completed and sand from the dunes filled in the low streets and bayous behind it. It was finished in July, 1904, a wall sixteen feet wide at the base with granite riprap filling twenty-five feet from the base to the water's edge. At first the wall went around the island for thirty-one blocks, then the U.S. government extended it around Fort Crockett.

To build it, the Texas legislature forgave all the county and city taxes for fifteen years, and authorized city and county bonds. The greatest task was faced by the people behind the walls where the land under every house, every school, every church and every other building in an area forty blocks long and twenty-two blocks wide had to be raised and filled from seventeen feet at the beach to ten feet at Broadway. Houses were jacked up and people walked narrow planks to reach their doors. All car tracks, water mains were elevated, all streets rebuilt. No vehicles were permitted in the section being filled. Galveston was the first city in the United States voluntarily to undergo such reconstruction without a single condemnation suit. In other years the sea wall was extended, topped with a wide road. The total cost was over nine million dollars.

There were five other hurricanes in 1900 besides Galveston's unforgettable disaster, and ninety-five authenticated hurricanes from 1900 to 1915, inclusive. The 1915 hurricane blew in all the way from the Cape Verde Islands, where for three years no hurricane had formed. It passed into the Caribbean between Guadeloupe and Dominica on August 10, moved west, south of Haiti, north of Jamaica, crossed Cape Antonio, Cuba. It had attained a fearful velocity of 120 miles per hour. This time its violence was preceded for twenty-four hours by exact warnings from the U.S. Weather Bureau. Damage was as high as $50,000,000. The business district of Galveston had five or six feet of water, rain and seepage from a tide twelve feet above normal. But this time only 275 people died. The great sea wall held. Galveston was the first city of the American coasts adequately to protect itself against the inevitable recurrence of hurricanes.

The great Galveston hurricane of 1900 made Dr. Isaac M. Cline into a hurricane expert. Later he was in charge of the New Orleans Weather Bureau. His dynamic dictatorship made his word law in the matter of hurricane warning in the dangerous season on the Gulf Coast and the Mississippi. There is no telling how much property damage he prevented and how many lives he saved.

Dr. Cline's first important contribution was a set of invaluable rules for finding the center and accurately describing the course and landfalls of hurricanes on the Gulf Coast from observations of storm swells and tides. He developed the important "horn-card" technique, from the sheets of transparent horn marked with the compass enclosed with old navigation books for charting wind directions. Like Piddington's *A Sailor's Horn Book*, his pamphlet, *Tropical Cyclones*, is a classic of hurricane knowledge.

When Dr. Cline died at ninety-one, in 1956, his brother Joseph, to whom, they say, he had not spoken in years, died a few days after him. Isaac was one of the most colorful, romantic, quarrelsome, opinionated and brilliant figures among American weathermen, on whose bitter experience the modern knowledge of hurricanes is in large part based.

2 *HURRICANES OVER FLORIDA*

1. *Miami in 1926*

For more than four thousand years the long flat land of Florida and the Everglades, as the sea water retreated from it, has offered no resistance to the passage of hurricanes.

The prehistoric Glades Indians who came shoving down around the Gulf Coast, to build their mounds and villages and dig their canals by the fish-haunted white beaches and the inner solitudes of the saw grass, knew them very well. The winds blew away their thatched roofs and the waves drowned them and their children, their canoes, their shell tools, their wooden godlings, their vegetable gardens and their fish weirs. Other hurricanes brought Spanish victims for the yearly sacrifices at which they prayed for protection and strength from the Master of Breath.

Yet there was no history of hurricanes over the Florida land until the uncertain first sailboats of white settlers ventured down the sandy beaches or oxcarts plodded south through the palmettos when men from Georgia and Alabama built shacks by deserted Indian mounds, by empty rivers and shimmering bays. They learned about hurricanes, then, chiefly from the Bahama people who were there before them.

They learned to set the corner posts of their houses deep and strong and tie their roof beams stoutly against the cutting, sliding winds. Palmetto thatch was knotted to ridgepoles, Indian fashion. Shingles were set Florida-style, nine nails to a shingle, no nail head

driven home, the shingles less than an inch apart, to allow for warp-
ing and swelling. The roofs were long and low, with deep eaves
against the heavy rains. The windows had wooden shutters. Boats
were brought ashore, or taken to some upriver lee, or Bahama-
fashion, sunk deep on the bottom. Everywhere, as in the Bahamas,
the rain-water cisterns had stout roofs, to keep out blowing salt
water and sand.

In north and inland Florida, houses were much like that, sometimes two rooms only, connected by a dog-trot or breeze way,
with the long roof over all. It must have been from the early days
that the English-speaking people began calling those great storms
"hurricanes." The exposed root mass of an overthrown tree is still
called "a harrican blow-down" or shortened as in the remark, "Better keep them kids away from them harricans. There's where the
rattlesnakes lays."

The most famous folk-saying about hurricanes may have been
brought to Florida early from the Bahamas but Florida people have
repeated it for generations as their own. Everybody knows it. And
from the fact that it does not mention November, when hurricanes
have been known to strike west to Central America, it may be believed to have originated in these latitudes. It goes, "June, too soon.
July, stand by. August, look out you must. September, remember.
October, all over."

The other folklore that everyone in South Florida knows and
enjoys repeating to newcomers may be of much greater antiquity
than the rule that has been taught in meterological courses since
1857, as a Dutch physicist first stated it, called "the law of Buys Ballot." Ballot taught that the observer, standing with his back to the
hurricane wind, will have the center of the hurricane on his left.
In Florida, from time immemorial they have said: "You want to
find out where the hurricane is? Stand with your face to the wind
and stretch your right arm straight out and you'll be pointing to
the center." It's all the same thing.

The fear of hurricanes was unknown to newcomers as railroads
crept down the long coasts and the first hotels were set among palms
on ridges overlooking inland waterways or bays or beaches. But
the hurricane jingle must have been heard by the first tourists who
came south as recently as the '90s, to Naples on its wonderful west
beach and on the East Coast, to the stylish hotels of Palm Beach.

On the Biscayne Bay the native Caribbean pine was cleared to make a grid of narrow streets and, as "Dade County pine," sawed up to make one- and two-story frame houses and stores. With a few docks and Mr. Flagler's big white and yellow wooden hotel by the river, this was the city of Miami.

No one but a few of the oldest homesteaders remembered the great hurricane of 1880 that struck where the hotels of Palm Beach would stand and on the almost uninhabited shores of Lake Okeechobee. Between 1885 and 1900, twenty hurricanes of known or doubtful intensity hit Florida. Few could have listed them.

In 1902 there were enough people in Miami to talk about the hurricane, with a single newspaper, the *Metropolis*, to report it. By 1903 there were a few masonry buildings among the frame houses, stores with corrugated iron awnings over the sidewalks and glaring white sand streets. That year eight tropical cyclones were listed, of which the third tore into the village of Juno up the coast and lashed Miami with winds of at least seventy miles an hour. Boats were smashed among the sea grapes and flimsy docks of the old waterfront. It tore up the two-mile-long wooden Collins bridge that crossed the bay to mangrove swamps and the beautiful empty beach. The Royal Palm Hotel company's cowshed blew down and corrugated iron awnings slid viciously along the rainy streets. There was greater damage to the small houses and fruit trees of Lemon City and Humbuggus as well as across the state at often-battered Punta Rassa. The first number of Frank B. Stoneman's new paper, the *News-Record*, later printed in the morning as the Miami *Herald*, carried the headline, "West Indian Hurricane Hits Miami." His lead editorial insisted that no more flimsy structures should be built in Miami.

Only one other hurricane in twenty-three years, in October, 1906, moved up the Florida Keys, drowning 124 workmen and wrecking barges, dredges, quarter boats and pilings by which Henry M. Flagler was shoving out his great Overseas Highway to Key West. The damage did not stop Mr. Flagler's construction of solid rock embankments where the shallow tides poured into Florida Bay. Across the deepest water his engineers laid trestles and bridges and it was a great progressive achievement to everyone but a few native Keys people. They said any hurricane could impound water behind those embankments that would wash out the best-laid railroad in the world. In Miami, Frank B. Stoneman's *News-Record* was the only paper to repeat the warning and ask Mr. Flagler to reconsider his engineer's plans. No changes in the solid embankments were made.

By 1926 the city of Miami sprawled out over the flat lands of Dade County like a huge fair. In an area six hundred miles long and sixty miles wide, from Fort Lauderdale to the south end of Dade County, there were 300,000 people, all excited about the future. Hardly a mangrove was left on Miami Beach, filled with pumped-in sand, with grass and trees, streets, houses, shops, office buildings, hotels and beach casinos, all brilliant in the sunshine. West as far as the Everglades real estate subdivisions had pushed sidewalks and ornamental gateways and auctions. In 1925 there had been over sixty million dollars' worth of new building and a frenzy of speculation that crowded the streets and hotels with people, sure they were millionaires already. Bank clearings had been well over a billion dollars.

But by the winter and spring of 1926 the fair and carnival, the boom and dizzy talk of millions, were running down. The flags were faded. Options were torn paper in the gutters. All that summer of 1926, as the crowds thinned out on the sidewalks, real estate advertising had made hysterical claims that the boom would start up again in the fall. Real estate companies such as Coral Gables, where the excitement had begun, were setting up more elaborate offices to flog the lagging market, although now many houses stood unfinished in the hot sun, and acres of shanties, trailer camps, tent cities, and flimsy stores were bleaching out.

No real estate office in sprawling Greater Miami was more remarkable than the office of Coral Gables at Miami Beach, on the ocean front, beside the stylish Roman Pool. It had cost $155,000. It was called the Salon Maritime. The main room was called a solarium, and centered by a tile fountain and surrounded by a promenade, all lighted by blue bulbs in bronze urns on columns that held up a sky blue ceiling and reflected splendor on models of Spanish galleons, antique velvet chairs, eight-foot-high marble cornucopias, a high marble mantel, two huge candelabra from a Spanish cathedral, seventeen Oriental rugs and a Steinway grand piano.

Dr. George W. Woollard waited for customers in his private

office, having just moved into the two-room private suite within, among Japanese silk panels, oriental chairs and steel filing cases.

The ocean beyond the entrance fountain and the long tan beach where bathers frolicked was clear green and curling crystal. At seven-thirty in the evening of the seventeenth of September a company official telephoned Dr. Woollard that storm-warning flags were being flown on the Miami docks. Nobody felt there was much to worry about. But no stars came out over the darkness, and the sea grew loud. By ten o'clock a wind was blowing so sharply from the northeast that Dr. Woollard went out and turned his big twin-six Packard coupé with its back to the stinging air. Getting back to the door was hard. Sand was flung into his face like needles. As he banged the great doors shut a little sea water came in. Presently by the blue light he saw the rugs were floating in twelve inches of water.

He went in and put on his bathing suit. His watch, which with a ring he put in a bureau drawer, showed it was midnight. It was the last time he knew what time it was, for two days. The electricity went out.

Tumult was rising outside. He managed to light a candle, and opened his office door just as the big front doors burst open and an enormous wave rolled in, scooped up all the furniture and swept it out again. His candle went out. In pitch blackness he heard all the windows crash open as two waves, one from the street and one from the ocean, filled the room with swirling sea water to his waist. Some dark object rolled against his kneees. It was a half-drowned policeman. For hours they stood on a table in water to their hips, roofed with the extraordinary howling-crashing-roaring of wind and rain and sea.

By the whiteness of waves they saw dimly the grand piano carried out through a door. Roofs over the windows collapsed, but not on them. The Roman Pool next door split in two, adding five hundred thousand gallons of fresh water to the ocean that rose around them. At dawn they hung to chandelier, lifting and falling with the waves.

It seemed to Woollard the wind was a little more quiet. He swam through a doorway, smashed a window and was trying to get out on a sanded bulk that turned out to be the piano, when the wind came up like a projectile from the south, knocking him back

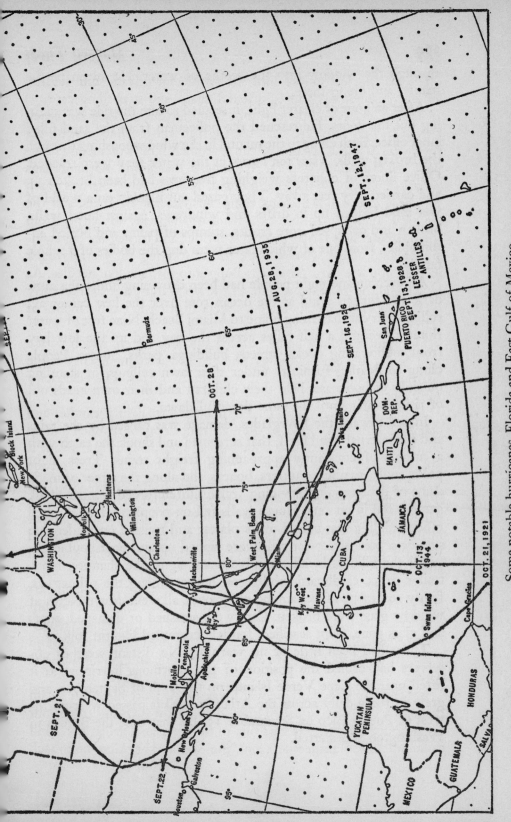

Some notable hurricanes, Florida and East Gulf of Mexico.

through the window into the seethe of water. He swam to the mantel and clung there.

After an hour of clearer light, it seemed to him the tide was sucking out the doors. He rescued the policeman from the sand-filled inner office. Both clung to the mantel in the wind whooshing through the broken walls. After ten hours in the water they were rescued. Office floors of concrete weighing five tons had been broken up and carried fifty feet away. They gazed out blankly on a world of wet sand heaped up in drifts and windrows, against hotel walls, broken and collapsed store fronts, stumps of palms and buried automobiles, from one of which later were dug the bodies of a whole family.

All evening and night people had been drowning under the same dark and furious wind as the ocean rose over the low causeway, rolling over cars hastening home to Miami Beach. Nine feet of water rioted three and a half miles across the bay and up the low bay front, obliterating docks, streets, buildings, parks, houses. People clung to floating furniture under their own ceilings, or standing on sinks or bookcases held their children and their own heads out of rising water until the same dreadful dawn.

Inland toward the Everglades, damage was caused by the rains and the infernal wind itself, that screamed and shook the earth with a rumble of constantly approaching freight trains. Trees, light poles, roofs, awnings, shutters, boards, slid along the street or made dams of debris against standing walls. Unreinforced cement-block garages fell in on cars. House walls fell on people. A half-finished office building was peeled of its plaster and twisted on inadequate supports. Steel street-car rails were ripped up and bent double.

All the billboards, all the advertising signs, the shanties, tents, trailer parks, cardboard subdivision houses among the palmettoes, flimsy real estate offices among old groves, all went down. Acres of window glass were broken. Cars were smashed or damaged, roofs and glass gone, paint scarified, fenders crumpled like tin foil.

There had been little or no warning. No distant weather observers had cabled the position of the enormous hurricane as it lifted near the Cape Verde Islands on the sixth of September, and grew in force daily across the Atlantic until it passed west-north-west of Puerto Rico on September 15. By that time the Bureau in Washington was alerted.

In Miami on the sixteenth there was no blood-red sunset, no long swells. On the blue, warm seventeenth there was no wind all day stronger than a pleasant nineteen miles an hour. People left work early to get to the Beach for a swim, played golf, went sailing. The *Metropolis*, the afternoon paper, was on the streets by four o'clock with a streamer that made news of a tropical storm somewhere south by east. People paid no more attention to that than to the Weather Bureau's storm-warning flags, black with red centers, snapping at the end of the municipal docks. Hurricane warning flags, red with black centers, were not hoisted on the docks until about 11 P.M. but no one noticed them.

People in the towns, subdivisions around, pineland, groveland or tomato prairies, never heard of a hurricane. Later that day hurricane flags were put up and all evening especially after 10 P.M. as the wind began to come faster and faster from the northeast, the Weather Bureau phones were busy sending out the word and asking that it be spread everywhere, that a hurricane was coming. By three o'clock in the morning the wires were down, the lights were out and the black driven water was foaming over the Beach, the bay and up the lowland.

The wind streamed across the beaten city at 120 miles an hour, when the anemometers blew away with tearing gusts against which no man could stand, that blew away roofs and houses and the instrument shelter on top of the Weather Bureau. People trying to crawl to safety on their hands and knees were killed by trees or bricks, as the wet ground shook and the searing voices of the wind lifted, over the roaring, higher—and higher.

At ten minutes past six, on the morning of the eighteenth, the wind stopped. The sun poured out hot, and hundreds of people, who had not the least idea that the calm center of the hurricane was passing directly over Miami, pushed away the heavy furniture against their doors, rushed out in hysterical relief, stared and climbed over the incredible piles of debris where streets had been. Houses left standing were plastered with a green mud of leaves. Everything was different, glaring, empty. The mild air smelled of salt, mud and sap. People poured out from downtown buildings where they had taken shelter. In the oppressive silence of which many complained, a hubbub of voices was lifting.

Only Richard W. Gray, the weatherman, after his frantic night taking instrument readings by flashlight, rushed hatless out into the strange streets to shout to everyone he saw to get back into shelter because the second half of the hurricane was upon them. Nobody paid any attention.

North of town or on Miami Beach the lull lasted only a few minutes. But in Miami, the beautiful quiet went on for thirty-five minutes, time enough for the whole city to open barricaded doors and come stumbling out over ruins, dazed with relief.

At 6:47 A.M. exactly, a gale leaped from the south, a smashing high tide of wind at over 128 miles an hour, that picked up debris and shoved people in a new cacophony of terror. Many were killed instantly by blown timbers or the falling of already loosened walls. Everything crashed. Water that had not run off the low ground was pushed back and higher up the bay, up the river, carrying boats and docks and sheds in a tidal wave of wreckage.

The hurricane moved away to drown people and obliterate the small boom town of Moore Haven on Lake Okeechobee and so northwest to fall with undiminished fury on Pensacola. But in Miami, when that day was over, the city built on wild promises and hopes, paper and unchecked speculation, like the acres of shacks and flimsy buildings and billboards, was gone. Blown away. There was left only sun-drying ruin, 114 dead, and damages estimated variously from fifty million to an extravagant five hundred million dollars. Twenty-five thousand people were homeless.

In the first day a citizens' committee was set up by which shelter, food and what building materials there were were at once made available to everyone who needed anything, along wtih hospitalization and nursing. The whole city was mobilized to relief work before the first trains could get south. People were fed at community kitchens. Doctors, nurses, repair crews went to work. A man whose roof had blown off could ask for a roll of roofing paper, sign for it and take it home. Martial law was at first declared, but it was unnecessary. The Citizens' Relief Committee was in charge of everything.

By the twenty-third, President Coolidge had appealed for Florida relief, the money to be sent to the American Red Cross. Three days later, the Citizens' Committee asked for relief. Supply trains with doctors and nurses began coming in over the cleared railroads from as far west as Chicago.

More than two-thousand workmen were hired for the long job of cleaning up the black bay mud that covered the city and the sand that covered the Beach, cutting up fallen trees, burning wreckage and collecting rotting fish. In a week the streets were passable and people who had done voluntary relief work for days and nights began to repair their own houses. The city commissioners waived all building permits for thirty days as the whole city and the county boiled up in a great wave of released energy and indomitable courage.

Then the American Red Cross arrived to take charge of all relief work, with its trained workers, its forms in triplicate, its endless questionnaires and red tape. To the people who still needed so much help, the professionalism of the great national organization still adapting after the war years, was a source of endless complaints and bitterness. It was years before most people in Miami had a good word to say about it.

But what Miami learned first of all about hurricanes was that only well-built buildings could withstand them. The city was filled with flimsy buildings, without proper storm bracing and roofs not anchored to walls, that had collapsed. The Miami Building Code was revised then and has continued to be revised until now it is used throughout Florida and has become a model to all hurricane-endangered cities. More than that, there was a concerted demand for better hurricane warning service, and better plans for hurricane relief which had an immediate and lasting effect.

In fact, no hurricane in the South made so many people hurricane-conscious as the '26, or more unforgettable history for all Miami people.

2. Okeechobee, 1928

That great lake, Okeechobee, like a hole in the long paw of Florida, was an almost unknown solitude while Miami grew into a bustling city. Its 730 square miles of water hardly deeper than a man's shoulders was a wide platter bright as new tin, colored like opals under a shell-pink sunset. It held rain water and river water from the Kissimmee and creeks flowing from the northward. For thousands of years the clear, fresh-smelling water, etched with reeds and crisp emerald water plants where the ibis and limpkin nested, had brimmed over southward through custard apple and willow jungles to the wide-open, curving river of saw grass and water, the Everglades.

Long after Florida became a state, that second largest fresh-water lake wholly within the United States was the center of a legend that if the Everglades could be drained it would be an empire of the richest land in the world. The few hunters, outlaws, and botanists who knew it first were followed by farmers who cut and burned away its south shore jungles to get at the ten feet of black muck where the lake overflowed.

From 1910 to 1920 there had been no hurricanes to brim the Okeechobee river basin. The canals dug from Fort Lauderdale and West Palm Beach to the lake were advertised enthusiastically as having drained the Everglades. There was a boom in Everglades land. Eager people came up the canals by boat to the flat southwest lake corner to a town, called Moore Haven. To the east they built Clewiston. In 1922, for ninety-five days, it rained. The lake rose four and one-half feet and seeped over the level lands. When that dried up, they built a long muck dike around the southern rim that would, they insisted, prevent all future floods. The grandiose plans for draining the Everglades with canals bogged down in dirty politics.

Still more men ventured to extend their vegetable fields south of the lake and the Miami boom increased the sales of land often under water. The hurricane of '26 that put a tragic end to Miami's wild hopes flattened Moore Haven's pitiful mud dike and drowned more than three hundred Moore Haven people.

Afterward, the roads crept again through the drying saw grass, as huge rectangles of beans, carrots, celery, cane fields reached out endlessly over the brown velvet earth to the horizon.

Small towns sprang up in a roar of trucks, and tractors. Shacks and huts jammed along the canals for the thousands of migrant field workers, chiefly Negroes. Before dawn the truck men shouted bids for the day's labor, in the long packed streets of Negro slums. By night the glaring saloons, pool halls, blaring juke joints, broke the dark centuries-old silence of the lake.

But in the towns there were neat small houses in green grass, churches, and voices of children after school calling across lots. Dark lines of bamboo and casuarinas marked muddy roads through

Bare Beach, Lake Harbor, South Bay, Belle Glade, Pelican Bay, Pahokee, Canal Point. On Torrey and Ritta Islands, within the dike, houses stood among bean rows plowed to the very lake water.

Twice in August, in the hurricane season of 1928 and twice in September, in the Caribbean, there were rumors of winds of gale force only. Over the lake country, in that time, three feet of rain fell. The muck ran with water. Ditches and canals were full. Lake water crawled up the dike.

On the tenth of September an American freighter east of Barbados fought huge swells of a monster hurricane that, with no human eye to see it, must have grown in violence all the way from the African coast. Winds whirling about the center left over 600 dead as it crossed Guadeloupe on September 12. On Thursday morning, on the day of San Felipe, winds about the center, 235 miles in diameter, damaged Puerto Rico $50 million worth and killed or drowned 300 people out of 200,000 homeless.

Hundred-mile winds were experienced in Nassau in the Bahamas, expecting the full force of that incredible vortex, but it moved nearer Florida and the hurricane-conscious East Coast waited breathlessly through Friday and Saturday, although the Weather Bureau seemed to feel it would not turn toward the land. The hurricane moved its terrible grandeur inland over West Palm Beach on the night of September 16.

At noon that day, Sunday, the people around the lake heard for the first time that the hurricane was moving toward them. The barometer at West Palm Beach went down to 27.43, the lowest up to that time. From South Bay, men organized to drive along the roads, spreading the warning, urging people to seek shelter. Women and children were gathered on a big barge on the lake. In Belle Glade, 500 people were crowded into the Glades Hotel and 150 in the Belle Glade Hotel. But hundreds of people, Negro and white, in shacks and farmhouses scattered about the enormous flat country, never heard anything about it.

By six o'clock darkness was thick in a howling gale straight across the Lake from the north. Automobiles and roofs rolled over in the streets. The wind was like the rolling of innumerable drums. The rain came like bursting shells. At the north end of the lake the bottom was blown bare of water, that was hurled straight across to the southern dike and the towns below it. Twenty-one miles of dried muck dikes melted under furious water that spread under the remorseless winds over the streets, houses, out over the endless farming country. There were no trees, telephone poles, no canals, no roofs left, but a beaten sea of water, from twenty-five feet at Belle Glade, with the horrible wind going over.

It is thirty flat miles from the coast to the lake. The hurricane took the invisible level land as it took the frictionless sea. It diminished only after it had moved northward.

In Belle Glade that night the crowded hotel had been pitched from its foundations, but it held, with the people in it. In the Glades Hotel, everyone moved just out of water to the second floor. Fifty houses and buildings in that town were swept away. Almost all the people not in the hotels died. Everyone in Pelican Bay was drowned, in the houses or trying to escape along the roads. People on Ritta Island climbed to their roofs and many were drowned as trees crashed into them. Packing houses full of people went to pieces. Some were saved by climbing trees, carrying their children. Many were killed by the fatal bites of water moccasins swarming up trees or along the tops of eastern ridges, just above the slashing water.

The people on the barge were safe.

The wind went down in the night but the rain continued like a cloudburst and the murmuring lake rose and spilled farther down into the Everglades.

Daybreak revealed a flat world of water to the horizon. The sun rose. Bodies of the drowned began to float to the surface with the bodies of cattle, hogs, chickens. Rafts of bodies extended among the drying wreckage.

Rescue workers and appalled elderly militia men, sickened Boy Scouts hastily brought in by the truckload and wading as far as they could along the lowering canals, were no longer able to tell white bodies from Negro. In a day or two the dead were beyond recognition, tied in long strings and towed behind launches to the railway platforms. Seven hundred were buried in one long trench in West Palm Beach. After the fourth day under the hot sun they could only be piled up and burned in great pyres. No one will ever know how many more than the estimated 1,800 to 2,500 died there.

But now the people of south Florida were roused again, to shame the confused and tardy state by demanding Federal aid for adequate flood protection. By 1930, President Hoover had approved a bond issue up to $5 million to support a well-engineered plan for state flood control over the Okeechobee-Everglades area of 12,000 square miles. A huge rock levee, 85 miles long, 34 to 38 feet high, which is 18 to 22 feet higher than normal lake level, was built all along the lake's southeast, south and southwest shores.

All the lake towns now, thriving with big business in cattle as well as sugar cane and winter vegetables, are cut off by the levee from all view of the lake. But like the sea wall at Galveston, it has saved innumerable lives from hurricane flood water since then.

3. *The Florida Keys, 1935*

It was hot white and mosquito-y all that summer of 1935 on the Florida Keys. There was always the threat of hurricanes like the one in August that whirled up the Atlantic and destroyed the fishing fleets of Newfoundland. But it was not the weather that was making the summer strange to the brown-faced, quiet people of the Keys, whose ancestors from over in the Bahamas or up from Key West had known more about hurricanes than any people on the American coast.

They knew exactly what was meant when a Bahaman said of the clouds before a hurricane, "See how they do send, low, low, low." They had known what the old Key West fisherman described when he said of a hurricane center, "And then there come a glistening calm."

Their seagoing ancestors had built the first stout small frame houses among lime and guava trees, under coco palms, near their boats pulled up in coves among the mangroves or along the shelly infrequent sands. They still lived as they always had, the people of the villages, Rock Harbor, Tavernier, Islamorada on Upper Matecumbe Key, and Matecumbe on Lower Matecumbe Key, and all the others, independent and close-mouthed. It was nobody's business whose people had been wreckers in the great days of wrecking or rumrunners in prohibition. Mr. Flager's railroad had brought construction jobs. Now fish guiding and charter boats, bait shacks, boat docks, stores, juke joints, fish-and-lime-pie restaurants were making good profit.

They never liked the high rock embankment down the middle of everything, where the railroad ran, that blocked up all the old channels between the Keys so that a man had to take his boat all the way down to No. Five trestle to get into the sheltered waters of Florida Bay. But now they were more bitter at the invasion of 716 very strange men.

There were, after all, only about four hundred Key people, closely related and clannish, like Captain John Russell, postmaster at Islamorada, and his seventy-nine kinfolks. By the beach lived Captain Edney Parker; his wife, who was one of the big family of Pinders; his ten children; his son-in-law Jack Ryder and their relatives. At Tavernier, Judge Lowe, the justice of the peace, was the head of the smaller Lowe family. He was called Doc in Miami, where he had been a deputy sheriff. There were Becoms on Windley Key, Sweetings on Lignum Vitae, and Alburys everywhere. They were keen-minded, intelligent, often well-read people, with a great deal of pride and much respectability.

The 716 strangers on the Keys were broken-down army veterans, forlorn stragglers from the bonus army that had marched on Washington. Some were drunks. Some were shell-shocked and half-crazy. Some were hard, useless characters. All of them, one way and another, were misfits.

They had been rounded up for the government by the FERA and sent down the Keys to get their misery and uselessness out of sight. They were quartered in three shack-and-barrack camps in the sun-blasted scrub between Snake Creek and the south end of Lower Matecumbe. They were supposed to be building a road but in nearly a year only two hundred feet were done. They worked only if they wanted to, got thirty dollars a month and all the food they could eat. They went fishing. Saturday nights after payday the saloons of Key West roared with the drunkenness of the alcoholics. There were fights in the camps. Many of the Key people, especially the women, were scandalized.

Yet some Key people (like Captain Parker, who worked at Camp Five), who had found many veterans to be lonely and friendless, were glad to befriend them. All that summer, there was talk about the veterans.

The Key people did not have to talk about hurricanes. Every man knew just where he would run his boat to shelter it, or even sink it with the engine out. All the frame houses had shutters, extra kerosene, extra food, were reinforced. Grandfather Becom on

Windley Key had built a house on quarried stone, that had stood through twenty years of storms. Some men had built special hurricane shelters, like Doc Lowe's, a small poured-concrete house set on a solid poured-concrete foundation, and over the whole thing two great chain cables flung and bolted into the concrete.

The State Veterans' Administration had set up a plan for evacuating them in case of hurricane, at the urgent request of Grady Norton, the head of the U.S. hurricane warning service, then in Jacksonville. The chief of the Key camps was ordered by his boss, the commander of the state veterans' corps in Jacksonville, to keep in constant touch with the Weather Bureau in Miami, and when it was necessary, order an F.E.C. train down from Homestead, the last mainland town, to take the men to an emergency camp north of Miami.

A hurricane, first recorded on August 31 northeast of Turks Island, had an unusually small center. It reached Andros Island with winds of phenomenal violence. But there was no one who could send proper reports of its progress. For a while there the hurricane was not even heard of. On the first of September northeast storm warnings were posted from Fort Pierce to Fort Myers, across the state. Caution was advised for the Florida Keys.

Everybody in Miami now gave the presence of a hurricane in the area a startled respect. By the holiday of Labor Day, the second of September, Miami streets resounded with hammering, as people boarded up. By nightfall, the sky was overcast, the rain came in blasts, and the gusty wind increased. Yet in another hour the rain had stopped and there was hardly wind enough to scuffle the bushes. People opened up doors and looked out of rooms lighted by lamps and candles and said, "I guess we're not going to get the hurricane after all."

About 350 veterans from the Keys camps, who had been brought up to Miami to see a Labor Day ball game, ranged the streets happily. But down the Keys people were already dying.

All that day Ray Sheldon, chief of the FERA veterans' camps at Upper Matecumbe had been calling the Miami Weather Bureau from Captain Ed Butters' hotel. Everybody on the line listened anxiously. The barometer was dropping and they knew the hurricane must be coming nearer.

The Miami Weather Bureau told Sheldon it might hit the Keys.

At 12:15 Sheldon told Captain Edney Parker to telephone the
Florida East Coast Railroad to send down the train that they had
been told would be ready and waiting at Homestead. The train was
not there. Orders were relayed to Miami. A train was made up and
left Miami at 4:25 P.M., arriving in Homestead after five.

By that time down the Keys, the light was cold and gray with
wind hurling whitecaps among the mangroves from a gray sea and
whipping the sand until it stung the faces of men boarding up their
own houses and the neighbors'. Boats were moved up coves. Men
and boys ran barefooted through the smarting rain to buy candles
and kerosene and canned goods at the little stores. Women peered
out fearfully from shuttered houses at the streaming palms and the
few cars driving the wet road, rain and spray scattering from their
wheels. Children and chickens were inside.

The barometers were still going down. The narrow land shook
a little with the waves' heavier pounding. At the veterans' barracks
the men packed up and moved out to huddle along the railway
embankment, waiting for the train. They had to cover their faces
because the stinging sand began to draw blood. Every once in a
while one would say, "It's coming. I hear it." It was the wind
coming in faster and faster over the bent trees with the high shaking hurricane rumble that sounds exactly like the never-ending
passing of a freight train.

Captain Parker had started to drive his truck home from Camp
No. Five, after he had boarded it up. The men hung around disconsolately. He and his son-in-law, a man of 240 pounds, a fifty-
gallon drum of insecticide and the truck, crossing the exposed
Whale Harbor fill, were picked up by a blast of wind and hurled
down toward the water. Struggling with the wheel, he got home in
time to board up and sit down to supper by lamplight, with all his
children around him. Like everybody else, he stopped constantly
to listen to the wind.

In the veterans' camps most of the men, with their bundles, still
sat by the railroad tracks, waiting. Some had gone back into shelter.
Some lay on their bunks and got drunk. Some tried to play poker.

The train had left Homestead after five o'clock, backing down
slowly. Sometimes the train crew had to stop and clear the tracks
of broken trees. A few Key people with their children, on signal,
boarded the train and went south with it into the storm darkness.

After eight o'clock, J. A. Duncan, the keeper at Alligator Reef Light, who had been clutching the rail of the lower platform to steady himself, caught the gleam of light on a black mass of water looming over. He jumped for the ladder and held on as tons of salt water crashed over him. "Ninety feet high," he said afterward. It was the nearly twenty-foot hurricane wave. The lighthouse men clung all night halfway up to the light itself, the cold iron jarring in their scalded fists. Wind or spray or both shattered the ⅜-inch glass around the light, and the lenses themselves. One of the sections of the lens was carried six or eight miles away and picked up on the beach unbroken.

The mounded wave reared across The Hawk Channel. The hurricane smashed down on a narrow ten miles of Keys from Tavernier to Key Vaca. The wind was flung like knives, 150 to 200 miles an hour with unbelievable gusts at nearly 250 miles that took everything. The people in the small houses saw black water bubble up over floor boards as roofs were sliced off and chaos crashed down on them. People hung on as they could, clutching children, heaping pillows over children in floating beds as houses tilted and spun off their foundations. Captain Parker's house with his wife and ten children, roofless, was swept south by the northeast wind into the welter of sea.

Doc Lowe, in his well-built house, buttoned his daughter's baby in his coat, tightened his belt, and got his family started out by lantern light for his hurricane shelter. The water rose up behind them. They stayed huddled in the small strong place that could not shut out the howling of the wind or the water. Something was lifting the whole place, the cables, the poured concrete. It trembled, tilted, cracked, tipped.

They got out into the wind and water, hanging on to each other, holding the children out of the smashing waves that pulled terribly at their legs, so that they staggered, bent over. Doc Lowe, ahead, groped for something, anything to hang on to. He found something that he could get his fists around. It was a little tree, its top bent almost level but its roots deep in rock. They huddled and held on while he took his belt and fastened it around him and the tree, too. The men, his son and his nephew, held the children's heads above the water and held on to him and the women clutched them. In the pitch blackness they had to fend off boxes, boards, floating things the wind and water hurled at them, every wave nearly drowned them.

A timber smashed down on Doc Lowe's head, knocking him insensible and into the water. They held him up, held each other up, held up the children. The tree stood.

There was a lull in that narrow ten-mile-wide hurricane. The Parkers found their wrecked house grounded on a beach a mile south. On Windley Key seven of the Becom family huddled in their car after their house had gone, kept the headlights shining through the rain over the waves that piled the debris high up the car's windward side. Five refugees saw the light and crowded in with the Becoms.

At 8:30 the ten cars of the train had been shoved backward as far as the Islamorada water tank. When the great wave struck, they were flung on their sides by the uprooted track. Only the engine was left standing. The thirteen people in the cars held themselves and their children out of water all night long.

All the buildings at Camp Five were smashed up and washed away.

The hurricane's narrow calm center lasted at Lower Matecumbe Key for about forty minutes and at the ruins of Long Key Fishing Camp, from 9:20 to 10:15, before the winds started up with even greater violence, up to 250 miles per hour. The barometer reading, corrected to 26.35 inches, was the lowest yet recorded in the histories of West Indian and Atlantic hurricanes.

By daylight, in that ten miles, there were only a very few people left alive. Everything was gone—roads, buildings, docks, viaducts, trees, the railroad and the bridges.

Of the innumerable dead, many were washed away and never seen again. Bodies were found hanging among overthrown and stripped mangroves, buried in sand and debris, rolling in sunken wrecks of boats. One hundred and twenty-one veterans were killed, 100 seriously injured and ninety were missing. One hundred and sixty-five Key people were killed and hardly any survivors were without injury. Out of seventy-nine Russells only eleven, and old man Russell himself, were left alive. The total death list mounted, in weeks of dreadful search, to 400.

The ruined ten miles of Keys lay like a leprous scar on the silky blue and green sea. The damage was done by the extraordinary winds and the hurricane wave. But the losses were increased by the rock embankment of the railroad that had dammed up the natural channels into Florida Bay. No one can say today whether the greatest damage was done by the piling up of the hurricane water, by the 30-foot rock fills, or by the undertows created by the irresistible force of its going out, that sucked everything away with it: men, wreckage, and the very sand under toppling concrete walls and foundations.

It was a strange and lonely tragedy. The Keys were completely cut off from the mainland. The bridge was out over the swirling current at Snake Creek. In Miami, nobody knew what had happened, as in the Keys the injured, hung up in trees, died of thirst, without help. It rained hard all Tuesday so that the living people, crawling about dazed, could collect rain water in buckets. The cisterns were choked with debris and fouling salt water.

Men in boats got to the mainland, walking up the roads to Homestead with the news. Homestead people hurriedly organized to go down and help. By Wednesday, with the white hot sun bringing stenches out of the ruins and the rot, the Key people had begun to organize their own relief. They groped in the ruins of stores for canned goods. The women cooked coffee and food for everybody over open fires. Others bandaged and gave first aid. Men under Captain Parker already were searching out the dying and bringing them to shelters. Drying clothing hung on the slivered bushes.

The boats from Homestead came down and the injured were moved to the hospital there, crowding the beds and corridors. Gangs of Negroes were brought down to work.

The first doctor to get down in a boat to ravaged Camp Five was Dr. G. C. Franklin of Coconut Grove. He found the bodies of thirty-nine men in a windrow, just as the last waves had left them.

A man sat calmly against a broken wall with a piece of two-by-four run completely through him, under his ribs, out over the kidneys. He refused the shot of morphine the doctor offered him, before he pulled it out. The man said that when it was pulled out he would die. He asked for two beers, drank them and said, "Now pull."

Dr. Franklin pulled, and he died.

There was no organized relief yet from Miami, except for a steady drift of volunteers, who went to work under Captain Parker discovering bodies. The Coast Guard sent supplies by five amphibian planes and a number of cutters. The National Guard was called out and regulations were imposed. There was friction between the officers and the haggard men of the Keys, going on steadily about their work of finding the dead. Boys, much too young, were sent down from the Miami CCC camp. Miami police helped identify veterans for burial in a Miami cemetery.

Then orders came down that the dead were all to be cremated. Captain Parker pulled a pistol on the National Guard officer who tried to stop him and Ed Albury from putting the bodies of Ed's wife and child in caskets. They were let alone as the smoke of pyres lifted into the mild air.

By the end of the week, the Red Cross arrived to set up an office in Tavernier, complete with trained workers and forms to be filled out. People who had been left with nothing were told now that to get help they must submit "plans for rehabilitation." There was a rising storm of complaints and bitterness, even more than there had been in Miami after the '26. But slowly, with Florida help as well, the people of the Keys who survived made something of their lives again. The veterans' group was broken up and those who had survived were quietly sent somewhere else.

Indignation for the veterans led the national WPA to open an investigation to settle the blame for the tragedy, especially for the fact that the train did not arrive until too late. But when it was realized that a state organization would be brought to question, the inquiry was dropped.

The hurricane had worked one good thing. The Overseas Railroad was abandoned. The channels were open into Florida Bay at last, and stayed that way, when a new roadway was built with bridges in place of solid rock causeways.

But while the Keys were still enveloped in the pall of their greatest tragedy, in little more than a month the fourth hurricane of that year of 1935 had made a strange hairpin turn up from its origin in the Sea of Colombia toward Haiti and Jamaica and down again to be dissipated against the mountains behind Honduras. It caused great land damage and 150 deaths. Florida paid little attention, however, until an even more freakish hurricane, October 30 to November 1, started up east of Bermuda where no hurricanes have ever been known to begin. Perhaps it was a storm that grew into a hurricane as it came crazily south past the Carolinas to the Bahamas, and then on a straight line to Florida where it scared the wits out of Miami before crossing the state and, out in the Gulf, looping back to Tampa. Its damage was not great but Florida people took toll for the wear and tear on their nerves, so soon after the Keys disaster, by calling it "the Yankee hurricane."

3 HURRICANES NORTH

1. September, 1938

New England people complained about the muggy heat all the late summer of 1938 and long after Labor Day. Rains brought no coolness to the autumnal bustle of school and work. Few people noticed the reports of three hurricanes within the Caribbean, the second of which invaded the mainland only at Louisiana. They were more remote to busy Northerners than the political turbulence rising in Europe.

The heat shimmered like a furnace over the even more remote oasis of Bilma, south of the middle Sahara Desert. Only an unfortunate traveling Frenchman noted that his barometer marked a small depression that crawled westward to the French West African coast, on September 4.

There the equatorial air drifts along the west-going edge of the strong trade winds. The monsoon winds gave the depression a twist as the trades carried it. The heated Atlantic air fed power into its rising whirl, and it blew west.

The trade winds might have carried it to Central America, over the frightened Antilles, except that just then, over the North American mainland, a wide front of cold polar air had pushed down as far as the southeasterly states. In the North Atlantic south of Newfoundland, a second high pressure lifted. Between these two moun-

tains a 300-mile low warm valley led like a great gutter straight to
the south coast of New England.

The whirl, drawing in speed and power from the moving tropic
current in which it was imbedded, turned and traveled northwest,
almost north, up that trough. Winds around the forward eastern
sector blew faster than one hundred miles.

This was the monstrous blot on the weather map that on the
eighteenth of September appeared suddenly off the anxious coast of
Florida as a fall hurricane.

In these days, forecasts and hurricane warnings for the Southern
states were issued by the U.S. Weather Bureau at Jacksonville,
Florida. The forecaster issued the first hurricane statement at 3
P.M. on the eighteenth. At 9:30 P.M. broadcasts warned that the
hurricane was 900 miles east-southeast of Miami, moving at 20 miles
per hour. The Bureau advised "all possible precautions" because
gales might reach the Florida coast by morning.

The whole coast of Florida stopped to board up, anchor boats,
watch barometers and wait. By the twentieth, the hurricane was
still far out, moving up that trough northward. The danger to
Florida seemed less. Caution was urged as far north as Atlantic
City and by all ships in the western Atlantic.

The hurricane moved out of the jurisdiction of the Jacksonville
Weather Bureau, into that of Washington. It had been reported as
a huge and dangerous hurricane. Now anything can happen to a
tropical cyclone as soon as it has moved out of the tropics. It can
swerve to the coast. It can fill up and disappear or move off to sea
with the Gulf Stream. Or, its whirl increased by the sharp contrast of cold air from the landward west and steamy air from the
seaward east, it can pick up speed and head north. The constant
warnings had driven all ships away from the hurricane, but two.
Each reported to Washington that, from its position, the hurricane
was diminishing.

The 9:30 P.M. forecast from Washington for the New England
coast read, "Rain, probably heavy Wednesday and Thursday
cooler." At sea, from New York to Maine, there would be fresh
southerly winds. Washington went so far as to report, with no
other comment, "a broad trough of low pressure extends from New
England south-southwestward to the tropic disturbance." Northeast storm warnings were ordered as far as Eastport, Maine. On

September 21, at 9 A.M., a tropical storm was mentioned seventy-five miles east of Hatteras. Small craft were warned to stay in port. Whole gale warnings were issued for New Jersey, Maryland and Delaware, but neither Long Island nor the Connecticut shore was mentioned.

Before two o'clock that afternoon in New York, white sheets of rain blew off the cloud-darkened tops of skyscrapers and crashed on streets shining with black water, taxi roofs spilling spray as soaked crowds herded squealing into subway entrances. Iron rain smashed flat the gray harbor water and swilled off the decks of tugs and ferries, laboring against the outdrawing tide. Invisible in blowing cloud a thousand feet up, the top of the Empire State Building swayed a little in winds streaming past at over 120 miles per hour although at street level, only twenty-mile winds snatched at rain, skirts, newspapers and umbrellas.

A forecast from the Boston Weather Bureau at the same time stated that a hurricane would move over New York up the Hudson valley. In New York, a few vacationing Florida people, calling up newspapers to ask about the hurricane, were answered, "What hurricane?"

It is true that few hurricane vortices have invaded New York, protected both by New Jersey and Long Island from every direction but the southeast. History remembers New York vulnerable to hurricane floods only on an incoming high tide. But even so the extraordinarily heavy rain that swamped the streets was an outermost western rain band of the monster then moving steadily northward. Safe within walls, thousands of radios drowned out the racket outside with the hysterical voice, all the way from Germany, of Adolf Hitler.

The hurricane had come much farther. Now for the first time in sixteen days, the feeble dust devil from the Sahara was feeling out the land with the accelerated speed of a gigantic slingshot. Nothing had stopped it. It built up and pushed a storm wave before it that grew bigger all the way up the empty reach of the Atlantic.

By noon on the twenty-first, over the eastern part of Long Island, the sun shone pallid under clouds racing high over from the south. Nobody saw them. Along the outer beaches, as thin as a long fishbone, white sand and bleached dunes that guard the bays and inlets and the massive island itself, an extraordinary tide was bursting. It muttered through the bright, rainless air across salt ponds, villages of old houses and elm trees, harbors full of boats, streets, summer cottages, clubs, schools, libraries, churches and people, from Fire Island to Montauk.

Some swimmers dared the curdled acres of foam. A few fishing vessels beat out into the sea. People breasted the wind to look at the magnificent surf. The thunderous fall of waves was felt in the villages and recorded in New York on Fordham University's seismographic instruments as if they were earthquake shocks.

The tide swelled up the sand, higher than the highest tidemarks. Behind came the ocean. The swimmers hastily left the water and climbed the dunes, twelve feet higher than high tide, where in the obscuring light the sand blew away like smoke. The rising sea ate the dunes like sugar. As it rose, an eighteen-foot hurricane wave lifted and raced across dunes, beach and salt ponds to the inner shore. Sand and bitter salt were blown far inland abrading painted walls, windows, tree bark, gardens, and people's faces. In water swirling where the beaches had been, the first hundred people were drowned.

Warnings were too late that were broadcast after one o'clock. At 2:40 P.M. phones went dead as poles were swept away. Eight minutes later, at Bridgehampton, the wind full from the dangerous east whined like steel saws at seventy miles an hour and higher. There was no light but streaming blur. Barometers went down to 29.65. The cutting rain flew level as the oldest of the elm trees began to hit the sodden ground. At half past three the terrible winds snaking about the vortex were dragged ashore over Long Island.

Some time between four and five the eye of the storm moved ashore also, centering on Bridgehampton. It reached for forty-three miles, from Brentwood, with a calm of fifty minutes, to Mattituck with a breathless five. Already, from Quogue Village to Moriches Inlet, where 179 houses had stood, there were left only the shells of twelve. The broken ruin of West Hampton was destroyed at 5:15 P.M. People, villages, trees and time itself, were swallowed up, from Southampton, Sagg Pond, Sagoponack, Amagansett to Sag Harbor, where the famous landmark, the great steeple of the Presbyterian Church, was snapped like a grass stem. Montauk was utterly cut off. It was all one wet mash of broken wood and mud and dead and injured people.

Neither the friction of the land nor the cooling air on one side slowed the vast locomotive of the hurricane along the trough. The 20-degree difference in temperatures between its eastern and western rims increased the wind's velocity. Besides that, currents like bombs of free cool air ripped from above to the heavier surface and stirred along the rim vicious local eddies.

The western section of the Connecticut shore was protected by Long Island from the long devastating hurricane wave. But not from the winds. At Fisher's Island near New London a weather tower was blown down at 120 miles per hour. The majestic vortex then moved ashore, centering its calm over New Haven and so on to Hartford.

But on the east-going shore the winds of the eastern sector piled up the Atlantic storm wave across the open end of Long Island Sound. With hardly any more warning than Long Island had had, Old Lyme was smashed, and Niantic, New London, Noank and Mystic. Boats and ships were hurled across docks and streets into houses. Railroad tracks and freight trains were twisted like string. In four hours, New London's ruins were a mass of flames carried by winds so powerful that high pressure streams from hoses held by firemen, staggering in salt water to their shoulders, were bent aside like grass blades or blown to mist.

The long peninsula of Stonington village, jutting out between salt inlets into the Atlantic, took the great wave as winds swung from the east to southeast and then southwest and was demolished. The southwestern shore of Rhode Island knew the same terror. Westerly, Watch Hill, Napatuc Point and Misquamicut were laid waste chiefly by the undertow as the hurricane high tide was sucked back to sea and entire settlements with it. Block Island's strong old houses on high land stood the wind well enough, but the whole fishing fleet and all the lobster pots were lost.

Charlestown Beach was wiped clean of houses and human beings by one walloping wave. It surged up green and pleasant Narragansett Bay, stripped Narragansett Pier, Warwick, Rocky Point, Pawtuxet Cove, Shawamet Beach. Yacht clubs were overturned and broken. The disaster was the worst, old-timers said, since the hurricane of 1869.

Up the bay that narrows into Providence River, beyond gas works, bridges, docks, ancient waterfront houses and warehouses, in the city where the river, below the steepness of elm-sheltered College Hill, has been almost roofed over with busy streets, nobody paid much attention all afternoon to the high winds. But at five o'clock when people were leaving offices, they looked out on streets awash with rain water and pieces of roof and signs swishing through the darkening air.

They were not aware yet that the high tide had not gone down. The wind screaming up the Bay held the high tide backed up, debris-laden, into the river and into its semi-underground city-confined channels. When the next high tide moved inevitably up past the narrows at Fields Point, bulkheads and lumber yards were smashed by a ten-foot tide. Loose lumber was stacked up against the Point Street Bridge, Weybosset Bridge delayed the roaring rush of water only a little, as the smaller rivers that Roger Williams had found so charming poured their loads into the swelling flood.

A wind nearly 100 miles an hour blew around the waterlogged buildings crowded with people. Water swirled through the streets covering thousands of stalled cars and street cars, tore up sidewalks and gutted cellars. Men who ventured out were swung off their feet in the current and had to be rescued by ropes flung from office windows. Some people were killed by falling walls. Flood tides rose as far as Pawtucket and Woonsocket.

The winds and floodwater had surged and burst up the eastern islands and coasts of Narragansett Bay, battering Newport, knocking to smithereens the fences and boatyards of Warren and Bristol. The winds crashed the tides eastward still up Buzzards Bay to South Dartmouth. Twenty-five people were killed at New Bedford. The hurricane swiped at the waterfront of Fairhaven and completely mashed the beach cottages and summer village of pleasant Mattapoisett.

At the same time the hurricane roared on the gray-shingled summer houses of Marion, Wareham and Onset and made debris of houses and boats at Bourne to choke the Cape Cod Canal. Falmouth seemed to explode in white spray.

From Woods Hole to Chatham, far from the eye of the hurricane, the south coast of Cape Cod was broken by the tide's dynamite, although the wind only switched at the dory gardens in Provincetown.

Inland, the rainy winds slashed at Taunton and old Bristol County towns, where single ladies in high, well-shuttered old houses peered out to see elms go down that their grandfathers had planted. The wonderful wineglass and fountain shapes of all those elms, that in meadows and by brooks had withstood many a so-called line storm, toppled like ninepins.

It had been raining heavily since September 17 all through central New England. Brooks and streams in that land safe from waves were tumbling, full and swollen, into the greater rivers. The Housatonic was rising, the Naugatuck, the Willimantic, the Natchaug, the Thames, the Quinebaug and dozens more, but especially the Connecticut. Hillsides were aslide with mud. Milldams bellowed. By Wednesday morning even before the Hartford Weather Bureau broadcast flood warnings, all those towns and cities set close about streams whose water power built the industrial wealth of New England knew they were in for trouble. Nobody mentioned the word "hurricane."

At 3:30 P.M. winds were blowing higher and higher. The damage of floodwater was increased a hundred times as the hurricane moving northward tore away, smashed and scattered everything broken or water-loosened. Bridges were slewed, lifted and dropped into the foam. All electric light and power blacked out in the screaming darkness. Houses were swept away. Entire apple crops, vegetables, tobacco in fields and tobacco warehouses were destroyed. Roadbeds were washed out. Trains were stopped.

The hurricane swept over Middletown and New Milford. By 4:00 P.M. it had cut off Hartford and four people were dead in the flooded streets. The Connecticut in its long curve through the city kept on blackly rising and men in boats rescued others from menaced and toppling buildings. One thousand men worked to build a sandbag levee along the dangerous half mile of river by the old Colt Arms factory. Thousands of people fled the city.

Farther east, in Norwich, the Thames River filled Franklin Square with twelve feet of water. In the business section every pane of plate glass was sucked out and smashed by the wind. Upstream mills were unroofed. Machinery and beams collapsed into the water. Willimantic was cut off.

The hurricane dragged its ruin northward across Springfield where the Connecticut, lashed into eight-foot waves, surged into the streets. Men, battered by wind and rain, worked feverishly to strengthen the north-end dike against the aroused force of the river. It held.

Floodwater from streams northward took the sodden towns of Monson, Palmer, Ware, before the hurricane blotted them out, and Chicopee Falls, the Holyokes, Easthampton, Northampton, Hadley, Amherst, Great Barrington. All roads and the Mohawk Trail, in innumerable places, were washed out or blocked by flung trees, poles and fallen boulders. A family from Newport were drowned when their car stalled on a bridge as the river rose over them. On the exposed sides of hills, trees and buildings were sheared off, and great swaths were cut in forests by winds higher than 150 miles an hour.

The city of Worcester and Worcester County, to eastward, for four days had fought rain damage and flood and had rushed food and medical supplies and rescue workers as the news of ruin spread from flooded valleys to the west. It extended its help eastward still to towns cut off from wind-lashed Boston which knew nothing of what was happening beyond its limits in Wellesley, Newton, Framingham, Concord and northeast to Lynn, Marblehead, and, on the flooded Merrimac, Lowell and Lawrence. Worcester was totally unprepared for its own disaster.

At four o'clock in the rain-darkened afternoon of that historic September 21, the hurricane's edge dragged over the city one of those savage eddies or twisters, winds over a hundred miles an hour, that continued for four blasting hours. At dawn, Worcester was unrecognizable.

Northward the center of the hurricane moved into New Hampshire and Vermont, over Keene, Jaffrey, Peterborough, the ruins of whose business sections howled up in wind-beaten flames, Laconia, Bellows Falls, Little Grafton, Ludlow, Brandon and all that countryside. For some the floods were worse than the winds. Montpelier, saved from high water by flood control dams built in 1935 by the Federal government, was shredded by winds still of hurricane force.

But now the drag and friction of the wooded hills and rising mountains began to slow up the whirling winds more than the whole crossing over and up the North Atlantic had been able to do. The eye was shifting northwest. On Mount Washington, in northern New Hampshire, over 6,000 feet high, the wind was the greatest ever recorded in a hurricane in the United States, with gusts of about 190 miles an hour. What was left of the hurricane disappeared over Lake Champlain.

It was without question one of the most dreadful disasters to have overwhelmed New England. Six hundred and eighty-two men, women and children were dead. Over 1,500 were injured; 93,122 families suffered property damage. Seventy-two million feet of wires were down. Over a quarter of a million telephones were out. Bridges, railroads, hundreds of miles of roads were useless. The total of the damage could never be reckoned. It was considered to be at least $400,000,000, the greatest then ever recorded in a tropical cyclone anywhere in the world.

Emergency relief for nearly 100,000 people was pushed in at once from all over the country, food, supplies and workers by the American Red Cross, the WPA, the American Legion, the Boy Scouts and other units from neighboring states and cities. Two thousand telephone men were brought in from as far west as Dakota, to put up poles and restore service. Bridges, railroads were rebuilt, roads cleared, repair work begun on buildings. Fallen apples in ruined orchards were harvested, bought by the government, restaurants and housewives, to save the growers from ruin. New England hummed with a great burst of Yankee activity in which thousands of unemployed men—since this was the great depression—found work.

The damage unique for hurricanes and to New England was the extraordinary loss of trees. Shade trees beyond counting, the American elms that beautified every town, city and countryside, avenues of chestnuts, oaks and maples had crashed and now had to be cut up and hauled away to repair houses and clear streets over which suddenly the sky was blank.

Worse, on the forested slopes more than four million feet of timber lay broken, the white pine which had been New England's first inland wealth, sugar maples, spruce and hardwoods. The over-all value to New England was almost incalculable because what the hurricane had thrown down was the growth of ten to fifteen years.

Many a town whose revenue came from timber taxes was threatened with bankruptcy.

The immediate danger, as the trees' ruin began to dry out in the October sun, was fire. The first spring dry spell would turn acres of fallen trees into tinderboxes, menacing the standing woods and hundreds of towns and cities. Men were put to work at once clearing fire lanes, setting up lookout towers. Roads were opened for firefighting crews, and water supplies developed.

At the same time the usable timber must be salvaged. If the most valuable white pine were left with the bark on until the next summer it would be riddled by insects unless covered with water. It was figured there were only a few months left in which one or two billion board feet could be salvaged at all.

For the first time studies were made of the effects of hurricane winds on forests. It was found that the first trees to be blown over were the brittle or shallow-rooted, and those exposed, across open swales, to the full force of the wind. The white pine had suffered most except on leeward slopes. Even-aged stands blew down, dependent on location, much more completely than uneven-aged. High trees above lower surrounding trees or on windward slopes went over. The damage was greatest on the tops and sides of hills. Where there were gaps or abrupt barriers, open places between slopes, along parks, golf courses and railway rights-of-way the velocity of the winds was increased as if in a wind tunnel.

There was, and is, no way possible of preventing forest trees from blowing down in a hurricane. But much could be done beforehand, even over a period of time, to reduce the losses. Early and frequent thinning of the crowns of trees allows ordinary winds so to bend the trunks and roots that they will develop a growth that will stand firm in higher winds. What the foresters call "stand borders and dense understories" slow down surface winds that make a cushion to force the dangerous winds to flow up and over the treetops.

Above all, in all the feverish cutting and clearing and salvaging of blown-down timber, enough seed trees must be left standing for future growth. Constant reforesting and care, undiscouraged and persevering in the face of hurricane menace, is after all the only assurance that the valuable great forests of New England can be maintained. Yet with all that, the remarkable thing was that thousands of elms and other old trees, like the great ancient elm of Weathersfield, Connecticut, survived.

What people complained of most even after much debris had been cleared away and towns were recovering, was the stinging, after-hurricane plague of mosquitoes.

2. *The Years Between*

For the first time in history, New Englanders had been shocked into recognizing that a hurricane could reach them. They quoted a report which listed this hurricane of 1938 as the ninth to hurt them in three centuries, although no official records had been kept much before 1870. On the whole, the disaster of '38 was thought to be a freak.

Their energetic clean-up of hurricane damage brought work and hope to a region much affected by the great depression. Many fine plans against future hurricane damages were made, seaside zoning laws, improved building codes.

But people forgot. In a summer or two, more flimsy cottages than ever were being built to the water lines. Only people at Montauk and Amagansett on Long Island seemed to be serious about sea walls and they were Long Islanders whose ancestors remembered more hurricanes than anyone else. Maples and quicker-growing shade trees like catalpas were planted where elms had been blown down.

One of the few cities which carried out with vigor a plan for protection against flooding by hurricane rains was the city of insurance, Hartford, Connecticut. The electric light company in Hartford built new structures on stilts so high that no future floodwater could ever reach the generators. A multimillion-dollar dike was built on both banks of the Connecticut River at the old Colt Arms factory, the greatest danger point in '38.

Dr. C. F. Brooks, director of the Harvard Observatory at Blue Hill in Massachusetts, and other Weather Bureau authorities insisted that the North Atlantic states were as much in need of hurricane observation stations and a well-organized warning service as

Florida had clamored for and received. A network of radio weather stations should be established.

Time went on. The hurricane was forgotten. No pressure was brought to bear on Congress for money for hurricane warnings or hurricane studies. Even later in '38 small attention was paid to the four other tropical cyclones, three in October and one in November, although people in Yucatán, Mexico and Texas were gravely affected. In 1939, the hurricane of October 12 to 18 that rocketed northeastward safely, far out to sea, was ignored.

In 1940, however, the first severe hurricane in forty years struck the Charleston-Savannah area, killing 50 people, and a few days later hit Port Arthur, Texas. In 1941, before Pearl Harbor, there were six, of which one hit Houston, Texas, and another with gusts up to 123 miles per hour went ashore just south of Miami, Florida, where forty advance bulletins from the Weather Bureau and the prompt energy of the people saved lives and prevented a great deal of damage.

Then the war shut down on the Atlantic its radio silence. Few weather reports could be received from ships at sea. The eight hurricanes of 1942 were inadequately recorded from island stations. Yet warnings of a very severe blow were so prompt and efficient in Texas and Galveston that 50,000 people were evacuated and only eight lives lost. An unusually late November storm overran Cuba and Belize in Honduras.

Ten hurricanes in 1943 occurred, all in the Atlantic but two that criss-crossed the Texas coast.

Planes were beginning to fly directly into hurricanes, with instruments to study pressures. An Army Air Corps plane flew twice from the island of Antigua into the center of the great hurricane of August 20 and 21.

Ten hurricanes in 1944 barreled through the Caribbean. The fourth, August 17 to 23, hit Wilmington, North Carolina. The fifth gutted the north shore of Jamaica.

In New England, few people had heard that the hurricane of 1815 had been followed exactly six years later by that of 1821. Now, with coasts blacked out and radios silenced by the war, there were almost no warnings of a violent disturbance which followed the track of the New England hurricane of '38, from Puerto Rico to Long Island. On the eighth of September, 1944, a weather officer tried to fly an army reconnaissance plane into it but winds of 140 miles per hour sheared rivets off the wings. The hurricane passed Hatteras, moved up the coast northeastward across Rhode Island and Massachusetts and along the Maine coast. Its hurricane wave met the outgoing tide and glanced off the coast. By the fifteenth it was blowing over Newfoundland and was lost off Greenland.

There was damage enough, but only one-third that of '38, on land, and only 46 deaths. At sea, 298 service men were lost with one destroyer, two Coast Guard cutters, a lightship and a mine sweeper. Three officers of the new Weather Division of the Air Corps flew a light bombing plane into the center of the hurricane that tossed them about in violent updrafts, and came out alive.

Men on Swan Island, a patch of sand on the edge of the empty deep north of Honduras, observed the great Havana-Florida hurricane of October 13–21, a dangerous freak bred in the Gulf of Colombia that threw big sponging schooners two and one-half miles inland near Batabano, blew at 167 miles per hour for twelve hours at Havana and swung across Florida from the west to Jacksonville, by the back door, as usual. The calm center was said to have extended 70 miles from Ocala to Jacksonville before it was off up the southern coastal states, up between Nantucket and Cape Cod and to Nova Scotia and a seagoing death.

Ten hurricanes were reported in 1945, of which the Florida hurricane of September 15, south of Miami at the Richmond Naval Air Station, wrecked three enormous dirigible hangars in one gust of 196 miles per hour, because somebody locked all the doors and the difference between the inside and outside pressure popped open the huge walls and roof like blown-up paper bags. Everything burned in the searing fires of high octane gas.

Wilmington, North Carolina, and Florida again caught two of the six hurricanes in '46. The curious thing about the hurricane that crossed the Florida coast at Fort Lauderdale was that it blacked out all communications at the Miami Weather Bureau. New Orleans had to take over Miami's forecasting task. Two days later the same hurricane blacked out New Orleans.

For the United States 1947 was a terrible hurricane year. The sixth, a tremendous Cape Verde blow, cut across the Bahamas to

Florida at Palm Beach and so across to Louisiana and Mississippi with damage of $110 million.

The ninth was famous because it was the tropical cyclone with which, as it proceeded up the Atlantic safely at sea, "Project Cirrus," a contract operation for the Army, experimented with dry ice. It astonished observers by turning directly left into Georgia and killed a man at Savannah. No one knew why. But the experiment was never tried again.

The chart of 1948 is all scratched over with ten hurricanes, three crossing Louisiana, two invading Cuba and Florida. Yet only one hurricane out of the twelve in '49 swept violently across land to Lake Okeechobee in Florida. This time, in spite of a few leaks, the great dike held which had been built along the lake's south shore. There was not much water damage.

In 1950 there were also twelve hurricanes of which an unbelievable eleven, the highest on record for any year, reached full hurricane intensity. Mercifully, most of them did not greatly affect land areas, except the one that did not spare Florida.

It formed on October 25 over the northwestern Caribbean as late hurricanes tend to do. As a low pressure area it had been under observation for several days and was still small as it moved past western Jamaica, crossed Cuba west of Camaguey and gained force over the Florida Straits. It was still small in diameter but vicious, as its five-mile-wide central calm plowed directly over Miami near midnight of October 17–18. At the Miami Weather Bureau, at the eastern edge of the eye, a fast gear was put on the triple register to double the time, so that it was judged that two miles were recorded in exactly one minute. A corrected reading gave the wind rate of 122 miles per hour with gusts of 150 miles per hour. The path of destruction was only about seven to ten miles wide through greater Miami north to West Fort Lauderdale. It was as sharply defined as the damage zone of a tornado. The hurricane winds continued north through Florida and into Georgia.

It was the most violent hurricane that had smashed down on Miami since the history-making '26, to which it could hardly be compared. It created $28,000,000 worth of damage in the two states, killed five people and caused 28,954 families to suffer loss. But the damage would have been much greater if the hurricane warning service of the Miami Hurricane Center, under Grady

Norton, had not been excellent. All areas enduring hurricane winds had warnings from eighteen to twenty-four hours in advance, a total of thirty-three advisories and warning bulletins. For everyone within earshot the quiet strength of Grady Norton's radio presence dominated the storm, as it did for an old Miami lady who said later, "There I was all through it, alone with Grady Norton."

For some unknown reason the Miami storm of 1950, when written up, was designated as "King." Hurricanes were becoming a matter of widespread interest and attention. Reports and warnings were printed in all coastal newspapers, broadcast to all radios. It was clear that there must be some way of distinguishing them, in any given year. During 1950, the alphabet designations, A, B, C, etc., or the American military equivalents, Able, Baker, Charlie, Dog, Easy, were being used for hurricanes for the first time, although not universally. The last hurricane of that long season was called "Love."

The twelve hurricanes of 1951 were called, Able, Baker, Charlie, and so on. Able was the earliest ever recorded in May but there seems to be a belief that in New Orleans this storm was given another name. George, the eighth, crossed Florida on October 2.

Charlie, the third, came in mildly enough through the Lesser Antilles from the Atlantic but grew to great intensity by August 17. Twelve hours before in Jamaica, radio warnings had blared. Hurricane Charlie was expected to move east and north. By the sixteenth its course ominously shifted. By 8:30 P.M. on the night of the seventeenth, its seething vortex crashed over the old town of Morant Bay along that rugged coast of St. Thomas Parish, beautiful with cathedral avenues of coco palms. Not a tree for miles along that shore was left standing. All the little houses, wood or masonry, along the coast and up the hilly slopes were broken like crates. The wild Yallahs Valley was devastated as its crops and topsoil were washed down into the mud-stained surf. The stormy vortex moved across that famous sandspit called "The Palisadoes" that reaches a skinny arm to shelter the harbor of Kingston, sinking ships and boats. Port Royal, a jumble of small frame gingerbread houses by the old church and Nelson's strong old fort, once the most famous of pirate hangouts, was swept clean, wharves, warehouses, rum shops, into the sea. Kingston was beaten by rainy winds of 125 miles per hour, drowned by mountain torrents. Roofs, palm trees, walls, fences, broken houses, jammed its streets. Westward the hurricane swept over Spanish Town and on through Savanna-la-Mar and its memories of century-old hurricanes and so, devastating every mile, out to sea toward Tampico.

Behind Charlie, five parishes lay in ruins. Houses and villages of the tilting plains, crops of coffee, bananas, cocoa and thousands of coco palms in seven other parishes were destroyed. One hundred and fifty-four people were killed, by drowning, by falling walls, buried under debris, struck by blown timbers. Two thousand people were injured. And in that island of crowding people, of innumerable small houses, huts and shacks, more than fifty-thousand people were homeless.

Ninety per cent of the great banana export trade was lost, and much of the coconut industry. Coffee, cocoa, were deeply affected and the local tree crops, as well as vegetables, wiped out.

Times had changed in the Caribbean, however. As morning came over the wreckage and stunned thousands of people began to murmur their losses and wail their deaths, the government of Jamaica, the Red Cross, the St. Johns Ambulance Brigade, the Jamaica Federation of Women, the police force and the Army sprang into action. A Central Hurricane Relief Committee with individual parish committees had been organized as a skeleton some years before. But the need of food for thousands, of shelter, of medical care, for the restoration of public services, for clearing roads, was so overwhelming that an over-all Emergency Hurricane Committee was set up at once for Kingston and St. Andrew Parish. Emergency orders for food and building supplies were cabled to Great Britain. Early in September H.M.S. *Apollo* plowed through an Atlantic hurricane to deliver 1,500 army tents from England. The people from the wrecked city slums were sheltered in schools, churches and public buildings. Tens of thousands were fed in more than twenty shelters in the cities. Gangs of men found employment clearing wrecked areas and setting up hundreds of wooden-floored tents, surrounded by drainage ditches, with showers and toilets for 9,000 people.

People from the ruined hill villages camped out in the mud of crossroads markets where truckloads of food were distributed as soon as roads could be cleared. Some crowded into the cities.

Enormous quantities of clothing were made and given out. For eight months free milk was given to babies. The government program of free lunches for needy school children extended to all children in the devastated areas. Gradually the relief kitchens were given up and food tickets issued but it was years before all the people were out of tents and temporary barracks in the city.

Money poured into the Hurricane Relief Fund. Two hundred fifty thousand pounds from the British government was added to the 144,000 pounds from Jamaica itself, and 141,186 pounds from the London Fund. Tiny, neighboring Grand Cayman sent 500 pounds, Turk and Caicos islands 300. Money was received from the Bahamas, from Australia and from the most remote members of the British Commonwealth. Canada sent money and planeloads of relief supplies. So did Cuba. The American Red Cross sent a navy shipload of building supplies.

It was no longer an island of small, self-sufficient individual farmers. Now it was overcrowded by a population for whom there was not enough land for the few crops, bananas, coconuts, coffee, cocoa, ginger, and some cattle, or work in the cities. There was a developing tourist trade. But the great mass of the people, almost illiterate, untrained in skills, living forever hand to mouth, were threatened with immediate destitution.

In ten days, a project was drawn up between the government and the All Island Growers' Association by which money was made available immediately for clearing fields and replanting them. Nurseries were set up to provide seedlings, cuttings and suckers to replace the bananas and all the food trees the hurricane had destroyed, not only for the coconut, banana and coffee industry but small farm and village dooryard trees, citrus, mango, avocado, akee, breadfruit, Cavendish bananas, and plantains.

Fishermen had been given immediate help to repair and rebuild their boats, so that they could return to work. A plan was set up to purchase and lease farm machinery, one for Farm Recovery loans, to extend over a number of years and include the most up-to-date help for proper soil conservation, drainage and water supplies. The United Kingdom made a grant of three million pounds and an interest-free loan of half that again, to put these plans to work.

The rebuilding of roads and government buildings, the rebuilding and enlarging of the University College of the West Indies, surveys and research in new ways to develop the island's industries, gave work to hundreds of men. The result of all this was a release of energy which had a part in the development of new island industries such as grapefruit and orange juice canneries, a cement plant, in an increased interest in cattle raising and the very hopeful tourist trade.

Crops such as bananas made a quick recovery. New schemes took time. The effect of the hurricane on the whole island was a slow social churning and upheaval.

Housing was perhaps the key to everything. It had not been difficult to lend money for the repair and rebuilding of middle-income homes, with a plan of guided self-help that gave a man a chance to do much of the building himself. Under the Urban Housing Scheme it was possible to clear land that had been occupied by city slums, or even land outside the city, buy it and redivide it into small holdings. A multitude of neat, small, one-room-and-porch cement houses appealed quickly to the displaced people of the tent slums. Thousands of landless people who found jobs quickly took over the houses.

Many men still without jobs signed up in groups for short-term periods in the United States, the bean and tomato fields of Florida and farther north. But recruited from Kingston slums, they had little or no experience as farm hands. In the United States they were dissatisfied, unsatisfactory and restless. Some disappeared in the vast country. Others returned with little or no money saved and bitter about American labor conditions.

In Jamaica the Urban Housing Scheme was in time considered a success. The Rural Housing Scheme, on the contrary, was almost a failure. It was true of the small emancipated Jamaica farmer that the dearest thing in his life was his bit of land. It had kept his family alive. The thatched huts, with their ancient Spanish walls of mud and rubble, leaked like baskets. Crowded families slept in wet mud, insect ridden. But such houses could be patched and repaired cheaply, although they were not any longer socially desirable. But one thing the farmer absolutely refused to do was to take money to build a new house by mortgaging his land to the government. A mortgage meant loss and ruin. The government agents eventually promised additional crop loans in case crop failures prevented payments. But the farmers continued to refuse all mortgages.

In order to get money such farmers could do one of two things. They could go down to Kingston and sign up for field work in the United States. Such skilled men made a far better impression on their American employers, earned more money and brought it home.

Others like these moved down from the devastated hill parishes to get jobs as waiters and hotel workers in the new hotels of Jamaica's north coast. Rents and food prices were so high they could save little. Their wages were low in spite of the unions and high tips from easy-mannered Americans. Rumors spread among them that the Labour government, whose power rested on the unions, had sold out to the hotel owners to prevent strikes hurtful to the valuable tourist business. The unrest among the workers decreased the prestige of the Labour government that later, for very many other reasons too, lost an election.

Meantime, the laws governing the rural housing problem were revised. The government learned that many Jamaicans held no proper title to land they had farmed and occupied for generations. Such knowledge became the basis for a new look at land ownership throughout the island.

The Jamaica hurricane of '51, therefore, set in motion a churning social change, a new era in the economy of the island. The time was ripe. No hurricane in Jamaica again, it seems safe to say, will bring the island so close to total despair.

It would have been hard to detect any evidence of cycles in the courses taken by the six hurricanes of 1952. Able crossed Puerto Rico on August 25, and accelerated along the Georgia coast and killed two people in flooded Pennsylvania. Baker, Charlie, Dog and Easy curved out to sea. Only Fox was severe, starting up north of the Canal Zone, killing 600 people in Cuba and darkening over the Bahamas. On Eleuthera and Watling's islands the hurricane-wise people saw the gray scud going over, "low, low, low," the hermit crabs piling up on higher land, the birds blowing away, the barometer falling in the greenish light as the surf hissed up. All the little houses up the narrow streets of island villages were boarded. The men sank their boats with stones or ran them up under cover. Children and chickens were cried in. When the hurricane winds shut down, only the steeples of a few little churches crashed in the bush. The people rode their swept islands as if they were stout boats.

The problem of naming hurricanes was still unsolved in the United States. Newspapers were critical of such names as "Easy" and "Love" for such disasters. Among non-English speaking people it was felt a more international code would be better, such as "Alpha," "Bravo," "Coco." In Catholic countries in the West Indies it had long been the dignified habit to name a hurricane for the saint's day on which it occurred, so that for years the people speak of the horrors of "the San Felipe" or "the San Mateo" of certain years. A fascinating book by George Stewart, called *Storm*, had just been published, in which a young forecaster, for convenience, named a Pacific storm "Maria." The San Francisco office had no such usage. Some weathermen insist that George Stewart's "Maria" had nothing to do with it. The fact is that hurricanes were given women's names for the first time in 1953, but for a few years, confusingly, the same names.

There was no rain over all the eastern seaboard of the United States that summer. Georgia, the Carolina beaches, eastern New Jersey, New York and Connecticut were drying up. In New England lawns and gardens were brown.

The first hurricane of 1953, Alice, made a curious loop over western Cuba. Barbara from outside the Bahamas, picked up speed as its center moved across the Carolina capes and over parching Pennsylvania, flooded inland rivers, canals and milldams, and killed one person. All those hurricanes seemed to be going up the meridian like trains on rails. Carol, a Cape Verde crasher, past Hatteras, to Bermuda and Nova Scotia, Dolly in the North Atlantic, Edna close behind, a big hurricane from the Leewards up into the cooling northeast sea. Florence went from Jamaica up the Gulf of Mexico to smack Panama City, Florida, with thousands of dollars of damage. Gail went north at sea.

The dry spell over Florida was broken. Hazel, of October 8–10, started up in full howling intensity out of the Yucatán Channel to cross Florida at Fort Myers with tornadoes along its leading edge that tore down the new mango groves of Pine Island, lashed Okeechobee and its dikes with rainy high water and killed oaks and palmettos along the ancient beautiful St. Johns.

In all the years since '38, it may be seen therefore, hurricanes

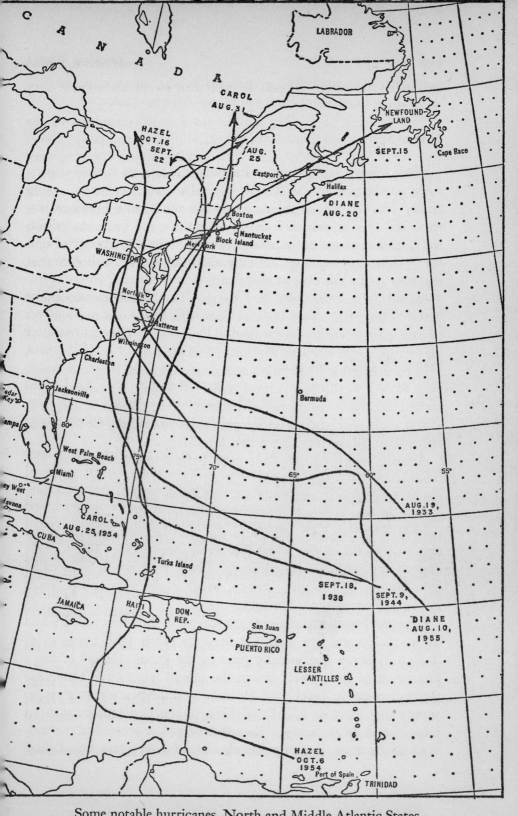

Some notable hurricanes, North and Middle Atlantic States.

rocketed everywhere. But an unusual number of them seemed to be invading the mainland off the North Atlantic coasts.

3. 1954

"Only about half as many hurricanes occur in drought summers, on the average, as during normal or wet summers," wrote Grady Norton, the hurricane expert of the Miami Weather Bureau. His comfortable dry drawl over the radio had encouraged and calmed more and more people in south Florida, listening through the preliminary warnings of hurricanes in the West Indies that might or might not overwhelm them.

Indeed, it was the third dry summer in the extreme southern states. A little rain along the east coast of Florida was not enough to dampen fires raging in the drying Everglades. The red rivers of southern Georgia crawled diminished to the sea.

In parts of New York State and almost all New England, however, from June through August, rains fell heavily. Summer people rocked disconsolately on rain-drenched hotel verandas, staring out at wet rocks and beaches under gray skies from Cape Cod and the north shore all the way down east into Maine.

Actually more people than ever before summered along the beaches of the Atlantic coast. People drove from as far away as the Middle West to swim and sail and fish in salt water. More cottages than ever before had been built between the long bare roads fringed with telegraph poles and the sand beaches, almost to the high-tide marks of the white-feathered summer sea. The highest dunes were marked with rooftops. There were whole villages of bath houses, boardwalks, casinos, beach clubs, restaurants, small stores, and everywhere cottages.

Southern beaches near rivers are stained dark, with mud, banked by magnolias and live oaks. Or they are white with ocean sand, backed by scrub and loblolly pine or the green swamps where a procession of motorboats churn the inland waterway. There are the endless lonely beaches of Hatteras and the new smart cottages among the dunes of Kill Devil Hill, or the populous beaches of Cape May in New Jersey. Thousands of people teemed in the sunshine and salt air up Long Island, around Narragansett and Buzzards Bay, petaled with white sails, the busy summer islands, Martha's Vineyard and Nantucket, all the way to Provincetown.

Few people remembered how Dr. Charles F. Brooks, director of the Blue Hill Observatory for Harvard University in '38, had described the conditions that must exist for a hurricane to strike New England.

Directly above the northwest Atlantic region in the eight miles of the earth's nearest atmosphere, he had written, there must exist a great difference in pressure and temperature between east and west. The general winds higher than the surface must be blowing northward or northwestward, in order to help drag the hurricane from the south or the southeast. And up the open sea from the West Indies a long low pressure area, between an Atlantic high and a high over the eastern mainland, must lead toward the northern, northwestern, or northeastern coasts.

The Weather Bureau was using the same women's names. So it was Alice again on June 24 that flushed out the dry beds of the Rio Grande and the Pecos Rivers with the highest water of record in Texas. Barbara was unimportant.

On the night of the twenty-sixth of August, however, Weather Bureau watchers reported a weak easterly wave or knot of winds showing up well east of Jacksonville, in the horse latitudes. Its name was Carol.

Many a Weather Bureau was checking it. A western high pressure area reached from the Rocky Mountains to the southern states. East another high stood at sea near Bermuda. North of the unsettled area where Carol hesitated like a great spider of rain and low pressure the two highs were joined by a narrowing neck. In two days, the highs, like moving mountains, drifted apart, leaving between them a low trough heading northward. The hurricane waves that Carol trailed up the coast seethed viciously over the islands as low as reefs, south of the Outer Banks. Hardy wild ponies descended from stock shipwrecked perhaps by earlier hurricanes, were drowned on Portsmouth Island.

Carol's idling engine suddenly picked up power from the warm wet stream of air heading with her into that trough. She began to move. Her gray rain-bands, like arms, began to whirl faster. By the thirtieth, Carol had strengthened into a great hurricane.

Over the crowded beaches of Long Island there were no general hurricane warnings. "The line storm is early this year," people said even as the dunes began to crumble under the white hurricane waves. But the New York Telephone Company alerted 4,000 installers, repairmen, splicers and linemen on "catastrophe routine," even before 13,000 telephones went out as the hurricane winds came howling over. John Telfer's cows gave one hundred quarts of milk less because they hated hand milking.

Easthampton elms that after '38 had been set back at a cost of $30,000 went down. Five thousand tourists and fishermen were marooned at Montauk when the ocean washed out roads and railroad tracks. Carol '54 was nowhere near as bad a hurricane as the '38 chiefly because Carol came over Long Island with an ebbing tide. But the damage especially to vegetables was bad enough.

Winds at 120 miles per hour were feeling out Block Island as the surf exploded higher up the beaches of Martha's Vineyard. The sea seemed to swell up over the land. Ponds were salt water. Salt water rose in the streets of Oak Bluffs. Gay Head was cut off. Vineyard Haven, West Chop, Edgartown and especially Menemsha were crushed by winds and heaped with a wet smash of wreckage.

Hurricane Carol was widening out her great course to 100 miles as she moved at 11 A.M. to the mainland, from New London, Connecticut, to the Cape Cod canal. Her center was at Saybrook. But there had been no word yet of hurricanes. The Weather Bureau, the afternoon before, had warned there would be abnormal northeast gales and abnormal tides.

The hurricane was far inland by the time the editor of the Vineyard *Gazette* had a chance to feel astonished that a writer from the West spoke of all this Atlantic coast as "hurricane country."

The hurricane wave crested up Narragansett Bay on the high tide, now, to hit Misquamicutt Beach with a force that swept away two hundred houses. In Newport, the famous old Casino collapsed. Three men in a car on an ocean-front estate were drowned. Ensign Thomas B. Farrey was drowned when his car was washed off the road by a giant wave at Jamestown.

Warwick was damaged more than in '38. In South Kingston, eight carloads of people who had fled from their cottages were stranded and many were drowned. Westerly and Watch Hill were overwhelmed by a 35-foot wave. The center of Providence—automobiles, busses and buildings—was flooded almost to the '38 marks.

The long narrow harbor of New Bedford under the winds and gray waves was a jumble of broken boats, docks, yachts, draggers, sailboats, trawlers, tugs and houses. Old men and babies died. Fishermen were washed off the scalloper *Redstart* and drowned. A boy was swept down the bay and never seen again. Two maiden ladies, Miss Henrietta and Miss Lucy Berry, snug in their old stone house at Wareham, were drowned. A dead baby was seen floating offshore, too far to be reached. Wareham main street stores burned even as the sea flooded to the ceilings. Firemen, in boats or floundering chin-high, struggled with their hoses. Everywhere the sea rose and ruined warehouses, factories and machinery with corroding salt.

Now hurricane warnings were flashing everywhere. Two thousand people on Cape Cod, from Bourne to Mashpee, left their homes for better shelters. Many of them returned to heaps of broken boards.

The vast whirling funnel of the storm ground its winds over the face of Massachusetts. In Boston, as a news photographer made his way in the wind and rain, he looked up and caught sight of the wooden spire of the Old North Church swaying. It cracked louder than the storm, and shuddered and heeled over and fell. The first spire, where the lantern had been hung to alert Paul Revere, had been knocked down exactly 150 years before, in the great New England hurricane of 1804. It had been restored, twenty feet shorter, in 1806. The first thing Boston people did after this was to build it up again.

The heavy apple crop of Worcester County was blown off by that time and corn fields flattened in Northboro, Westboro and Shrewsbury. The winds were more furious and vicious south and east than they were at Worcester, that after rain like sheets of lead at 12:30 took the eye, bright with sun and white clouds. Yet as it passed, the winds were wild enough to blow Harry R. Davis to his death from a downtown building when he opened a door on a fire escape on the tenth floor, and was swept off. By 4:30 in the afternoon in Worcester it was all over but for grief and the heavy work of cleaning up.

The coast of Maine had no warnings. Trees went down on the islands. Boats and docks were broken by high waves. As Carol went on into Canada, flooding everything but gradually losing strength, she left behind her forty-five dead and millions of dollars' worth of damage.

Already, on the Cape, in Boston and in Worcester, and in Miami, Florida, by September 2, the newspapers were announcing the fourth hurricane that season. It was 725 miles off Jacksonville, Florida. This was Dolly. All New England, cleaning up debris from Carol, was anxious. Radio warning stations were set up. Weary rescue and relief workers pulled themselves together. Disaster relief organizations moved into high gear with twenty-seven National Red Cross experts establishing a five-state center in New Bedford. The stricken areas, Bourne, Falmouth, Mattapoisett, Westport, Dartmouth, were sealed off to everyone.

Dolly curved harmlessly northeast of Nova Scotia.

Four days later the news was flashed everywhere that hurricane Edna, observed north of Puerto Rico as an easterly wave, by nightfall had become an intense hurricane, moving rapidly northeast. By the tenth the South and North Carolina coasts were fully alerted and anxious. Waves broke across inland highways. The people of the Outer Banks of Hatteras were boarded up. By midnight the center went by sixty miles at sea, headed north-northeast. Outer winds brought floods to lower New York State.

By the eleventh, at 11:30 A.M., it was announced that the eye of Edna was off Nantucket. On the coast of Maine the warnings went on continuously. Cars were ordered off roads. Schoolhouses were opened for refugees. A baby girl was born and christened Edna. Everyone was strainingly alert.

On the Maine coast the winds were rising to ninety miles per hour. By evening, the power failed and many places were blacked out for a week. Trees went over. Shingles blew like birds. Boats were washed ashore by high waves.

But by ten o'clock it was all over and moonlight whitened the booming, bursting magnificence of the surf. Edna had crossed violently the tip of Cape Cod, the Bay of Maine, Eastport, and vanished toward Greenland.

New England not only heaved a sigh of relief and went back to its cleaning up, but also got mad. There were too constant announcements of "hurricane coming" that did not say where it was going. Yet the general alarm was almost the only announcement possible in face of the fact that the Weather Bureau lacked money, equipment and experts who could study these tropical cyclones on their dying and often erratic courses through the temperate zone. The protest indicated that Northern people were learning about hurricanes the hard way.

Even so, few people in New England noticed that, as Edna died, Florence leaped into life out of an easterly wave of disturbance in the Gulf of Mexico off Yucatán, on the eleventh of September, and just at hurricane force crashed southwest into the Mexican coast at Veracruz, and so full into the mountains rising behind the narrow coastal plain. The mountains killed her but not before her winds, without warning, had knocked down flimsy houses and huts in and around the battered old city and flooded the steep short rivers that drowned five persons and all the streets.

Thirteen days later a storm named Gilda, with winds just fast enough to be called a hurricane, made a short dotted line on the map, in a jab from the original disturbance in the Sea of Colombia to the north coast of British Honduras. The record says, "There was some damage but no casualties." But in Tegucigalpa, Honduras, it was thought that it would be at least two years before the damage of the three days' floods could be forgotten. Six hundred and thirty square miles of valley and banana plantations were under water, with thousands homeless. Thirty-four thousand employees of the United Fruit Company were affected. Prompt rescue work by American agencies prevented loss of life. But 5,000 banana workers were laid off by the United Fruit Company and many joined the gangs of jobless in the banana port of Tela where they were influenced by Communist labor agitators.

For the small farmers whose hillside farms were swept clean even of soil and boundary markings the Honduran government, with the aid of American funds, gave out tools and seed and offered credit and new land elsewhere. Their long painful recovery got slowly under way.

All but three hurricanes that year of '54 were born in the Atlantic. In a little more than a month Dolly, Carol and Edna had sprung up not far off the islands, within the 60th and 75th meridians of longitude. It was as if some enormous disturbance in the upper air had hung all that time over the Caribbean from the Lesser Antilles to the Atlantic.

But not Hazel. The greatest hurricane of '54 rose far east in the
Atlantic. There were no ships to send warnings until October 5,
when its winds already of ninety miles per hour flicked at Barbados.
Within the arc of islands it shifted northward and seemed to hang
for several hours almost stationary in that empty tropic sea, south-
southeast of Jamaica. But its turbulence was so great that an observation plane, trying to penetrate to the center, was jolted and a
crewman injured. Then Hazel started up, loaded with power from
the steamy air around it, and moved suddenly almost at a right
angle northeast, straight for that long lower jaw of Haiti.

Jacmel, the run-down small Negro city that faced the open sea
within a two-mile harbor, rises on low slopes that eastward lift to
the great battlement of the Morne la Selle. Jacmel seemed to take
the whole baffled fury of the hurricane, in torrents of rain that
scoured the soil off the rocky slopes and savage winds that seemed
to slice off the whole rising façade of the city, so that its ruins
clung like ranks of gutted honeycombs. The same thing happened
at Jérémie, under the winds of the northeast sector. Hundreds of
lives were lost on that steep coast and thousands had no homes.

The circular hurricane winds were slowed to forty miles an hour
by the hilly peninsula. Mole St. Nicholas, at the tip of the northern
jaw, felt it pass up the Windward Passage, but there it gained
strength and moved and whirled with renewed savagery.

Behind it at Jacmel and the Haitian south coast there was utter
destitution. Nothing could grow in the denuded soil. Trees were
gone that were used for boats' masts. The boats were gone. Cut off
even from the rest of the Haitian world by the lack of roads, little
or no help was sent to the forty thousand homeless and starving
people by the helpless Haitian government. A year later a Haitian
Red Cross official traveled through the dead land and reported that
the starving people had just energy enough to drag themselves from
their shacks to hunt for wild yams and morning-glory roots and
green mangoes. Many had died and many would die of tubercu-
losis and of hunger. The United States government, at the request
of the Haitian Red Cross, sent in 2,000 tons of beans, rice and
cooking oil. The Haitian government was asked to set up shelters
where the children at least could be given needed care. There is no
evidence that anything constructive was ever done. On the whole,

the people were left to live by what resources they could muster or die by themselves.

Hurricane Hazel, the eighth of '54, blew northeastward up the Atlantic. Eastward a high pressure area rose over the sea. To the west a long steamy trough turned toward the land. Her circular winds accelerated to 130 miles per hour as she turned northwestward, squarely toward the coast of the Carolinas that juts out into the Atlantic. Before her, in her great fetch across the sea and the the Gulf Stream from the Bahamas, she pushed a rising wall of waves.

After a busy day's work of charting the progress of a disturbance that would become Hurricane Hazel, on October 9th in Miami, Florida, Grady Norton went home and died. He was awarded posthumously the Department of Commerce's gold medal for exceptional service because he was credited with having cut the average death toll in major hurricanes from 500 to five.

Warnings screamed along the Carolina coasts as the rains began. In the late season the beach resorts were not crowded, but many people who owned their own cottages were staying later. By every resource of every Weather Bureau and community—radio, telephone, television, newspaper, Coast Guardsmen knocking on beach house doors, by word of mouth—the news was spread of the coming violence. Radio stations in the Carolinas sent out warnings all night long on the fourteenth, and continuously throughout. All utility companies, transportation industries, businesses were forewarned. All these advisories as to the path, location, severity and velocity of the hurricane were accurate, fast and pinpointed. Neighbors called to neighbors. Cars were stopped and warned. Men set off in rowboats to reach people living on isolated islands. Barometers were falling. Gusts were shaking trees. The sea rose up in gray and bursting white. The dun skies lowered and scudded heavily over.

The mass evacuation that followed saved thousands of lives. The problem, on those endless island beaches north from Georgia, is that they are connected with the mainland by bridges or causeways only at long intervals. To escape, people must ride for miles along roads parallel to the sea already storming up the sands. The heavy rains fill the roads. The rising winds fret and worry at exposed cars, even on the bridges. People who were forced to abandon their cars in sand flowing like water were exposed to sand-blast, rain-blast, wind-blast.

The hurricane moved majestically at North Carolina about 9 A.M. on the fifteenth of October, from the South Carolina line to Cape Fear, with winds from 90 to 106 miles per hour and blasts, near and east of the eye, at 150 miles per hour. Twenty-foot waves came racing up the shores on top of a ten-foot-high tide. Rain was like drumfire. Light was a dreadful twilight in which there was only the terrible pounding, shaking, screaming freight-train uproar of water and of wind.

From Pawley's Island, South Carolina, to Cape Fear, North Carolina, the entire ocean front was obliterated. All signs of human life vanished in watery smoke. Miles and miles of houses built behind ten- to twenty-foot dunes exploded as the seas and winds crashed over the sand hills. The long paved road vanished, broken up or smothered. Blown debris was ground to mush and washed west into the swamps, the inland waterway, the woods beyond. Myrtle Beach, Windy Hill, Crescent Beach, Cherry Grove, in South Carolina, with their stores and businesses, were incredibly devastated. There was one death. In North Carolina, Captain Fulford of the shrimp boat *Nina Fay* reported that the eye of the hurricane, about fifteen minutes of calm, passed near Holden Beach at 11 A.M. on the fifteenth. Of Long Beach's 377 buildings, 352 were utterly destroyed. At Holden Beach 200 were gone. Ocean Isle was swept bare; Robinson Beach, Colonial Beach, Wrightsville were badly damaged. One-half the taxable wealth of Carolina Beach was swept away. The old town of Southport was devastated by wind and the wild seas broke in the house doors along the waterfront and crashed huge shrimp boats up to verandahs. Nineteen lives were lost in North Carolina. The estimate of the damage, chiefly by sea water, mounted higher than $136 million.

Hazel blew and whirled through Virginia, the District of Columbia, Maryland and Delaware, Pennsylvania, New Jersey and New York State. Winds cut swaths in forest trees, blew down power poles and towers, plate glass store fronts and roofs, destroyed apple crops, poultry houses, tobacco barns. The losses by power failures and by the floodings of rivers, lakes, dams, the destruction of roadways and shade trees were astronomical.

The hurricane, in New York State, through Binghampton and

Buffalo, had become a huge extratropical cyclone, with heavy rains and many gusts of more than ninety miles per hour.

The United States Weather Bureau had forecast that the hurricane would carom off the Alleghenies and lose force eastward. At 9 A.M. on the sixteenth the Dominion forecaster Fred Turnbull, at Malton, Ontario, predicted that the center of Hazel would jump the mountains and head for Lake Ontario. He had been watching a cold front which had left the Yukon a few days before, moved south across the Canadian prairies, crossed into the United States and continued east to Chicago, when it turned north, heading for Toronto. If it had been a day earlier or even a day later, nothing much would have happened. But he saw the cold front moving up as hurricane Hazel, its winds slackening somewhat, swirled across Lake Ontario.

Fred Turnbull had been instructed to make no broadcasts, only bulletins in the regular newcasts. But Friday, Turnbull appealed to the local radio station for air time. One station refused. He made four broadcasts, warning the people that the hurricane would reach Toronto Friday night and that, in conjunction with the cold front, they must prepare for the heaviest rainstorm the city had ever seen.

Many people heard his warnings. The Dominion Weather Bureau received over two thousand phone calls. The Toronto Hydroelectric Corporation took his warning seriously and had their repair crews standing by. Most of the people in that well-populated area, however, had not the slightest idea what a hurricane or hurricane rains were like.

The hurricane that was moving into Canada with a path as wide as Windsor to Kingston, with winds of ninety miles per hour and gusts to 120, with the cold front converging on it west of Toronto, was made incredibly more dangerous by the very geography of the country about Toronto. The city's waterfront extends for miles along Lake Ontario. North of the lake the land rises as steep as a roof in watersheds of more than 377,600 acres, scored deeply by four rivers and their branches carrying down more than six billion gallons of water. West of the city the broadening Humber with its West Branch and Black Creek is as steep between Bolton and Sunnyside as the whole fall of the St. Lawrence to the sea. West in deep cuts in the land run Mimico and Etobicoke creeks. The Don flows to the lake east of Toronto. Everywhere in the well-settled countryside, pleasant, tree-shaded towns are scattered along the high banks of these rivers. Near the city great roads like Queen Elizabeth's Way go straight across the rivers on more than forty bridges. In the whole system there were not more than four mill-dams and these were open. Up in the hills rain had been falling for two days.

It was over this steep lakeside region, deep-grooved with rivers, that hurricane Hazel from the Caribbean collided with the massive cold front from the Yukon and Chicago. The hurricane pushed the cold front west of the Humber and all the water vapor was condensed into an explosion of rain that from Malton to Guelph fell like curtains of lead. Over Brampton in forty-eight hours fell an all-time record of eight inches. Downtown Toronto, that had had winds of only forty miles per hour, had a deluge.

By seven o'clock that night Toronto skies were clearing as the hurricane moved beyond. People went to parties and the usual night life began gaily. The Hydroelectric Company phoned the Dominion Weather Bureau to ask if it would be all right to send home their emergency crews. Only Fred Turnbull at Malton still sent out warnings that the worst was yet to come. Not many people believed him. The Weather Bureau itself insisted later it was not responsible for warnings because it could not predict floods.

One of the most pleasant streets in town on the steep west bank of the Humber was always quiet tree-shaded Raymore Drive. There was a drop of twenty-five feet between Thistleton just above Raymore Drive and Scarlet Road below it. Black Creek joined the Humber across from it on the east. Raymore Drive children were always envied by other children because the river ran down there below their back gardens.

The children of Raymore Drive had gone to bed long before midnight. Upriver, 113 tons of water per inch of rainfall for each of those nearly four hundred thousand acres had been added to the usual billions of flow since 6 P.M. Water up there was already flowing across the bridges. About midnight, when lights suddenly went off, a Raymore Drive mother opened her back door and was engulfed to her waist in swirling black water. The black street beyond her front door was running ankle deep in river water. There were creakings in the house walls and screams and cries from the other houses. She woke her children and hurried them out as her husband hurried to warn some elderly neighbors. The Raymore Drive people floundered to higher streets. A church was hastily opened and lighted. Children were put to bed in the pews. More and more people were brought in. The air was filled for miles with the shaking roar of rivers in terrible flood.

Children and old people, unrescued, were swept away and drowned as acres of grassy banks and pavements and roadways were swallowed up. Bridges were going. In Toronto, cut off from all communication with the west, laughing people were leaving late parties, glancing up at the stars and calling out that the storm had passed. Houses, buildings, stores, garages were then collapsing down into the wild cataracts of the rivers.

On the Little Don River three men in a car plunged fifteen feet down into an invisible forty-foot gap where a culvert was washed out. The car was carried five hundred feet down the river as the men managed to climb to the roof and roped a tree and clung to it. In Weston, people took to their roofs as the river tore houses from their foundations and were rescued at dawn by the aerial ladder of a fire truck. Humber Boulevard, Porter Avenue, Cordelia Avenue flowed with water from Black Creek, that rose fifteen feet and surged downhill in a black wave that overturned and swamped cars with people in them, carried away houses with people clinging to the rafters. Trying to rescue three men, five firemen drowned. Hundreds of trees, light poles, fuel pumps were swept away, trailers and trailer parks and forty concrete bridges. Rivers to west of the greater watershed rose fourteen or more feet. The sewage plant at Kitchener was gutted. Sixty families were homeless at Bridgeport, fifty at New Hamburg. Hardly a house was left untouched and many had vanished in Woodbridge, where the ruin was greatest. No one knew how many were drowned or injured in that catastrophic night.

No dams went out. It was said afterward that six dams, closed, would have held back 35 per cent of the water and saved many lives.

Sunday morning, the sixteenth of October, 1954, there was a strange yellow light over the city. Rain was still falling. At once the whole metropolitan area began marshaling its fullest forces of relief, beginning with its new metropolitan police force and fire departments. The Reserve Army was called out, army engineers, soldiers, Boy Scouts, Girl Guides, the Sea Cadets, officers and crew of H.M.S. *York*, the Red Cross and dozens of welfare groups and hundreds of volunteer workers. Relief began pouring in from the rest of Canada and the United States.

What the first helicopter saw, flying low to pick up people stranded on the roofs of houses, was an enormous triangle of destruction that had been a valley of neat and pleasant towns, from Bradford and Becton in the north, to the mouth of the Humber. It was now a steep and glistening avalanche of wet mud and indescribably tangled debris. Already there were furtive figures of men here and there, looting and robbing the still wet dead. Everything within the reach of the high waters that was not smashed was soaked. Basements, floors, walls were dank with sliding, evil-smelling silt. The sky rained and brooded over two hundred men who began wading and poking about for dead bodies. Helicopters hovered and signaled from above where other bodies could be made out. Stenches rose from trailers rolled over in mud. Eight hundred men with flame throwers began to clear and burn wreckage that covered streets. Men with lifeboats probed the bottoms of streams. Hospitals were overcrowded. Doctors, nurses, volunteer workers came in from everywhere.

A pall of smoke from the flaming debris began to hang over the city and the countryside. Up and down the rivers there was a clatter of small gas pumps pumping out basements. Loudspeakers from cars and helicopters blared orders. "Do not drink the water." "Go at once to the nearest Red Cross station for your antityphoid and antitetanus inoculations." Haggard women were putting out mud-soaked rugs and sodden mattresses, mopping walls and porches. There were innumerable muddy gashes on hillsides where houses, gardens, trees, raspberry patches, had vanished. Solemn-faced people helplessly stared about them. The damage was in the one hundred millions.

Hurricane Hazel had blown northeastward, out of North America, beyond Greenland, even, it was reported later, making its winds felt off Norway. Insurance rates went up everywhere.

The year 1954 saw no more hurricanes. It was estimated later that the property damage in North America of the three hurricanes,

Carol, Edna and Hazel, amounted to one billion dollars. They killed over 150 people.

4. *1955, 1956*

The disastrous hurricane season of 1954 called up a storm of protest against inadequate hurricane warnings, as Northern people began to recognize they were more vulnerable than they liked to think.

A freak tropical cyclone called Alice, south-southeast of Puerto Rico, disappeared westward, either the last of '54 or the first of '55. It kept the protest alive. The newspaper talked about the hurricane late in January, 1493, that Columbus had encountered on his return voyage, but Dr. Brooks of the Blue Hill Observatory insisted that that was not a circular storm but only two severe, if typical, Azores blows.

The protest against the previous closing of several northern weather warning stations, however, was effectual. In March, a resolution submitted to the House of Representatives from eighteen coastal states asked for an appropriation of $5 million to provide an intense hurricane study and an emergency hurricane warning system. It would provide four upper air observations daily instead of two and additional observations in new areas as well as increased staffs at the important forecast centers, Boston, New York, Washington, Miami and San Juan, Puerto Rico. They asked the reopening of the four stations just closed, additional observations from ships at sea and hurricane warning service flying squads at regional offices at New York and Fort Worth and radar observations at other than weather stations, with high tide warnings, weather-ship stations between Norfolk and Bermuda and a careful program of information, warnings and special broadcasts.

At all costs, it was insisted, the great loss of life and property must be reduced. It was argued that if the public could depend on accurate warnings it would be more ready to take precautions without panic. The bill was passed with additional money for a study of ways to improve the service.

On Thursday, June 17, 1955, at 12:01 A.M. at the Weather Bureau headquarters in Washington, Dr. Reichelderfer, the director, threw the switch that officially opened the hurricane season. An enlarged teletypewriter service hooked up from Maine to Texas, with Portland, Maine; Providence, Rhode Island; Hartford, New Haven and Bridgeport, Connecticut; Atlantic City, New Jersey; Wilmington, Delaware; Richmond, Virginia, and Raleigh and Wilmington, North Carolina.

July 31 was blistering hot, and dry. Many day's temperatures had gone higher than 90° F., before a hurricane called Brenda with winds up to sixty miles per hour formed in the Gulf of Mexico and moved up into Louisiana. Every nineteen years, the people of the swamps and bayous believed there must be a hurricane. There had been more than that. The men and big boys moved the boats as far inland as they could. The old men and the women and children stayed in the little houses shuttered tight against the leaping cold air, the cold rain, the hissing water. As the saying was, they saved what they could and lost what they must. Now, for all the warnings, over the flooded and wind-ravaged marshes, seven lives were lost and $200,000 worth of damage was done.

The northern summer resorts had only four days of peace in August. On the fourth, 800 miles out in the Atlantic east of the French West Indies, a well-formed hurricane was spotted with winds already at 100 miles an hour. As hurricane Connie, it leaped into headlines everywhere up the Atlantic coast and in Puerto Rico. It was moving west-northwest at 14 miles and on its northeast sector the squall bands lashed out at 125 miles per hour.

It edged northward beyond Puerto Rico. South Florida and the Bahamas quivered to the alert. A Navy Neptune plane from San Juan, piloted by Lieutenant Commander Raymond Newman, flew three turbulent missions at a level of 500 feet into the clear eye of the storm. A B-29 Air Force plane flown by Captain George Newkirk, specially equipped for taking hurricane data, lost its engine in the vortex and was forced down at Nassau.

The hurricane moved on.

Off St. Augustine, it slowed a little. There was a low pressure trough moving east to sea ahead of a high pressure over the mainland, but Connie did not connect with it.

All the forces of the Weather Bureau were marshaled. Red Cross headquarters in Washington ordered thousands of volunteer workers to stand by for the Carolinas. Sixty-six jets and propeller craft were flown west from the Marine base at Cherry Point, North

Carolina. The Navy ordered aircraft carriers and other big vessels in Hampton Roads, Virginia, to sea and flew two transport planes out of the South Weymouth, Massachusetts, Air Station. A Navy antisubmarine plane being evacuated out of Hampton Roads crashed and killed two crewmen. Private beaches were closed along Narragansett Bay and fishing vessels were tied up at New Bedford. On Long Island, ocean-front residents were urged to leave their cottages.

Heavy swells smashed waves up North Carolina beaches up to the doorsteps of beach cottages. The hurricane drifted. Swells more than ten feet high came in north of Wilmington, North Carolina, at Topsail Island and over the sea wall at Holden's Beach. Everywhere along the coasts thousands fled. Business was at a standstill. Winds and high waves trailed damage up the beaches. The hurricane bore inland near Morehead City, North Carolina, and went sixty miles west of Hatteras, smashing at villages from Myrtle Beach, South Carolina, to Wilmington and along Pamlico Sound. On August 12 its path was declared a major disaster area.

On the eleventh, another hurricane, Diane, had picked up speed to full hurricane power, over one thousand miles east of Miami, Florida.

Connie's winds were slowing but her rains flooded New Bern, North Carolina, knocked out electric light and power systems as she took an erratic course to northwestern Pennsylvania, flooding the hills. There were forty-one deaths by automobile accidents, drowning and electrocutions. New York City under "Hurricane Alert" was badly damaged on the thirteenth by the fringe gales of more than sixty-seven miles per hour and terrific rains, as the hurricane itself spread northeast of Pittsburgh and diminished in heavy rains across Lake Erie, leaving forty-three dead. The whole northeast, especially Connecticut that had been hot and dry, was waterlogged with its rains.

There was Diane, howling up the Atlantic south of Bermuda. At Coral Beach, Hamilton, the first giant hurricane wave washed Mrs. John Bastin out to sea and ran a British ship aground on a reef. On the fourteenth the hurricane swung toward the exhausted coasts of South and North Carolina. An Air Force reconnaissance plane from Bermuda tried to penetrate Diane's eye from 1,500 feet to

10,000 feet. The dangerous winds were an impenetrable wall of roaring air.

But as Diane turned toward the mainland, its winds were diminishing to thirty miles per hour. Rain, cataracts, avalanches, curtains, rivers of rain, cloudbursts, were let down abruptly for twenty-four hours over Virginia, Maryland, Pennsylvania, New Jersey, New York and New England. The earth, already saturated by Connie's rains, could absorb no more. All the brooks, the streams, the rivers began to swell and rise.

In the Pocono Mountains at Stroudsburg, Pennsylvania, Brodhead Creek rose thirty feet in fifteen minutes, drowning fifty people who had already fled to what they thought was higher ground. Before Diane had wandered harmlessly out to sea beyond Boston, relief work was begun in the Poconos as a fleet of helicopters rescued 235 passengers from a stranded Lackawanna Railroad train.

The rain storm came over from lower New York State across Poughkeepsie into northwestern Connecticut. The mountains squeezed the water out of the heavy clouds as if they had been sponges.

On the night of August 18 in Connecticut, the Naugatuck, the Mad and Still rivers, the Connecticut, the Farmington and the Quinebaug, in their ancient channels, were rising faster and faster. In the night in the Naugatuck Valley, there were sudden shouts, "River's rising. Get out—get out." The hoarse voices cried in all the river towns but there was no time. The Naugatuck's gentle flow of 17,000 cubic feet per second was increased to 59,000, three and a half times greater.

There was no adequate protection for the hundreds of towns and cities in the lower lands and river plains as the enormous dark volume of water rose out of the rivers over everything down to the Sound.

In Winsted, the Mad River lived up to its name, tore up the streets with twelve feet of raging water and isolated the town for two days. In Seymour and in Woonsocket, Rhode Island, the floods ripped coffins out of cemeteries and carried them downstream. In Putnam, Connecticut, the flood destroyed a magnesium plant and all that night hundreds of barrels of burning magnesium floated on the water in the streets, with metal bursting 250 feet in the air in white-hot flaming fountains.

The two hurricanes together brought the greatest disaster ever known in Connecticut, where a hundred people were killed and known damage went to $200 million.

In Massachusetts, across the Concord River, the 50-foot span of the Old North Bridge where the Minute Men had defied the Redcoats, went down under crushing flood waters. Old buildings, old houses, strong old factories at the water's edge, and people huddling on the roofs, were swept away from far beyond the river banks.

In all more than 310 people died. The total of damage was over $1.5 billion.

Six eastern states were declared disaster areas by President Eisenhower as the helicopters carried the first relief supplies pouring in from the untouched parts of the state and from all over the country. Squadrons of trucks, loaded by hundreds of volunteers from the collection places, were driven to relief points, as martial law was declared in the flood area. Auxiliary police with sidearms were sent in to help protect battered homes and stores from looters and sightseers even as another army of volunteers with tools from everywhere began shoveling yellow mud and refuse and destruction from the huge raw scars that had been pleasant valleys and busy towns.

All banks accepted flood relief funds. Additional Federal relief grants were announced, $500,000 to New York State, $1,000,000 each to Connecticut and Massachusetts.

The new system of coordinated relief between Federal, state, municipal and private agencies, went to work for the first time when the governor of Connecticut called on the President of the United States to declare the flooded districts a major disaster area. This time there were no complaints against the Weather Bureau's hurricane warning system, or even the flood warnings. Relief was as prompt as possible in so great a disaster. It would have been more prompt and help would have come more quickly if there had been a better system of communication. A civil defense radio network that would communicate with every corner of the state was one of the first recommendations in the recovery program.

On the twice-damaged Carolina beaches meantime, rescue work was already giving place to repair and rebuilding in sparkling blue weather as all the beach resorts tried frantically to save the last of their tourist season. From Carolina Beach, with over $4 million of damage, through Wrightsville up to Morehead City, Oregon Inlet and Hatteras, hammers were sounding and shovels scraping away sand. Southward, Kure Beach, Wilmington, Southport, Long's Beach and Holden's Beach were opening their piers and rooming houses, bathing pavilions and restaurants. Already, cottages that had twice been battered or washed away from high tide marks were being set up again on their old foundations. People seemed to feel that where bathing and fishing were so good, the occasional loss of easily rebuilt cottages did not matter.

The twenty-ninth of August saw headlines in every Atlantic Coast newspaper that a hurricane called Edith, the fifth that season, was drifting slowly out in the Atlantic, where Bermuda felt its winds as it moved away.

Even as the National Red Cross announced that its flood-relief fund drive had brought the most prompt response in history, ten million dollars, hurricane Flora was announced on September 4, east-northeast of San Juan, Puerto Rico, and two thousand miles east of Miami, Florida. But before Flora went off to sea hurricane Gladys blew westward, to bring tides four and a half feet above normal to Corpus Christi, Texas, on September 6, and dump eleven inches of rain over the Rio Grande valley, threatening floods to south Texas, and flooded out 60,000 people in Mexico City. It was a bad year.

Early that same first week in September, forecasters were advised that a strong low pressure system had just moved off the continent of Africa into the Atlantic. An airliner reported squalls and shifting winds south of the Cape Verde Islands. Then there was silence until September 12, when hurricane Hilda was located north of the Dominican Republic, roaring at full force almost due west. On September 14 the Grand Caymans were swept clean, just as another hurricane, Ione, was discovered northwest of the Windward Islands, going north.

Hilda went west, to cross eastern Cuba and Yucatán with ruin and death and head straight for Tampico on the Panuco River in Mexico, cutting the highway from Laredo to Mexico City and working millions of dollars' damage to the oil industry. A thousand people were injured and over 204 killed as the rivers rose under the heavy rains. Tampico was isolated and without help as Hilda died in the mountains. One-fifth of the city was homeless. There were no drinking water, lights, electricity. Churches, schools, movie houses were full of refugees. Government food stores were opened. Mexican Air Force planes began a shuttle service carrying in food, medicine, clothing and blankets. Government officials were flown in to speed sanitation and relief work but prompt organization work was lacking. The effect of the hurricane floods would be felt for months if not years.

Ione was there still, far away, but watched by every Weather Bureau on the Atlantic Coast. It swerved toward the United States with eighty-mile winds. An Air Force plane found very heavy turbulence as it tried to penetrate at 19,000 feet, in snow and heavy clouds.

Four states were alerted for hurricanes. Ione with 115-mile winds, moved beyond Palm Beach, Florida. Everyone knew now that she was a very dangerous hurricane. The red-and-black hurricane flags went up from Hatteras to Cape Cod.

Blowing northwest, Ione went ashore across the often hit Carolina beaches, and overwhelmed Morehead City, Washington and Belhaven, North Carolina. High waves smashed over piles of debris. Winds blew at 100 miles per hour. Heavy rains raised high water in the streets. There was five million dollars' worth of property damage. North Carolina's peanut crop was ruined.

Ahead of Ione, Weather Bureau warnings shouted from every radio. People were in hysterics. New York City officials went into a panic of preparations. Airplane flights were canceled. Rescue workers, extra policemen, Coast Guard ships, the Mayor and his Board of Planning and Operations, all leaped into high gear.

Hardly a breeze stirred in Maryland. A Princeton professor of astronomy, John Q. Stewart, said the Weather Bureau was depending too much on radar and airplanes and forgetting to watch the barometer. His barometer had not fallen at all. He believed Ione would not amount to much.

Ione curved harmlessly out to sea before the hurricane warnings were quiet. Newspapers and Professor Stewart and people generally were perfectly furious with the Weather Bureau, which had broadcast only general warnings.

The Weather Bureau said it was almost impossible to say exactly where a hurricane would go, out of the tropics, when it invaded the land. What had happened, they decided, was that the jet stream, one of the great high altitude winds, had suddenly veered downward as far as Virginia, pushing the diminished hurricane out to sea.

It was late in September. The cooling air to the north at this time in the fall puts up a barrier that hurricanes seldom penetrate. Yet when on the twenty-third a vicious great hurricane suddenly hurled out of the Atlantic over Barbados, with winds of 127 miles per hour, all the Atlantic Coast was anxiously aware that thirty people were killed there, and 40,000 were homeless. The next day, the twenty-second of September, was strangely dull and dark in the beautiful rocky island of Grenada, 98 miles southwest of Barbados. The sea was dull gray and roaring about the rocks of the Grenadines. Winds poured over. The radio blared warnings. Policemen on bicycles hurried along country roads among the spice groves to warn the people to take shelter. At noon two cannon were fired, but the frightened people knew what was coming.

By evening for five hours the hurricane winds and rain and high seas had swept across the town, the harbor, the houses. A pier with warehouses collapsed. Rivers flooded. By dawn the island was a heap of wreckage. Nutmeg, coconut and cocoa plantations were destroyed for years to come. Two hundred people were dead. Neighboring islands sent help. British and American relief ships crowded the harbor. With government aid, slowly, only after a year, the island had begun to recover.

Hurricane Janet had already moved west through the empty sea of Venezuela, which few hurricanes invade. Janet was delayed and kept its course uncertainly, but touched with its outermost winds the almost hurricane-free Dutch islands of Curaçao and Aruba.

The U.S. Weather Bureau and the Navy were following every mile of Janet's progress. On the twenty-sixth, a Navy Neptune plane of the Hurricane Hunter Squadron flew out of Jacksonville with nine crewmen and two Canadian news photographers aboard.

The hurricane was now gaining in speed and intensity. The last clear message from the plane was heard early in the morning of the twenty-seventh, when Lieutenant Commander G. B. Windham reported that he was beginning to penetrate the turbulent swirling wall of clouds about the eye, at only 700 feet.

For two hours after that messages were received but in the shrieking static could not be heard. Winds about the eye were probably blowing at 150 miles per hour. The plane was never heard from again. Eight Navy planes and two ships searched all over the quieting area. It was the first hurricane hunter plane ever to be lost in the Atlantic-Gulf-Caribbean sector.

Directly ahead of Janet, northeast of the Central American Cape Gracias a Dios lay tiny Swan Island, where for some years the U.S. Weather Bureau and the Navy have maintained a hurricane observation station. Swan Island is nothing but a dot of sand with palm trees, a tiny village of people more or less native, and the Navy Seismo Building, a Quonset hut, a mess hall and a Weather Station manned by a few Americans.

On the twenty-seventh of September the seas were very rough. The increasing wind uprooted coconut trees. The Weather Bureau men made all possible instrument readings and transmitted them to Miami before the antenna blew away. The seas and winds were increasing, ripping the Weather Building apart. Seven men huddled in the kitchen of the mess hall. Everything else blew away. The refrigerator exploded. At 150 miles per hour the roof went off and they were soaked with 500 gallons of diesel fuel as the tank fell. They managed to dash through raging wind that blew them along with the rain to the covered Navy building.

The eye of the hurricane was approaching. In the half quiet they dashed out to help the desperate native people, men, women and children whose houses were gone. The sky was hazy as milk. After thirty minutes as they crowded in together, the rain began again, the building shuddered, the winds shrieked at hurricane force for four hours more.

The next morning, all but a very few of the 10,000 coconut trees on the island had been snapped off at a height of fifteen feet. There seemed to have been no very high hurricane wave but the beaches were covered with dead fish, almost all with their eyes popped out.

Late that day the first planes dropped food. In two days the U.S. Navy landed to evacuate the island.

But hurricane Janet had gone straight on its course to the coast of Honduras, where it obliterated almost entirely the town of Corozal.

It killed 200 people and injured thousands from the Gulf of Campeche, cutting a path across Yucatán among the old cities and the small thatched houses and the wide fields. Chetumal, the old Spanish capital of the district of Quintana Roo was completely cut off from the rest of Mexico. Heavy seas broke over it and shattered hundreds of houses. Some houses just seemed to explode. A lighthouse with its keeper was blown away. The dead lay about the streets. The Mexican government began evacuating women and children by a fleet of government and private transport planes from the destroyed city.

The city of Veracruz was hurriedly making preparations. Hurricane warnings were screaming in Tampico to the north already hit by two other hurricanes that month. Thousands of people fled as the first light rain fell on the coasts. The rivers were rising again.

The hurricane whirled ashore north of Veracruz piling up high tides as far as Brownsville, Texas. Four hundred miles of coast felt the winds of 114 miles per hour. Hundreds were homeless. Tampico was three-quarters inundated, with 60,000 refugees, many crowding on housetops. The Panuco and Tamesi rivers went on rising. Power and light were cut off. Bodies floated out to the Gulf. Nobody knew how many were dead. A strange peril came from hordes of rattlesnakes that were swept down by flood waters, and from water moccasins which the people on the housetops had to fight off.

From the Sierra Madre Oriente Mountains rising abruptly behind the narrow coastal plain, against whose heights the hurricane beat itself out, its load of rain was dumped into the rivers already swollen, that flooded the villages and cities.

Relief came slowly to Veracruz and Tampico, from the Mexican government still using all its facilities toward evacuating the homeless from Yucatán. U.S. Navy helicopters buzzed over Tampico, rescuing refugees huddled on rooftops. Navy planes worked back and forth over the Caribbean looking for the lost hurricane plane and wrecked ships. The U.S. Army, Air Force and Marines, the American Red Cross and the Salvation Army rushed a seventy-passenger clipper plane of Pan American Airways with supplies and to help evacuate people.

Relief work was still going on feverishly in Mexico as a last off-shoot of tropical cyclone Janet survived the Mexican mountains and swept, and later died, across the Gulf of Lower California. Hurricane Katie slowed and picked up speed again across a sparsely settled area of the Dominican Republic and vanished northeastward into the Atlantic.

There were remote places where the effects of those hurricanes would go on for years, such as the Mexican town of Jicaltepec, in the little hills above Veracruz, across the river from Nautla. Over a hundred years before, it had been settled by French pioneers who introduced vanilla in the rich soil brought down by the rains every year from higher hills. It had been a pretty village of brick houses and gardens in the French manner, prosperous until the river, which was their first way to market at Nautla, silted up and the government put a new road a mile back on the other bank. The town was dying before hurricane Janet's dreadful floods reduced its neat houses to piles of rubble and washed away the huts.

There seemed no help at all for Jicaltepec. Its people were lost in despair, unable, it seemed, to do anything for themselves, until before Christmas a unit of the American Friends' Service Committee moved to the village not so much to bring relief supplies as to help and encourage the people to start clearing up the silt and rubble. That winter the people began to take an interest in rebuilding the plaza garden, with a bandstand, repairing and whitewashing houses for widows and the destitute, and finally rebuilding their school. When the Friends' unit left, Jicaltepec, with renewed spirit, was planning what could be done to build up its old prosperity.

That season of 1955, with eleven hurricanes, was the most extraordinary and disastrous of modern times, to date.

As if that year was the climax of some vast condition, perhaps of the upper air, the following years, 1956 and 1957, were curiously anticlimactic.

In 1956, there were eight storms, chiefly of subnormal intensity, with the greatest damage in the Caribbean Islands and Mexico. The northern Atlantic coasts were not affected, nor were they in 1957, except for hurricane Audrey, the first that year, that blew north up the Gulf of Mexico. Warnings were sounded for Louisiana but the people of the swamps and bayous were not moved. "I wasn't much afraid," one woman said, "because the Lord told us He would never destroy this earth with water again." But Pecan Island, Creole, Grand Chenier and Johnson's Bayou were rolled under by the waves. Dead bodies, fuel tanks and wrecked fishing boats were swept into the main street of Cameron. Three hundred and fifty people died and the living fought for life on any bit of dry land, with invading alligators and moccasin snakes.

The Ohio River Valley, western Pennsylvania and New York felt the last of the hurricane's life northward. It died in Canada.

But after the terrible hurricane histories of the last nearly twenty years, 1957 seemed like a pause, a breathing spell in the endless and unrelenting chronicle of menace.

There was no question but that in other years they would return.

BOOK EIGHT

WHAT'S TO
BE DONE?

1 PROTECTION

1. Against Wind

For thousands of years man considered catastrophes such as hurricanes an evil so vast he was helpless to protect himself against them. They could be only the anger of gods whose laws he had broken or whose saving power he had in some way forfeited. His only hope for security lay in magic.

It did not work. Records of a staggering increase in damages and deaths have piled up, not because hurricanes have grown greater or more frequent, but because on coasts which once the terrible winds had almost to themselves, people, cities, roads, bridges, factories have spread so thickly that wherever a hurricane invades the shore there is something human for it to destroy.

No thinking person is unaware that somewhere in the season along this enormous region and its islands a hurricane will loom. People choose to think that in their locality a hurricane is a very rare accident.

In New England, after two seasons of hurricanes, many people clung to the idea that it could not happen again in fifty years. Yet it has been clearly shown that as often as every two and one-half years tropic disturbances head northward into the temperate zone that only a wide variety of weather chances keep from crossing inland. The general belief in the magic power of modern science, little understood as it is, has induced the comfortable faith that by another season "they" will be stopping hurricanes in their tracks.

This combination of blind faith and heedlessness accounts for the fact that only in a few places hurricane conscious citizens have demanded better warning services, regulations for protection from them and a continuously stepped up study of their nature. Only after the last great hurricanes hit New England was such a clamor

327

raised for national protective measures that Congress was forced for the first time in history to appropriate money adequate to an extended and combined study, a better warning system and an over-all program of relief.

Yet for all that, after 1957, in which only one hurricane damaged Louisiana, that appropriation, in the interest of economy, was cut down. There was little or no public protest.

All the thousands of hurricane stories boil down to this, that even with all modern scientific developments, a man and his family can be alone in a hurricane, as cut off by extreme peril from any human help as the first naked Indian who ever died in one.

In fact, in modern times the property loss by hurricanes has increased so astronomically that no man alive can figure the total of it. It has been the modern boast that hurricane deaths have decreased. Perhaps in comparison to all other accidental deaths the percentage is slight. But there have been from one to four hundred deaths in each hurricane that has reached land in the last few years. Such loss still comes about because, among the unpredictable hazards of hurricanes, individual risk is still a grave one.

In the last analysis, all the warnings, all the knowledge of all the scientists will do a man little good when the hurricane breaks about him, if he has had no thought, no common sense, no foresight for himself and his own. It will never be known how many people have died or been injured because they paid no heed to warnings. Or how many lost their lives or property because they took no thought to the simplest principles of safe building.

From his earliest history man learned to shelter himself from the wildness of weather by building a house. The things which can be done to keep a roof from blowing away and house walls from crashing in under pressure have been studied and are simple enough. It is extraordinary that tens of thousands of people in countries subject to hurricane winds and waters live contentedly in houses that can give them no protection whatsoever. The shocking thing is not only that cities must have building codes and police powers to keep people ordinarily safe but that there are so few cities which have and enforce building codes adequate to protect all their people in hurricanes. In unincorporated country areas, of course, there are no requirements at all and it is left to common sense and tradition to provide them.

If the city of Miami, in Dade County, Florida, were as old as Charleston, South Carolina, it, with the mainland and Keys of south Florida, would undoubtedly be known as the American continental region most frequently invaded by hurricanes. But it was not until the great hurricane of 1926 damaged the hastily built masonry buildings of the boom-time city that Miami people began to learn about sound hurricane-proof building. Its building code was re-written then, and revised and improved many times since, always more strictly, under the demands of architects, insurance under-writers and public opinion. Its provisions are copied in Dade County and by very many other counties and cities in Florida.

The Miami Building Code is intended primarily to ensure that buildings are built strong enough to withstand winds that have been known to increase from 75 to 185 miles per hour. Racking gusts have been recorded as high as 200 miles per hour. Their power for damage is almost unbelievable since the force of the wind increases not just according to the velocity, but to the square of it. So if a wind of 80 miles per hour exerts twenty-six pounds of pressure per square foot, a wind of 150 miles per hour produces the startling pressure, on a completely exposed surface, of 112 pounds. That is the power of wind which can shake a house as if it were a cardboard box, or hurl a narrow lath, as if it were metal, straight through the trunk of a palm tree or force a mush of wet leaves or rags through the smallest chinks in a wall. It forces rain water like mist into every least crevice, in walls or under panes of glass.

There is not only this direct pressure on all the windward surfaces of a building, but what is called the negative pressure on the lee side, a suction as powerful as the direct force. Over a sloping roof the tearing flow of a hurricane wind, if not broken by small irregu-larities, may exert the kind of negative pressure that a wind current over an airplane wing exerts to pull it upward. The same wind force can pull walls and plate glass windows outward, like an explosion.

The first problem of building has always been that of holding a roofed building up. Hurricanes have made clear that a building also must be held down.

Old-time Florida people have always considered that wooden buildings stand hurricanes best, if they are properly braced and tied, because of their flexibility under pressure. In the town of Burrwood, Louisiana, there were no frame buildings standing after a number of hurricanes at the beginning of the century, except those which were held together by sixty-penny spikes, known as a Burrwood finishing nail, driven into heavy timber.

Masonry is another thing entirely. Because the tremendous wind pressure of a hurricane can force water into a concrete wall it can be so saturated that it becomes crumbly and weak. So today the Miami code requires that all walls except those of one-story dwellings must have vertical columns of steel reinforced concrete set at intervals between the blocks.

To that end, masonry buildings that are to have wooden floors must have a poured concrete footing in which steel reinforcing rods are set at intervals. The frame must be braced and a poured concrete lintel or tie-beam of the same width which extends around the house must extend down into the window frame. Steel rods must be embedded in the concrete beam. The plate, which is the next wooden member above the tie-beam, must be bolted down. Straps underneath the plate are secured to every second or third rafter. The strength of the framing of the rafters is specified and the details by which it is braced to the ceiling rafter. A wooden decking or special weatherboarding covers the rafters with felt or tar paper fastened on and tarred. The tar paper keeps the water out but if it is not properly fastened down to the wooden decking, hurricane winds can peel it off from the ridge to the eaves.

In Miami, the hurricane of 1950 touched off a big postwar Veterans' Administration housing scandal when countless roofs of GI homes were blown off because of careless and inferior construction. As a result, the U.S. government required stiffer building restrictions for government-mortgaged properties everywhere and the Miami Building Code was again made more strict.

It has long been proved that a house or building can be made so strong that it can live through the highest hurricane winds yet known.

There are also many precautions the wise householder must take, as any local weather bureau now broadcasts, when a hurricane is imminent but before the immediate winds rise to seventy-five miles per hour. Doors must be braced. All weak places should have been repaired or reinforced. A house should be provided with heavy wooden or steel shutters permanently, or easily attached, which should be closed on the windward side as the winds pick up speed, and left open on the leeward. This serves to equalize the inner and outer pressure without which windows may be sucked outward and the roof blown off. Heavy branches or boards blown through the air may crash through unshuttered panes of glass and let in torrents of rain. It is better in any case for the people who must sit and wait to be inside a half-opened house. Too many people delay to put up their shutters because they hate that feeling of being shut in.

Because during a hurricane electricity is interrupted or cut off when necessary, living is reduced to much more primitive level. Any resourceful people can provide themselves beforehand with the things that are essential to their living. There must be some way of cooking and lighting, such as kerosene, solidified alcohol or bottled gas. There must be kerosene lamps, candles, flashlights and extra batteries, battery radios, tubs full of clean water, plenty of canned goods, dry ice if refrigeration fails, rope, nails, tools for emergency repairs, rags and newspapers to stuff in broken windows, through shutters or under doors, a first-aid kit for injuries. Many a broom handle lashed with a clothesline has held broken shutters shut. Many a heavy piece of furniture has held a door firm that the wind tries, like a savage beast, to burst open. Dry clothing and blankets will keep out the damp hurricane chill.

Out of doors, long since, all the loose things should have been put away—porch chairs, pails, ladders. Dead trees must have been taken down, vines pruned, even old trees topped that might go over when the ground is saturated. Cars must be put in garages so well-built that the roof or walls will not collapse on them. The brakes should be set and windows slightly opened. The gas tank should be full. Water in swimming pools should be lowered two feet below normal, the electric pump removed from underground filter pit after valves are closed. All electricity must be turned off at the supply panel. Boats should be taken out of water and sheltered or well-secured fore and aft in a sheltered harbor, to stout pilings, on lines long enough to ride the high water. Safe anchorage should be chosen and arranged for long before trouble arises. In the Bahamas, after the engines are removed, people sink their boats deep below the waves. Larger boats and yachts should be taken as far up inland rivers as possible just as all airplanes are flown far from the hurricane's likeliest course. Invalids in the family should be removed to a safer place.

Not just the householder but cities and towns everywhere must also prepare to protect themselves. Fire departments, water departments, waste and garbage removal departments must be prepared, not only for the hard work that will come afterward but to clean things up beforehand so that litter and tree branches and refuse and uncollected garbage will not be blown all over everywhere as the great winds begin.

2. Against Water

For all the astonishing force of hurricane winds, greatest damage and loss of life comes from water, in wind-driven waves and hurricane floods.

Therefore where a house is placed in relation to bodies of water which hurricanes can affect is of the greatest possible importance. It has been proved again and again that a house can be built to withstand winds at the highest speeds we know. It would be a remarkable house indeed that is unaffected by the pounding shocks of hurricane wave action or the irresistible sucking outflow of sea water or the attacks of rivers swollen with hurricane rains and wild for sea level.

It is only recently that engineers have begun to study the menace along shore of hurricane surges. They rage across reefs, beaches, dunes and sandspits, invading harbors, rivers, tidal basins, docks, streets, cellars and subways.

They are doubly dangerous when they push the water of the high tide or the moon tide far past their usual marks. They are triply dangerous when their pressure holds the ebb tide from running out of tidewater rivers so that the next normal high tide can push the accumulated waters back and higher still.

Hurricane surges have left shocking changes behind them all along the islands and coastal beaches. Dunes crumble before them. Tides cut across long sand islands and carve new inlets from the sea to inland waterways. Old inlets are closed as hundreds of thousands of tons of sand are swept along and deposited in new places.

When the worst winds of the hurricane have passed and their pressure no longer holds back the impounded tides, an even graver menace which few structures can resist comes with the dreadful sucking action of the outgoing water. The very sand is sucked out from under otherwise sound houses, which stood the wind pressure and the waves, so that, undermined, they collapse. Such a force tears up and twists railway lines, retaining walls, concrete piers.

Early records from the West Indies tell of heavy iron cannon pushed from the sea walls of forts and rolled along harbor bottoms by the combined action of waves and undertow. One of the freaks of hurricane action on Carolina beaches was that hundreds of heavy refrigerators, stoves, washing machines and food freezers from destroyed cottages were rolled and pushed along by wave action until they were half-buried like rocks in sand edging a new-cut inlet.

Far inland, from coastal plain to foothills after the hurricane winds have passed with the tremendous downpours of its rainy sector, the other great danger crashes down unsuspecting valleys in floods as irresistible and terrible as the hurricane itself. The whole watershed has been soaked and gives off water rushing with the full weight of gravity down to inland lakes or bays or the sea. The coasts of Mexico, the valley of the Rio Grande have known such floods for centuries. In the last few years several hurricanes turning inland have brought flood destruction in Virginia, Pennsylvania, New York, New England and Canada.

The first and perhaps the only rule for safety in hurricane tides is to put the building where the highest high water will not reach it. At sea level it must be raised on high and stout pilings. It has been impossible to prevent the building of beach cottages too near high tide marks. With every year in which the whole population of the United States has increased, more and more people feel the fascination of the summer sea. Atlantic beaches that always have been empty but for sea birds and wrecks and the hardiest fishermen's families are now crammed with cottages, with villages of hotels, restaurants, filling stations and bathing casinos.

The only safety then, when the warnings go up and the Coast Guard men come knocking at doors, is to get the children, the old people and the pets into the car and get out.

Even that is not an easy as it sounds. The great problem of these long coastal islands from Brownsville to Montauk is that the single road running through them for miles lies parallel to the ocean beaches and may already in low places be covered by the smoking march of the waves. There is rarely more than one long causeway or bridge in seven or eight miles connecting these islands to the mainland. With the wind strengthening and water coming over, it is difficult and dangerous enough to arrive at the causeways, from which many a car has been blown as the storm increased.

It takes hours to get off some of the Florida Keys. The new settlement of Key Biscayne at Miami is exposed to the open sea to the south, and miles from the low causeway which could be washed over even as cars race to the mainland. The linked islands off Charleston have only one slightly higher place of refuge and only one long bridge miles distant from the farthest beaches. There are hundreds of other such exposed islands, where already too many people have died.

Many true islands have no easy escape at all, even by boat or airplane so that building on pilings, or as high up on slopes as possible, is the only chance of security.

The danger of high hurricane waves, to worried Weather Bureau men and Coast Guard officers, is such that in many cases they feel it is better to advise evacuation of the whole population to shelters and bear their scolding if the hurricane does not arrive, than to lose a single life.

Not enough local officials, and certainly the people of few ruined cities or areas, have demanded adequate hurricane protection.

The first concerted civic effort of this kind was the great sea wall of Galveston, Texas, built after the 1900 hurricane by the heartfelt cooperation of all the citizens. After the 1915 hurricane the wall was so thoroughly strengthened and extended that Galveston, although visited by many hurricanes since, has never experienced such losses and deaths.

The Railway Extension over the Florida Keys, whose solid embankments across once open water were a partial cause of the inexcusable loss of life in the Labor Day hurricane of 1935, has been abandoned. In its place an open roadway has been built with miles of open bridges which allow the normal ebb and flow of tides into Florida Bay. But the hurricane-conscious people of south Florida have constantly to be on the alert to prevent ambitious real estate men and builders, with some politicians, from trying to connect the Keys with the mainland by solid causeways that would still endanger them, instead of bridges.

It has been said that a wide beach is a greater protection than a narrow one. Some people, as on the islands north of Hatteras, pin their faith for hurricane protection on a series of offshore reefs, although such reefs have been no help to Florida. The truth is, that not enough is known about beach erosion prevention. The people of some localities like Montauk at the eastern tip of Long Island have for generations prided themselves on their knowledge of the proper building of sea walls. Yet the whole business of breakwaters, jetties and groins has been left to the whims of beach property owners. A confusion of groins has often increased beach erosion and certainly has been no help in hurricanes. Some engineers are earnestly trying to promote a series of coastwise conferences on beach erosion, which might be the beginning of a very important over-all study of Atlantic beaches in hurricanes.

The control of floods caused by hurricane rains upstream in river systems in congested areas is probably the most difficult and complicated of all after-hurricane problems. It is also highly controversial. Some engineers say that total flood protection is impossible. Some say that even a small attempt at local flood protection is worth trying. The difficulty of the problem is increased by the density of the population.

The state of Florida again set an example of good flood protection, after the hurricane floods of 1928, when all Lake Okeechobee spilled over into the southern mucklands, with a dreadful loss of life. The state asked the help of the U.S. engineers through the Federal government. A huge rock levee, built all around the southern rim of the great lake, has successfully protected the lake towns and the great vegetable and cattle lands from any such flooding. But in addition, to maintain a proper water supply for the East Coast cities, in wet times or dry, and regulate the water table, an enormous system of canals, dikes, pumping stations, and water conservancy areas are being constructed throughout the northern and middle Everglades for the benefit of the East Coast counties.

There is actually no central agency that collects flood damage figures and tries to bring some uniformity to the chaos of flood regulations, or the lack of them. Even the Weather Bureau, to which the study of floods was transferred in 1890, had decided that it can give an accurate forecasting of floods over a short period of time only. It has not yet solved the difficult business of prophesying what a hurricane will do and where it will go once it has moved inland in the temperate zone.

In 1936 a Federal Flood Control Act was set up which appropriated $63 for flood control on main streams by the U.S. Engineer Corps, for every dollar spent on the improvement of watersheds and watershed control by the U.S. Department of Agriculture. In 1954 Congress passed the Watershed Protection and Flood Prevention Act to provide a program by which local groups can cooperate and receive assistance from the Federal government for the best uses of water in the upper reaches before runoff. This was to be supplementary to the work for downstream flood control by the U.S. engineers. It has not yet been thoroughly worked out.

The water flowing in innumerable streams, and river systems branching across two or three northeastern states, from the hills to the sea, was the source of all New England's wealth. Mills and factories were crowded on their banks, with houses of owners and workers and their villages spreading out on the river plains. The rivers run down the center of most New England towns.

The outstanding example of good local protection from flood water was the building of retaining walls along the Connecticut River in the manufacturing district of Hartford, Connecticut, which it so often flooded since the first flood records were kept from 1600 on. The flood walls, built after the 1938 hurricane, have never been topped by water.

Other mills were set downstream at tidewater so that their goods might be loaded directly on ships. So New Bedford and the manufacturing cities along the Sound, the bays and salt river mouths of southern New England were ruined, factories, machines and warehoused goods, by the assault of hurricane waves, just as the fifty-two Connecticut towns along the steep valleys of the Naugatuck, the Torrington and the Quinebaug were drowned in the floods of 1955. The only prevention possible would be a concerted movement on the part of factory and mill owners to move their industries high enough beyond all danger of flood water. There have evidently been only sporadic individual attempts at doing this and no wholesale moving thought of except the great effort begun by the state of Connecticut for wholesale relief, recovery and future flood prevention, which will be discussed.

2 *RELIEF*

In the crises of hurricanes, in the last analysis, men and their families are alone, with their own courage and their own foresight. It is afterward when the wind has gone away and people wander dazedly under clearing skies staring at wet wreckage and calling to the missing, that they realize that no man can long survive disaster by himself.

The first problem is always to get the word of disaster out of the ruined and isolated place. Even while the last of a hurricane is raging, exhausted men have risked their lives to row a boat or swim a river or struggle along a torn-up railway track out into an unknowing world. It is difficult in this day of radio to believe how absolutely cut off from human help were any hurricaned West Indian islands when the sailing of supply ships from mother countries was prevented by politics or war. It is even more difficult today to believe that only in a very recent hurricane towns on the south coast of Haiti were so cut off that it was weeks before any relief at all was sent.

Old cities in out of the way places along unfrequented coasts like Yucatán, villages hidden in jungles, flooded towns in the foothills above Veracruz, have often gone for days without help, because of the difficulties of communication. Even then the Mexican government, its disaster organization and resources strained by the need of evacuating the old and the injured by airplane, has had to call in the aid of American naval vessels and planes, and the International Red Cross, even to begin to handle the emergency.

Indeed, the long history of hurricanes about the Atlantic, alone, shows that man's sense of responsibility toward the sufferings of his fellow man in a great nationally felt calamity is only a very recent development. Yet in the United States, where today the word of disaster is flashed out by radio, telegraph, telephone, and newspaper headlines, and organized relief begins to pour in, circumstances exist in which a community could still be cut off for days from human knowledge and human help.

There is no help that can be given to a stricken people that is so important as the unorganized, purely spontaneous help of neighbors. The first man in a sailboat who makes his way to help the people on a nearby ruined Bahama island, the first man who comes plodding down the beach to the hurricane-swept place, the first man over the broken bridge, are the rescuers who count most to the survivors who are already searching out their own injured and dying, and the women who are binding up wounds with whatever clean cloths they can find and lighting the fires under the community kettles. Neighbors are the ones who first feed the hungry, round up the children, search out the missing, get the old people taken care of, put up makeshift beds and shelters and get things going.

That is why all people in hurricane-likely areas must be trained and ready for immediate disaster work. By the nature of things, on the initiative, drive, courage and trained ability of survivors and neighbors the welfare of a ruined area may have to depend for days.

After the hurricanes of 1926 and 1928 and with the local bitterness against the then inadequacies of the American Red Cross, the people of Miami and the lower east coast of Florida attempted to set up a network of local relief units and train their own groups of hurricane relief workers. But no relief can be entirely local. The whole resources of the nation must be made available as soon as possible.

In the West Indian islands and the remoter coasts of Central America the whole picture of relief was changed by the coming of the airplane. Even then at first the organization of relief suffered from confusion, inadequacy and lack of planning.

Airplanes were probably first used after the terrible hurricane of September 3, 1930, that ruined almost all of Santo Domingo, only a few years stabilized as a republic. San Domingo city, San Pedro

Macoris, San Isidro and faraway towns like Azua were leveled and desolate. Hospitals with no roofs or broken walls barely sheltered hundreds of people wounded by cement blocks and galvanized iron roofing hurled about by the winds. The dying lay on dirty floors. There were food riots. General disorder and panic increased.

President Trujillo called for aid to Colonel R. M. Cutts, commandant of the U.S. Marine Corps still occupying Haiti. Marine Corps planes immediately brought in the only relief supplies which the city had for four or five days. A new Naval attaché to the Republic was flown in and made Food Administrator. An American Naval officer from the Haitian Service d'Hygién was put in charge of the wretched hospital situation.

Supplies came from Cuba and Puerto Rico. Dutch and British ships came in with hospital units, doctors and medicines. Five days after the hurricane the American Red Cross representative was flown in. The Dominican Red Cross was better organized. As soon as possible, the American turned over the work to local governmental officials.

Already, Pan-American Airways was beginning to extend its services by seaplane from Miami everywhere throughout the Caribbean, where for some years it was the most important general air carrier. Hurricanes were the greatest possible menace to its operations. In 1927 and '28 there were not a dozen weather stations in the whole area. By 1931 Pan-American had established its own hurricane watches in twenty-two countries in the hurricane region. It also and of necessity became the first relief service available, and it has always maintained this service without charge.

In 1931, in the hurricane that destroyed Belize, Honduras, the Pan-American radio installation, which its men struggled all night to keep out of the rising waves, sent out the first message for help to the outside world. Its barracks were the only large building left standing, where refugees could gather and from which relief supplies, sent in by all available planes from Miami, were given out. Pan-American planes were the first into San Juan with relief after the hurricane of September 26, 1932, at Tampico in '33, where Pan-American men were called on to organize relief work for the American Red Cross and in '34 in June at San Salvador and Cozumel, Yucatán.

After five years, the U.S. Weather Bureau and the Weather Bureaus of the other hurricane countries organized their own hurricane services and warning stations but Pan-American still maintains its own weather office, in control of its own planes. It brought help after many other hurricanes; Bahama Red Cross supplies to British Honduras again, medicines from New York to stricken Barbados, after hurricane Hazel, two iron lungs to Tampico, and, regular 70-passenger clipper services in shuttle flights carrying refugees from Tampico to other Mexican cities. Now many other airplane lines, covering the Caribbean like the Pan-American, put all their equipment freely at the service of devastated areas. The Mexican and Cuban governments now use all their own planes for such relief work.

The use of helicopters in such disasters was demonstrated in hurricane Janet, when ten U.S. Navy helicopters from U.S. Aircraft carrier *Saipan* flew low over flooded Tampico and snatched people from treetops, roofs and sandbanks. Helicopters hovered over flooded river areas for a dozen different purposes in the hurricaned regions of New England and Toronto, Canada, of recent years.

The Second World War changed at once the character of hurricane relief in Florida. Relief, which included emergency work in the event of enemy attack, was reorganized under Civil Defense, a network of local units organized and directed nationally. Everywhere, a system of emergency medical aid stations, hospitals, transportation corps and rescue workers was set up by the people in their own communities. The Red Cross had a valuable place in all this, lending trained workers for first-aid drill classes and emergency relief. Supplies of all kinds were collected and stored in emergency storerooms. Paper systems were simplified. Since it was wartime, the whole tempo was increased and all workers had to be efficient and constantly vigilant.

After the war, the Civil Defense organization was retained and hurricane work was coordinated under it. It is surprising to realize that for all our American faith in our own promptness and generosity, the first law to set up an over-all National Disaster Relief, as it is now known, was enacted by Congress only as recently as September, 1950. It has been constantly revised and no doubt still needs improvement on every local level to keep it prompt and effective. But it was a great step forward.

The Act provided an orderly and continuous means of assistance by the Federal government to the states and local governments, in a close relation, to alleviate suffering and damage in great national disasters.

A hurricane has destroyed, and blown on. The survivors, the neighbors, the police, firemen, local doctors have sprung to work. The Civil Defense Council has called out its organized and trained rescue workers, nurses, medical aids, alerted hospitals, health personnel of the local health department and men and women volunteers for all sorts of prepared special services.

The disaster is immediately seen as too great for local abilities to handle. The governor of the state declares martial law and all the state's forces are called on. They are not adequate either for relief or for the expensive difficult process of reclamation and first recovery. Then the governor may formally request that the Disaster Relief law be invoked. He must certify the need for Federal assistance and give assurance of the expenditure of a reasoned amount of state and local funds for the same purpose, under Civil Defense, and the direction of the state Civil Defense coordinator.

The President then declares the district is a major disaster area. At once, the organized resources, public and private, of the nation are called out. Among Federal forces, the Coast Guard, under a separate memorandum for peacetime, controls all civilian small craft. The Army, Navy and Air Force perform all services necessary to preserve life and property, to help repair and replace local public facilities, to clear debris and wreckage, to provide emergency shelter and make contributions to state and local governments. Surplus Federal supplies and equipment are donated or lent to the state, but Federal aid is always supplemental to state aid. Predisaster plans have been worked out between such Federal departments as Agriculture, Commerce, Defense, Health, Education and Welfare, Interior and others, among which are included the work of wreckage clearance, emergency repair, aid for repair, reconstruction of bridges and highways, assistance, nursing, food and relief to survivors and every other assistance necessary to put the people and their community in working condition again.

The weakness in the plan lies in the fact that as the states were by no means equal in their disaster facilities, each had to enter into a separate agreement with the Federal government, which not all of them have done. Most of the coastal states, however, aware of constant danger and the advantages of Federal cooperation, now participate.

It was not the only weakness in modern relief work. At the end of the 1954 hurricane season in which, in the northern states, there was a desperate failure in getting to the rest of the world news of the disaster, Charleston, South Carolina, was selected as the center for an amateur radio hurricane warning service to be called the Coastal Emergency Network.

In South Carolina, 762 ham operators, well organized for state emergency work, at their own expense had worked day and night to get out weather reports, relief needs and messages to and from the afflicted people. After hurricane Hazel, the U.S. Weather Bureau had cited for distinguished service four local amateur radio groups, in Charleston, Georgetown, Myrtle Beach and Florence. Other southern states had good amateur radio organizations but there was no related organization between the states. The ham radio operators hoped to extend the new network from Key West to Norfolk and eventually all the way up and down the coast. The hope was that operators might be equipped, or equip themselves, with trucks and cars with adequate two-way transmitters. There seems to be no official attempt to set up such an emergency system which is still left to the vigilance of the amateurs. As usual, when the immediate emergency is over, the energy to complete so obviously important organization has seemed to lag.

The Federal Civil Defense Administration has a formal understanding with the American Red Cross, which describes their shared responsibility for the distribution of relief supplies in a distressed area. Nowadays, Red Cross activities are carefully organized at the local level, with local volunteers trained in clerical and other procedures. In Florida, before the hurricane season, there are all sorts of special training assignments. The Red Cross is responsible also for providing immediate mass care, food, shelter and clothing for all distressed people. It cooperates with local public health in services in nursing, emergency medical stations, hospitals and transportation. But always under Civil Defense.

This tremendous coordination of activities for Disaster Relief was put to its first test following hurricane Diane on August 20, 1955. Its effectiveness was demonstrated in the first and only serious hurricane disaster of 1957, when in June hurricane Audrey created havoc over 1,500 square miles of Texas and southwest Louisiana. Hundreds of people died because hurricane warnings were not heeded. The town of Cameron was a waste of pitted mudholes where houses had been. There was no light, no roofs, no food. Four months after the Disaster Relief Administration and the Red Cross had gone to work, 1,474 families had been assisted, 1,190 families provided with household furnishings, 1,295 with food and clothing, labor and materials financed to rebuild 731 houses. The town of Cameron and the district around it was on its feet again.

Of all private utilities, the most important service that must be restored after a disaster is that of the electric light and power companies.

Telephone companies in many places put their wires safely underground. Many are seeking to improve their cables, like the Narragansett Electric Company out of Providence, Rhode Island, in an area damaged by ice storms as well as hurricanes. For the many tree-lined streets and roads, their company, since 1946, use a nonmetallic shielded type of cable which does away with the need for pruning trees. It remains in service in spite of fallen trees and poles and has a high resistance to hurricane winds.

Many cities require power and light companies to bury their wires. But in Florida the utility companies do not extend their wires underground outside of the main business districts. Light poles and wires come crashing down as hurricane winds blow roofs or trees on them. Power is often interrupted as a hurricane nears. The company has to resume service as soon as possible after the height of the winds has passed, first of all to such public necessities as hospitals, water works, sewerage and food storage plants, radio stations and gas stations. Trunk power lines must be opened as soon as it is safe and the public constantly kept informed.

The Florida Power and Light Company, in the hot summer before every hurricane season stages a full dress seven-hour hurricane drill. Under a predetermined plan emergency crews are ready to be brought in from all over the state, or nearby states when necessary, fed and housed. The plan itself is based on a complete decentralization, in which some twenty-eight local stations are set up, each equipped and ready to restore power in its own district.

As many as seventy-five employees, volunteer office workers and so on are trained in special classes, four hours once a week for six weeks, with 500 linemen and service men and supervisors, to man the separate stations.

The day of the drill, it is assumed that the city is devastated. The emergency crews are already at their stations. They receive the word of damage from men with walkie-talkies who tack up white cards on poles so that the crews will know what the damage is. The central office is equipped with ten battery receiving and sending sets, so that, as the work of repair continues, its nature and progress is marked with pegs on a great central board. Where transformers are gone, complete substations may be moved around on trailers. Auxiliary gasoline-powered generators that are available for immediate rental are listed, ready to be set up for important public services. All necessary wire, all possible supplies are at hand in emergency storerooms. Large quantities of dry ice are on order, ready to be trucked in for use as local refrigeration.

All over Florida on the day of the hurricane drill, area substations hum like frontline battle stations, as the war against hurricane damage is tried out.

A similar decentralization plan was decided to be the most practical in Pennsylvania by the Philadelphia Electric Company and proved its worth first with hurricane Hazel in 1954. Service was then completely restored in five days.

The Major Emergency Plan of Operation, which the Boston Edison Company had had set up for its far-flung lines in eastern Massachusetts, was revised completely after the 1954 hurricanes. After a study of the Florida system, it was decided that a very complete program of decentralization under a central control center was the most efficient method.

Other power companies in other states once hurricaned are making new studies. It is the opinion everywhere that the problem is to estimate the damage quickly, to determine at once how much help is needed and get it on the job fast.

3 INSURANCE AND REBUILDING

Ever since the fourteenth century in Europe, it has been considered that the cheapest and best way for a man to provide against losses is insurance. Americans are accustomed to insurance for everything from burglary to unemployment. It is inevitable that people should try to turn to insurance to make up for losses and damages in hurricanes. But the surprising thing is that while injuries and deaths in hurricanes and hurricane floods are taken care of under the usual accident, health, or life insurance, property damage in hurricanes has never been successfully handled by insurance or considered by insurance underwriters a profitable risk.

For flood risks, private insurers offer protection only for movable or personal property. Immovable property, like bridges or tunnels, can be insured under an all-risk policy. Flood damage to motor vehicles is insured under comprehensive coverage. Inland marine policies cover all sorts of things in transit, tugs, yachts, or goods in storage on piers and in warehouses. Many personal things, jewels, furs and art objects, are covered by floater policies.

That leaves an enormous amount of property, private, commercial or industrial, for which no flood risk insurance is offered. Even home mortgages insured by the FHA, except for Veterans Administration guaranteed or insured home mortgages, are not covered by flood risk.

The problem is to define the nature of hurricane risk.

If damage occurs in a hurricane flood, right to recover hinges on whether the damage was caused by wind or water. Wind damage is allowable. Water damage may be contested, so that insurers actually have the opportunity to decline to pay for damages caused solely by water in a hurricane. Standard extended coverage insures against direct loss by windstorm or hail, but not by wave action, high water or overflow, whether driven by wind or not. Damage inside a building must not be caused by water, rain, snow, sand, or dust, whether driven by wind or not, unless openings in roofs or walls were first made by wind. No insurance is offered against interior wall seepage, such as happened in Washington, D.C., as a result of hurricane Connie in 1955.

It may be seen from this that insurance companies have protected themselves with the greatest care from liabilities in relation to flood, wave action and rain, the greatest cause of property damage in hurricanes. The reason is clear. In such catastrophes as hurricanes, loss by water is almost inevitable. To pay the annual losses, it was found in a long study of flood insurance possibilities, would force the rates so high that the general public would refuse and has refused to purchase such insurance. The total of losses from any one such catastrophe would bankrupt the strongest insurance company.

However, a new study of the problems is being made in hope that some form of flood insurance can be made both beneficial and profitable.

Wind damage insurance, on the other hand, is the only kind practicable in hurricanes because everyone is exposed to wind losses of one kind or another. Windstorm loss such as followed hurricane Diane in 1955 hit hardest on states not usually associated with floods, but it was taken care of under the standard extended coverage in use on residential and commercial properties in New England and the Middle Atlantic states. The largest single loss in 1955 amounted to about $1 million which occurred when hurricane Carol blew off a roof on a textile plant in Fall River, Massachusetts. The roof had not been properly anchored. Even so, insurance losses that year were not large in contrast to the total amount of insurance written.

Following the hurricane losses of 1955 there was an increasing demand for a government administered nation-wide flood insurance program which would, of course, include hurricane floods. Studies are still being made with an eye to preparing several such bills but the problems involved are so complex that it is understandable if no Federal action has been taken.

Federal as well as commercial private insurance against hurricane losses, therefore, may be seen to lag tremendously behind the increasing efficiency of immediate relief. It has become only one phase of the problem of long-time recovery from hurricane devastation which in these modern times requires all the resources of Federal, state and local governments hand-in-hand with private enterprise strained to its utmost.

Certain forms of assistance by certain Federal agencies, under the Disaster Relief Act, have the effect of long-term rehabilitation. The FHA is authorized to issue mortgages, under certain terms, on single family residences which have been destroyed in the major disaster area. Lenders may be authorized to permit suspension of loan payments for a year and on home repair and modernization loan payments for two years, as well as to extend the mortgage term from twenty-five to thirty years and to reduce the amount of down payment to 5 per cent.

Federally owned housing units and trailers were made available for an indefinite time to 232 families in Pennsylvania, Connecticut, Rhode Island and Massachusetts after hurricane Diane. The Urban Rural Administration is authorized to make grants up to 50 per cent of cost to regional, metropolitan and county planning agencies for replanning areas subject to recurring disasters, and to provide loans and grants for regular urban renewal projects. After hurricane Diane the URA advanced thousands of dollars to such flooded ruined cities as Scranton, Pennsylvania and Waterbury, Connecticut, and to such organizations as the Connecticut Development Commission and the Rhode Island Development Council.

These are only partial measures, however. Nothing could illustrate better the huge problem of permanent recovery than the story of what went on in Connecticut after that state and others of New England were drowned and destroyed by fresh-water floods caused by hurricanes Connie and Diane in 1955.

Destruction was most complete in the valleys of the Naugatuck, the Torrington and the Quinebaug river systems. The Naugatuck Valley with its cities, Torrington, Waterbury, Naugatuck, Seymour and Ansonia, is typical. In the course of a hundred years it had become the center of a bronze and brass industry with a dense working population. When the floods stopped all production, not only all those people but industrial activity all over the country was affected.

The valley itself, like so many others, is less than fifty miles long, steep-sloped, and narrow. The mild-seeming river rises among pleasant hills at 2,000 feet with the greatest incline and runoff in the upper valley. It joins the Housatonic at 200 feet. The cities with the river running through them are huddled on the narrow river plain, only nine miles at the widest, and are completely vulnerable to floods.

The soil upstream in the Naugatuck Valley is too thin to absorb much rainfall although fully two-thirds of its two watersheds were well forested, with a good deal of cropland. The upper ground had been bone dry for three and a half weeks in the extraordinarily hot weather before the first hurricane, so that it could have stored an ordinary rainfall. But not the more than eight inches that fell from August 12 to 14 in hurricane Connie, and thirteen inches from hurricane Diane that pounded the already saturated earth in forty-eight hours on August 18 and 19. After that, the average river level rose from two feet to twenty-four feet.

In the terrible emergency which followed, the state of Connecticut was faced with the most desperate problems of relief and recovery in its entire history. They could not have been solved without the cooperation of all governmental and private agencies and the work and good will of thousands of citizens. Future flood-control plans had naturally to wait on the people's distress. But the Flood Recovery Committee, appointed by the governor, at once set up a subcommittee for flood control to be planned as far as possible along with recovery. The committee stated its hope that recovery plans should not perpetuate old errors or merely restore the obsolete or inadequate, nor limit opportunities for a new approach, "which are the only potential good in any disaster." The committee urged that the state, in concert with other New England states and New York, take steps to obtain early congressional funds for a sound over-all flood program.

It was apparent at once that no over-all flood-control program had ever been set up in the state of Connecticut. And as time went on it became equally clear that the committee's hopes for concerted action with neighboring states was merely a hope. Nothing has evidently been done about interstate plans, admittedly a very devious affair.

The work of preventing flood disasters within single states like Connecticut is difficult and complicated enough. It seems to divide automatically into two parts. The first problem is that of controlling and channeling flood water so that flood crests can be lessened and flood water run off harmlessly without dangerous encroachment on the human life around it. It is a technical problem dependent on the will and desire of the people of the basic locality subject to floods, without whose approval nothing can be accomplished legally. The second and even more intricate one is the problem of removing the people from and keeping them out of the flood water.

Before the disaster there were two bodies at work in the state, the State Board for the Supervision of Dams and the State Flood Control and Water Policy Commission, both undermanned, with very little money. Whatever they had been able to do was not much. They were given new powers by the Flood Recovery Committee, in cooperation with the studies by the U.S. engineers.

The State Board for the Supervision of Dams was set to work at once on an inventory, apparently for the first time, of all the dams in the state. After two years, dams in fifteen towns out of 154 have been mapped and inspected, with recommendations for repair and improvement. Additional sites were selected for two flood-control dams above Torrington, one above Winsted, one above Putnam. Other sites were being studied for three dams on the Naugatuck and three on the Farmington.

Of the innumerable destroyed bridges to be rebuilt, and the many new ones, some will have improved approaches and be built to allow the harmless passage of from five to seven times the amount of flood water.

The three desperately wrecked valleys, the Naugatuck, the Farmington, the Quinebaug with their fifty-two towns and cities, were considered as three over-all regions for which the U.S. engineers were making studies and long-term plans for flood control.

Other planning programs with their local problems must, by state law, be left to the will and foresight of the individual communities. Each must ask approval for Federal and state aid to share the financial burdens of programs planned by U.S. engineers and regional planners. By 1957 fifteen had already organized such programs and others were waiting approval.

A state law of 1955 provided that any Connecticut town, city or borough might vote to request the Commissioner of Agriculture for advice and assistance to begin a soil conservation and flood prevention project for the control of flood water for the watershed area in which the town is located. Eleven towns requested and were approved for state and Federal assistance: Windsor, Woodbury, Stafford, Granby, East Granby, Farmington, Westport, North Canaan, Norfolk and Simsbury.

The emphasis on the will and freedom of the individual community in matters of flood protection is even more clear in that other more difficult matter of human engineering, keeping the people away from the floods. The river plains were always centers of population in Connecticut, because the work was there, in humming mills and factories near the source of water power. With electricity and turbines it is no longer necessary for a mill to be on a river bank or a mill stream. But to move old established industries and commercial establishments away from their own land to safer new lands, and to move the houses and buildings of citizens who have always chosen to live by the river, is an undertaking of extraordinary complication and delicacy in any democracy.

Public buildings, schools, firehouses, courthouses and so on, in many flooded places, are being relocated on safer lands. The committee strongly recommended that legislation be enacted so that shopping and business districts and industrial sections might be moved completely away from flooded areas. Details of financing were carefully worked out. Any township could make itself over, if it chose to.

The problem of replanning for flood safety and rebuilding in all these towns is made even more difficult by the fact that the state of Connecticut is constantly encouraging and hoping for the establishment of new business in all these often flooded industrial valleys so that, in the next few years, it confidently expects to see an increase there of a million new people, with 400,000 new jobs. No planning is on the boards which can keep up with that.

At the most, in these years since the hurricanes, fifteen flooded municipalities have begun to accomplish something in the way of town planning and redevelopment. With no later hurricane to keep people alert, that is probably remarkable.

Through twelve of the badly flooded towns and cities, U.S. engineers were able to establish ninety-three miles of encroachment lines of excessive flood danger within which no buildings might be built. In these ruined areas many towns were setting up parks or public parking areas or such commercial undertakings as floods could not damage. Yet pressure to rebuild in ruined areas was so great that legislation to allow towns to declare a building moratorium within a flooded area had to restrict the moratorium to only six months and to only a single disaster. Ordinary zoning laws needed to be strengthened by additional legislation, to hold against the demand for immediate rebuilding.

The Connecticut Development Credit Corporation was set up to give help with the state's faith and credit, where Federal funds were not available, specifically to hurry up the process of relocating damaged commercial plants with housing, where they could expect to be safe from floods and resume their businesses as quickly as possible. The corporation's financing plan took care of condemning lands for removal, but all under the control and subject to the plans of the towns themselves.

After two years the state of Connecticut was still struggling with these enormous recovery problems, chiefly financial. It meant the outlay of millions of state and Federal money for repair and replacement of public property, for tax refunds, for temporary and permanent housing. Twenty-four redevelopment projects in sixteen municipalities were being carried on. Flood-control studies were still being made, with no over-all plans visible.

Finally, legislation was provided for the establishment of Regional Planning Authorities, to take over, at the request of all the towns and cities within one river-controlled region, all this work of town planning, redevelopment, watershed and flood control. Not even the devastated valleys of the Naugatuck, the Farmington and the Quinebaug, seemed willing to put their problems in the hands of such single control. Only one regional planning authority, therefore, has ever been set up, the South Central Connecticut Authority, centered at New Haven.

Crowded Connecticut has probably done as much as or more about future floods than any other state, except for uncrowded Florida. Yet although all these people must endure, in the same catastrophe, the same expectation of danger, loss and death, they have chosen to protect themselves only by such haphazard and incomplete methods as these, which the next hurricane will put to the test.

4 *WARNING AND RESEARCH*

A single engine airplane, a small light AT-6, a little later than noon of July 27, 1943, rose up like a blown leaf over Texas to fly straight into the dark churning cloud mass of a hurricane. There was nothing official about the flight. Nobody knew that Major Joseph P. Duckworth had asked navigator Lieutenant Ralph O'Hair to join him in the only plane he could use without special permission, for the fun of finding out what a hurricane was like from the inside.

Major Duckworth, the head of a school for instructors in instrument flying, was teaching the Air Force that there was almost no weather a competent instrument pilot could not fly a plane through. Always before, the only way planes could fly was by avoiding, if possible, all weather disturbances. Now they had taken off from Bryan Field for hurricane-threatened Galveston, on instruments, through winds increasing from 80 to 100 miles per hour. Over Galveston they had radioed an astonished operator that they were turning and heading straight into a visible loom of cloud.

They were flying in from the west, on the milder left-hand sector, but already, as the cloud scud whirled by them, white and growing grayer and darkening with lashing rain, their tiny plane was bounced and tossed so that Major Duckworth could hardly keep it in control. Rain floods roared like shot on the fuselage and blotted out the glass. Static cut out his radio. His single engine throbbed and strained like a faithful heart. They were flying at four to nine thousand feet, in increasing blackness that threw them about and sickened them.

In the next moment, they had burst out of that dark violence into pure shining brightness. Far around them, as they floated under a great circle of blue sky, they looked up at towering high walls of foaming white cloud. They could soar to a mile or a mile and a half and they did not top those snowy ramparts walling them in. Below they could look down to a patch of the brown earth.

They tried to get down to it and land. Lower, the rough air caught them too dangerously near the ground. It was as if they were caught like a fly in a leaning tower or cone of cloud and circular winds which dragged them along, slowed down there by the friction of the surface. To get out, there was nothing to do but fly straight through the smashing, tossing, rainy, thundering and lightning swirl of the far wall, all over again.

They made it. They were the first airmen who had ever flown a plane into and through a hurricane. When they got back to Bryan and reported in, a weather officer, Lieutenant William Jones-Burdick, complained bitterly that he had not been taken along. Major Duckworth promptly took off with him in the same little plane and flew the hurricane all over again. The record the weather officer kept on that flight was the first ever made of conditions through a hurricane and the central calm. They proved then that the greatest hazard of such a flight, besides the battering the men must take inside it, was the static from the tremendous rain. The engine was also likely to be cooled to the danger point.

Major Duckworth later received the Air Medal for that flight of his. He had undertaken it out of sheer high-spirited curiosity, but the award recognized the fact that his courage and initiative opened a new era in hurricane research and warning.

After Pearl Harbor there was utter radio silence on the Atlantic and Pacific oceans, where the American navies moved among the enemy. There was no way of telling when or where storms or tropical cyclones would move more devastatingly than any foreign fleet across the bows of our ships. The vast empty spaces of the Pacific were particularly dangerous, as a typhoon could pick up speed for hundreds of empty watery miles before it could be located by instruments on board ship. Because it was so imperative to know more about the nature and progress of such whirlwinds the Army and Navy cooperated in flights of weather reconnaisance aircraft on triangular courses that would touch only the outer edges of the high winds. No attempt was made to follow Major Duckworth's penetration into the cyclone's eye until 1943 when volunteer flyers, especially trained and equipped in old bombers, converted B-25's, flew out from Presque Isle to measure the strength of sea-level winds. They flew blind at less than 1,000 feet over rugged seas, in woolly white fogs as low as 200 feet over the reaching wave crests. Sometimes turbulence twisted and strained their wing surfaces so that dozens of rivets popped out. But they brought back new facts about weather and about hurricanes.

One of those planes, caught in the rough updrafts of the massed cloudy outer walls of a hurricane, reached to the heart of peace within and released the first radiosonde balloon from an airplane into a hurricane. Such balloons, now in common use, are equipped with a tiny radio transmitter which sends back a combined record of temperature, barometric pressure and humidity at various heights. This first one swept up as high as 56,000 feet in the hurricane's sky-tower sending back the first sketchy scientific picture of that all-important core of the whole cyclonic structure.

That year also the men who had been cursing at what they called "weather clutter" on the screen of an instrument invented for detecting enemy aircraft, because it obscured their view of airplane targets, began to realize they were watching an astonishing and revolutionizing new picture of weather. The instrument was the microwave radar. They were looking at pictures made by echoes of storms.

A short pulse of radio energy, generated by a transmitter, is beamed toward a target. Some of it that hits the target bounces back to its source where it makes patterns on a radarscope. The time it takes for the pulse to be sent out and come back is the measure of the distance between transmitter and target. They found that what they stared at on their screen was a picture of snowflakes or raindrops, all in related motion, from which the microwaves bounced back. They were looking at the pattern of storms and hurricanes which the screen presented exactly as they were, that for the first time could be studied.

The radar screen can give a nearly continuous picture of an approaching hurricane, but not for more than 200 or 300 miles, because the beam is straight and goes off into space as the earth's curve drops away from it. But that was better than anything the weathermen had ever had before.

The development of radar for the use of weather studies made it possible that radiosonde balloons could be traced by radar. And that the always difficult wind measurements could be taken by complex electronic radar equipment called rawin.

The tremendous step forward of radar, probably the most sensational to date, was being studied and adapted for weather use as the old B-25's of the Fifty-third Weather Reconnaissance Squadron were flying out daily over the Pacific Ocean from Tacoma, Washington, over the Atlantic from Newfoundland to Bermuda and from the Azores. They were searching out bad weather that would have intercepted the planes from Europe bringing home the troops. What they learned of taking off across icy runways to fly close to the wave tops through blizzards, helped them with the first official flight to penetrate a hurricane in 1944. As the Army Air Force's First Weather Reconnaissance Squadron's Hurricane Patrol, in 1945, they flew twice a day from West Palm Beach, June to December, covering the coasts of the eastern Atlantic, the Gulf to Mexico and the southern Caribbean. Sometimes turbulence tossed an old B-25 so that it stood straight up on a wing and safety belts could not keep the crew from smashing their heads against the cabin's walls. In pounding rain that raised the racket of a boiler factory they were soaked to the skin by wet blowing in through every joint.

The men learned, with bruises, wrenched backs and broken bones, everything that a hurricane could do to a plane trying to penetrate it. The worst and most dangerous tossing, lifting or sudden dizzy dropping for hundreds of feet came from the boiling turbulence of eddies in the rising air currents within the walls of cumulo-nimbus clouds. The remedy was to fly lower. But at low levels in winds over sixty knots they learned a sickening roll and sliding yawing and pitching for which the remedy was to climb. And even as they burst out of the clouds into the silence of the eye, in the sudden change of wind velocity, the plane could fall off sidewise, down into the churning visible tossing of the sea.

It became clearer that for both safety and accuracy high air speed was necessary for hurricane-hunting planes. In ten years the Air Matériel Command had reconditioned seventy-two four-engined B-50 outdated bombers into weather planes for the Air Weather Service, some of which flew the 1950 hurricane safely at sea and were knocked out sitting on the ground as the hurricane came over land. The Navy Hurricane Hunter Squadron, from the

Jacksonville Naval Air Station, by 1955 had logged 76 flights with 63 eye penetrations, 32 of them at the low levels which were the special field for study by the Navy.

The next year three Super Constellations, huge flying laboratories, were in service for hurricane observation. They were equipped with three-dimensional radar sets and electronics equipment, and were on the way to being able to define a hurricane as to location, intensity and shape without getting into the greatest wind velocities.

The old planes with plenty of space inside had become the 2V Neptunes of the Airborne Early Warning Squadron 4, now known as the Hurricane Hunters. They are so crammed with instruments that technicians and crewmen must crawl through hatchways and tunnels to get to the spaces no bigger than closets where they sit belted tight, walled in by the equipment of their special tasks. They see nothing else.

These flying weather laboratories are propelled by engines of more than 5,000 horse power, since speed is now all-important in high-level flying. They are caapble of remaining in the air longer than fourteen hours.

The work of ten men is devoted solely to carrying into the hurricane and safely home again if possible, the one all-important specialist: the aerologist, or weatherman. Pilot officer and flight engineer command crew chief and crew of enlisted men, all with highly specialized training; two or three navigators with their tables, slide rules, dividers, visual aids and loran sets, which by measuring radio waves, from two different stations, constantly tell the plane's position and the speed and direction of the wind; the radio operator and his relief, who every five minutes sends a message to the nearest weather control.

The weatherman is thrust out into space, enclosed in a Plexiglas bubble on top of the plane or in the nose, alone with the instruments, compass, barometer, radio altimeter, regular altimeter, clock set at Greenwich time and radarscope, by whose continuous findings he interprets the conditions of the sea, the air, the pressures, the winds, the clouds, the hurricane.

With all these men and things the plane moves somehow through the hurricane mass and orbits around its center at varying levels. Sometimes it is low enough to see the tossing, bucking, churning and boiling of the foam-marbled sea below that space. Now like the imprisoned birds it skirts the solid white balconied and pillared walls, now high up where the thin dome of cloud may bulge into brightness almost into the stratosphere.

The men, blind and cramped within the plane's interior, know only the peace of untroubled air. It is the weatherman in his airy bubble who stares out almost unbelievingly at the white splendor of that place where the hurricane centers. It is undoubtedly one of the most extraordinary natural phenomena which man has ever succeeded in observing.

After that, they must go home through the same extreme discomfort and danger by which they came in. The first weather plane not to come through a tropical cyclone was flying in the war in the South Pacific. The first lost in this hemisphere was the Navy Reconnaissance plane under Lieutenant Commander Windham with a crew of eight men and two Canadian newspapermen who disappeared in hurricane Janet on September 26, 1955. Their last message was "Beginning penetration."

It was from the developments of war flying that weather specialists learned that many preconceived ideas of hurricanes were not true. The airmen learned that often they could fly to the center of the hurricane by spiraling in along some calm, even sunny alley between the turbulent arms of the hurricane, called "rain bands." They began to see that hurricane structure was not at all a doughnut of cloud with a hole in the center. The photographs of hurricanes which moved across the radar screens showed that a hurricane was an asymmetrical swirling concentric circle of cloud and squall lines. Each one was different, each one with complexities no one had yet adequately studied.

The simple concept of a single calm eye or center was refuted by a newly discovered idea that there were not one, but three centers. The center of wind circulation, generally known as the eye, was not necessarily the point of lowest air pressure or the point about which the spiral rain bands rotate. The three centers may be twenty miles apart. The new idea shows how inadequate and complicated hurricane detecting and forecasting really is.

But perhaps the most far-reaching discovery followed the experience of bombing planes trying to take off from Japan. Engines going full speed, some found a vast mysterious wind holding them in their tracks; others, aloft, in a similar wind current, could make no headway at all, for all their horsepower, against its incredible force. The newly discovered wind type came to be considered a planetary wind or jet stream, such as have been found to blow around the world in great dipping variable waves, and has been believed by some scientists to have a great effect on the tracks northward of hurricanes.

After the war, there was no immediate attempt to do research in the new air discoveries. The U.S. Weather Bureau, now grown into one of the most important of all governmental scientific services, with its hundreds of trained and devoted men, was still not equipped to do the research work, especially in hurricanes, the results of which the public increasingly demanded. Only from Florida, with Texas next, had there come any sustained public outcry for better research and more complete warning services. The North that for years had called all tropical cyclones "Florida hurricanes" was roused out of its calm detachment by the shocking hurricane catastrophes of 1954 and 1955. Its disgust at hurricanes fastened first on the inadequacy of the Weather Bureau, handicapped as it was, to predict exactly where a hurricane, over land in the temperate zone, was going. The clamor brought out the fact that there were not enough hurricane-trained men north of the Mason-Dixon Line even to begin to be able to send out adequate warnings, and indeed nobody knew enough to give them training. Nobody knew enough about hurricane surges, that did the worst of the damage, or could anticipate and predict a hurricane flood.

So under this new burst of pressure, Congress was moved to appropriate funds large enough to develop a new system of hurricane warning stations.

Observation stations were set up almost every twenty-five miles along the Gulf and Atlantic coast from Texas, around Florida to North Carolina. They were manned by volunteers who send observations to the nearest U.S. Weather Bureau when the hurricane season begins to breed its alarms. Ten such stations in south Florida report to the Miami Weather Bureau. Under the direction of the Chief Forecaster and hurricane expert, Gordon Dunn, the Miami office, as the most important hurricane forecast center, is undertaking an intensive study of the forecast problem.

After the appalling list of the dead in Louisiana in 1957, caused by the indifference of the general public to the warnings about hurricane Audrey, it was decided by Washington officials that broadcast warnings which now follow reports of a hurricane being watched must be made so clear and blunt that people will be forced to prepare for the disaster threatening them. The Weather Bureau cannot order the evacuation of an area but they can urge it. Of course, if the hurricane fails to arrive, public indifference mounts, if not actual resentment. The efficiency of the whole warning system, therefore, may be seen to depend on the accuracy and reliability of the forecasting.

All this mass of figures from the observation stations is used by the central forecasting offices of the Weather Bureau. But the methods now in use are all acknowledged to be vague, fragmentary and impractical under the crushing challenge of a hurricane's immediate presence.

The most usual method is called "the statistical approach" which might well be designated as historical. This was developed by C. L. Mitchell and I. R. Tannehill. All known past hurricanes were chartered by the months in which they occurred which showed a general tendency in hurricanes to move here or there according to the time of year. José Colon computed their frequency in sixteen principal directions. The forecasting method, therefore, based on an average of past performance, was a rough and fairly accurate guide for the generality of hurricanes at a given time.

The second has been called the "path method" which projects the probable track of any given hurricane by a study of its known forces, and what, on the basis of what has already happened, is likely to continue to happen. This method has been successful very often, so long as the hurricane is not a freak and does not change course and speed as it so often does on approaching the mainland. It has already been shown by hurricane Carol in 1954 and Ione of 1955 that over land in the temperate zone it is as yet almost impossible for any forecaster to be sure whether a hurricane will lose speed or accelerate, and how its movements will be affected by the surrounding air currents.

A new technique called "high level steering," often used successfully by Gordon Dunn of the Miami Bureau, consists in a study of the level at which the circulation of winds in the vortex seems to disappear and move in the direction of the great high air current which directs it.

It has long been the hope of meteorologists that high speed computers would be developed for the use of numerical techniques in immediate forecasting. In 1955 the Weather Bureau announced plans to start test runs on International Business Machine Corporation's new electric data processing machine, called a giant brain. They believe that the machine can be fed complicated equations based upon hurricane facts of wind velocity, temperature, barometric pressure, humidity and so on, which the planes record on the spot, and turn out in a few hours weather forecasts it would take mathematicians days to work out. In this way, the hope is, the direction and track of a hurricane may be broadcast with precision in from twenty-four to forty-eight hours.

The difficulty of the mathematicians and of the high speed computer is of course the difficulty of all forecasting, that not enough is actually known of a hurricane to figure it. Since for each unknown there must be an independent equation, the list of equations itself would seem to the untutored mind to be so astronomical as to stagger even an electronic intelligence.

The clamor on the part of the Northern states for greater forecasting accuracy influenced Congress to vote funds with which to begin a concerted and intensive hurricane study to continue for thirty months from the spring of 1956. It is sponsored and coordinated by the Weather Bureau with many meteorological experts, the Army, Navy, Coast Guard and Air Force, such as the Air Force Cambridge Research Center and a number of universities with meteorological laboratories such as the Massachusetts Institute of Technology, the University of Chicago, and the Florida State University at Tallahassee. The great radar station of the University of Miami, nearest to the heart of the hurricane region, was added to the Bureau's radar stations; so were the long-range radar eyes at Cape Hatteras, at San Juan, Puerto Rico, and at Nantucket, which can detect and track storm clouds over an area of 200,000 square miles. Forty-two other short-range radar stations have been installed from Boston, Massachusetts, to Brownsville, Texas, and at Swan Island in the Caribbean. Even newer radar units have been ordered for delivery in 1958 which by varying wave bands and pulse lengths can measure clouds and see raindrops before they fall. Such radar eyes will be tied in a major network that may even do the work for the hurricane-hunting planes and study also conditions not just within hurricanes, but surrounding them on all sides.

A Research Operations Base was set up beyond the Airport at West Palm Beach, Florida, with a corps of weather specialists, under R. H. Simpson and R. C. Gentry. Through this the whole program of information and analysis has been flowing, long enough for a very significant preliminary report to have been published.

To supply the Research Base constantly with data a dense network of cooperating rawinsonde stations, with especially equipped aircraft for research flights, with rocket reconnaissance of hurricane cloud systems, was set up throughout the West Indies, to operate continuously for the thirty-month research period. They include eight stations operated by the U.S. Air Force, three by the U.S. Navy, two by the British, two by the French, two by Cuba and one each by the Dutch, the Dominican Republic, Mexico, and Colombia. Soundings were to be attempted above 80,000 feet.

Especially instrumented aircraft, one B-47 and two B-50's, are assigned to the project by the Department of Defense and operated by the Air Weather Service. They move from near the surface to 40,000 feet. During hurricanes they attempt to fly in the storm area at the same time, one from 1,000 to 8,000 feet, the second from 15,000 to 25,000, and the third, entering at 30,000, will climb to above 40,000 feet. Each will be packed with the most advanced weather-measuring equipment, vortex-, aspirator- and stagnation temperature probes, infrared absorption hygrometers, sea-surface temperature-radiometers, D-value computers, automatic wind-measuring and cloud physics study equipment.

Rocket launchings are made under the direction of the Office of Naval Research in an attempt to photograph the entire hurricane cloud system and its environment.

Storm surges, rainfall and weather trends are being studied by various departments of the Weather Bureau and the U.S. engineers.

In the quiet and orderly building beyond the wide spaces of the West Palm Beach Air Field, eleven research tasks have been assigned to eleven teams. They will study the phases of hurricane circulation and structure; energy processes and hurricane energy budget; momentum transfer within the hurricane and between the hurricane and its environment; the dynamics of hurricane movement; the conditions antecedent to hurricane formation; an analysis of errors in observation made in the tropics; large-scale energy transport in the tropics and from the tropics to other areas; physics of hurricane clouds and precipitation; artificial modification and movement; forecast application of findings of the project; the possibilities of the hurricane beacon, a radio balloon designated to float at constant pressure in the eye and signal its position as an aid in studying circulation in the eye and possibly in tracking the movement of the storm center.

All these special studies, it has been intended, will be published in scientific journals and monograph series for the widest possible circulation.

The work was well begun in 1956. Yet by 1957, when no hurricanes had affected the North in an entire season and even Florida had not been threatened, the interest of Congress in this research, so important to the welfare of the whole eastern seaboard, began slightly to weaken. Budget cutting was in order. Defense demands were most urgent. There was a time when Weather Bureau officials were in grave fear that the service of the three research planes' studies would be given up for economy's sake. At the last minute, however, Congress was argued into continuing the three weather planes for another year.

It cannot be imagined by the most uninformed of legislators or uninterested citizens in general that the huge problems of these hurricanes which from time beyond memory of man have harassed these shores can be solved in any thirty months.

The present studies, like the new light thrown on the structure of hurricanes by the cloud shapes moving across the radar screens, have shown clearly how incorrect many scientific concepts of hurricanes have been. It is not now considered enough that airplanes take readings within a hurricane. They must study the whole area of sea and air and wind currents about the central disturbance. The great field of the upper air and the jet streams must be better known. Already the few facts established have opened the way to new questions which as yet no man can answer.

The questions which the general public asks most constantly and anxiously, it should now be clear, cannot be answered accurately. Is there a cycle in the movement of hurricanes, and where will it turn next? Will hurricanes continue to damage the Northern states, and why? Will they overwhelm Florida again? The Weather Bureau specialists do not answer because they know how much more they need to know.

No satisfactory answer can be given to that other constant popular demand, "When will they start to control hurricanes?"

Fantastic suggestions used to be made about blowing up hurricanes with great island stockpiles of explosive. Since the successful seeding of rain clouds with dry ice, people often ask why hurricanes are not dispersed by seeding. Yet the only attempt proved nothing. The development of the hydrogen bomb has caused hundreds of people to argue that such a bomb be used "to blow a hurricane to pieces."

The answer to that is always that although the force of the hydrogen bomb is almost unimaginable, the forces released in and by any hurricane are so much greater, clearly beyond the grasp of the average mind, that such a bomb would be no more disturbing to the colossal dynamics of the great spiral than one of its own minor eddies. Control of hurricanes might come, as precision forecasting may, when the weather scientists have had an opportunity to learn and measure exactly the complex of forces that triggers them, the formula for the vast cloudy heated-air machinery that keeps them going under the formidable movements of the upper air which they begin to think are their supreme controls.

What no man has yet learned is the relation of the mystery of this extraordinary climax of our weather, the hurricane, to the ultimate and magnificent mysteries of this world and our universe and all space.

BIBLIOGRAPHY

ALEXANDER, W. H., "Hurricanes; Especially Those of Puerto Rico and St. Kitts." *Monthly Weather Review*, Vol. 33, 1905. Washington, D.C.

ANDREWS, CHARLES M., *The American Nation. Colonial Self-Government.* Harpers, New York, 1904.

———, *The Colonial Period of American History: The Settlements.* New Haven, Conn., Yale University Press, 1939.

ARCHER, LT., *Circumstantial Account of the Wreck of His Majesty's Ship Phoenix.* London, 1810.

BARBOUR, THOMAS, *The Birds of Cuba.* Cambridge, Mass., Harvard University Press, 1923.

———, *A Naturalist in Cuba.* Boston, Little, Brown, 1945.

BARCIA, DE, ANDRES GONZALES (ed. Anthony Kerrigan), *Ensayo Chronologico.* Gainsville, Fla., University of Florida Press, 1951.

BARTRAM, WILLIAM, *the Travels of* (ed. by Mark Van Doren). New York, Facsimile Library, 1940.

BEARD, J. S., *Forests of the Windward and Leeward Islands.* New York, Oxford.

BELLO, FRANCIS, "Hurricane." *Fortune*, August, 1956.

BENTON, GEORGE S., "More Hurricanes in Your Future." *The Johns Hopkins Magazine*, October, 1955.

BISHOP, MORRIS, *The Odyssey of Cabeza de Vaca.* New York, Century, 1933.

BODSWORTH, FRED, "Why We're Getting More Disastrous Hurricanes." *Maclean's Magazine*, Canada, September 15, 1956.

BORDUE, ERICH, "Some Hydrological Aspects of the Flood of August, 1955, in a Connecticut Valley." *The Geographical Review*, Vol. XLVII, No. 2. New York, 1957.

BOYRIE-MOYA, EMILE DE, "Monumento Megalitico y Petroglifos de Chacuey." Ciudad Trujillo, R.D. Serie VII, Vol. XCVII, No. I. Press of the University of Santo Domingo.

BROOKS, CHARLES F., *Why the Weather?* New York, Harcourt Brace, 1935.

———, "Hurricane into New England; Meteorology of the Storm of September 21, 1938." Washington, D.C., 1938. Smithsonian Report.

———, "The New England Hurricane of September, 1944." Blue Hill Observatory Reprint No. 5, 1945.

BROOKS, C. E. P., *Climate Through the Ages*. New York, McGraw-Hill, 1949.

BROWNE, CHARLES A., "Thomas Jefferson and the Scientific Trends of His Time." *Chronica Botanica*, Waltham, Mass. 1944.

BUNTING, DONALD C., "A Comparison of Six Great Florida Hurricanes." Gainesville, Fla. (Unpublished ms.)
SEE Latour

BURNS, SIR ALLEN, *History of the British West Indies*. London, Allen and Unwin, 1954.

BUTLER, O. M., "New England's Storm Tossed Trees." *American Forests*, Nov. 1938.

CALVERT, E. B., "The Hurricane Warning Service and Its Reorganization." *Monthly Weather Review*, Vol. 63, 1935.

CARR, ARCHIE, *High Jungles and Low*. Gainesville, Fla., University of Florida Press, 1953.

———, *The Windward Road*. New York, Knopf, 1956.

CATE, MARGARET DAVIS, *Early Days of Coastal Georgia*. St. Simon's Island, Ga., 1935.

CAUGHEY, JOHN WALTON, *Bernardo de Galvez in Louisiana*. Berkeley, Cal., University of California Press, 1934.

CHAPMAN, FRANK M., *Camps and Cruises of an Ornithologist*. New York, Appleton, 1908.

CHARNEY, MITCHELL V., *Jean Lafitte, Gentleman Smuggler*. New York, 1934.

Chronological History of Charleston, Charleston, S.C., 1700–1894.

CLARKE, MARY HELM, *Major and Minor Keys of the Florida Reef*. Coral Gables, Fla., 1949.

CLINE, ISAAC M., *Tropical Cyclones*. New York, 1926.

———, *A Century of Progress in the Study of Cyclones*. New Orleans, La. 1935.

———, *Storms, Floods and Sunshine*. New Orleans, La. 1935.

———, "Tides and Coastal Currents Developed by Tropical Cyclones." *Monthly Weather Review*, Vol. 61, 1933.

CLOWES, ERNEST S., *The Hurricane of 1938 on Eastern Long Island*. Bridge-hampton, L.I. 1939.

CONNECTICUT FLOOD RECOVERY COMMITTEE: "Report to Governor Abraham Ribicoff." Hartford, Nov. 1955.

———, "Manual for Flood Recovery Program." Hartford, Jan. 1956.

———, "Report on Flood Recovery Program to General Assembly." Hartford, Jan. 1957.

CONNOR, JEANNETTE THURBER, *Colonial Records of Spanish Florida*. Deland, Fla., Florida State Historical Society, 1925.

———, *Jean Ribaut*. Deland, Fla., Florida State Historical Society, 1927.

———, *Pedro Menéndez de Avilés Memorial* (tr.). Deland, Fla., Florida State Historical Society, 1923.

CROUSE, N. M., *The French Struggle for the West Indies*. New York, 1940.

DALCHO, FREDERICK, *An Historical Account of the Protestant Episcopal Church in South Carolina*. Charleston, S.C., 1870.

Dampier's Voyages (Masefield Edition). London, 1906.

DAVIS, H. P., *Black Democracy*. New York, Dial, 1929.

DEFOE, DANIEL, *The Storm or a Collection of the Most Remarkable Casualties and Disasters Which Happened in the Late Dreadful Tempest Both by Sea and By Land*. London, 1704.

DELAWARDE, J.-B., *La Vie Paysanne A La Martinique*. Fort-de-France, Martinique, 1937.

DUNLOP, J. G., "Spanish Depredations." *South Carolina Historical and General Magazine*, Vol. XXX. Charleston, S.C. 1929.

DUNN, GORDON, "Aërology in the Hurricane Warning Service." *Monthly Weather Review*, Vol. 68, 1940.

SEE ALSO Namias.

ELLIS, MILTON (ed.), *A College Book of American Literature*. New York, 1954.

ESPINOSA, FR. ANTONIO VÁZQUEZ DE, *Compendium and Description of the West Indies* (tr. Charles Upson Clark). Washington, D.C., Smithsonian Institution, 1942.

———, "A True Account of the Voyage and Navigation Made by the Fleet of New Spain and Honduras of the Year 1622." Abstracted from the Spanish of Original, 1623, by Mark F. Boyd. Tallahassee, Fla. 1952. (Unpublished ms.)

ESQUEMELING, JOHN, *The Buccaneers of America*. (ed. W. S. Stallybrass). New York, Dutton.

FASSIG, OLIVER L., "Hurricanes of the West Indies." Bull. X, 1913. Weather Bureau, U.S. Dept. of Agriculture.

FAYE, STANLEY, "The Contest for Pensacola Bay and Other Gulf Ports, 1698–1722." *Florida Historical Quarterly*, Vol. XXIV, No. 3, Jan. 1946, No. 4, April, 1946.

Federal Disaster Insurance. Report of Committee on Banking and Currency, U.S. Senate. Staff Study No. 1313, 84th Congress, 2nd Session, Washington, 1956.

FEENEMAN, LEVIN M., *Physiography of Eastern United States*. New York, McGraw-Hill, 1938.

FROUDE, JAMES ANTHONY, *The English in the West Indies*. New York, Scribner's, 1888.

FRAZIER, R. D., "Early Records of Tropical Hurricanes on the Texas Coast in the Vicinity of Galveston." *Monthly Weather Review*, Vol. 49, 1921.

GAGE, THOMAS, *A New Survey of the West Indies* (ed. A. P. Newton). New York, McBride, 1929.

GARRIOT, E. B., "West Indian Hurricanes." Weather Bureau, U.S. Dept. of Agriculture, Washington, 1900.

GIBSON, COUNT D., *Sea Islands of Georgia*. Athens, Ga., University of Georgia Press, 1948.

GONZALES MUÑOZ, ANTONIO, "Notas Historicas Sobre Ciclones." *Boletin de Observatorio*, Epoca IV, Vol. I, 1 and 2, La Habana, 1945.

GOODLET, JOHN C., "Vegetation Adjacent to the Border of the Wisconsin Drift in Potter County, Pennsylvania." Harvard Forest Bull. No. 25, Petersham, Mass. 1954.

GRAHAM, S. B., and NEWMAN, ELLEN, *Galveston Community Book*. Galveston, Texas, 1945.

GRAU, SHIRLEY ANN, "Storm." *The New Yorker*, Sept. 24, 1955.

GRAY, R. W., "Florida Hurricanes." *Monthly Weather Review*, Vol. 62, 1933.

GRISCOM, LLOYD, *Modern Bird Study*. Cambridge, Mass., Harvard University Press, 1945.

Gulf of Mexico. Its Origin, Waters and Marine Life. Fishery Bulletin 89. Washington, D.C., 1954.

GUPPY, H. B., *Plants, Seeds and Currents in the West Indies and Azores*, London, Williams and Norgate, 1917.

GUTIERREZ-LANZA, P. M., "Apuntes Historicos Acerca de Observatorio del Colegio de Belen, Habana." Havana, 1904.

HAKLUYT, RICHARD, *The Principal Navigations, Voyages, Traffiques and Discoveries of the English Nation*. Everyman.

HAMILTON, ALEXANDER, *A Few of Hamilton's Letters* (ed. by Gertrude Atherton). New York, Macmillan, 1903.

HANNA, A. J. and K. A., *Lake Okeechobee*. 1948. Bobbs-Merrill.

HANNA, KATHRYN ABBEY, *Florida, Land of Change*. Chapel Hill, N.C., University of North Carolina Press, 1948.

HARING, H. C., *Trade and Navigation Between Spain and the Indies*. Harvard Univ. 1918.

——, *The Buccaneers in the West Indies in the XVII Century*. London, 1910.

HARRINGTON, M. R., *Cuba Before Columbus*. New York, Heye Foundation, 1921.

HAURWITZ, BERNHARD, "The Height of Tropical Cyclones and the Eye of the Storm." *Monthly Weather Review*, Vol. 63. Feb. '35.

HAYDEN, EVERETTE, "West Indian Hurricanes and the March Blizzard of 1888." Reprint from the *American Meteorological Journal*, New York, 1889.

HERSEY, JOHN, "Over the Mad River," *The New Yorker*, Sept. 17, 1955.

HORGAN, PAUL, *Great River*. New York, Rinehart, 1957.

HOWARD, R. A., and PROCTOR, G. R., "The Vegetation on Bauxite Soils in Jamaica." Cambridge, Mass. 1957. (Unpublished ms.)

HUGHES, RICHARD, *In Hazard*. London, Chatto and Windus, 1938.

"Hurricane Damage Legislation." *The Congressional Record*. Washington, D. C., Mar. 28, 1955.

IRVING, WASHINGTON, *The Life and Voyages of Christopher Columbus*. New York, Putnam, (no date).

——, *The Companions of Columbus*. New York, Putnam, (no date).

KNAUSS, JAMES O., *Territorial Florida Journalism*. Deland, Fla., Florida State Historical Society, 1926.

KNOX, DUDLEY W., *A History of the United States Navy*. New York, Putnam, 1936.

KORGANOFF, ALEXANDRE S., "Le Naufrage de la Nuestra Señora de la Concepción." Paris, France. *Miroir de l'Histoire*, April, May, 1955.

LABAT, JEAN-BAPTISTE, *Memoires des Nouveaux Voyages Faits Aux Isles de l'Amerique*. Paris, 1722.

LAS CASAS, *Journal of the First Voyage to America by Christopher Columbus*. New York, Boni, 1924.

LATOUR, M. H., and BUNTING, D. C., "Radar Observation of Florida Hurricane, Aug. 26–27, 1949." Bull. Series. No. 29, Engineering Progress at the University of Florida. Gainsville, Fla., Oct. 1949.

LAWRENCE, ALEXANDER A., *Storm Over Savannah*. Athens, Ga., University of Georgia Press, 1951.

LECKY, S. T. S., *Wrinkles in Practical Navigation* (Revised, William Allingham). New York, Dutton, 1919.

LOVEN, SVEN, *Origins of the Tainan Culture, West Indies*. Goteborg, 1935.

LOWERY, WOODBURY, *The Spanish Settlements in the United States*. New York, Putnam, 1911.

MACKAYE, MILTON, "We're Cracking the Secrets of Weather." *Saturday Evening Post*, Philadelphia, Sept. 11, 1954.

MADARIAGA, SALVADOR DE, *The Rise of the Spanish-American Empire*. New York, Macmillan, 1947.

——, *The Fall of the Spanish-American Empire*. New York, Macmillan, 1948.

MAHAN, A. T., *The Influence of Sea Power on History*. Boston, Little, Brown, 1890.

——, *The Influence of Sea Power upon the French Revolution and Europe*. Boston, Little, Brown, 1892.

——, *Lessons of the War With Spain*. Boston, Little, Brown, 1899.

——, *Sea Power in its Relations to the War of 1812*. London, 1905.

MARTIN, SIDNEY WALTER, *Florida During Territorial Days*. Athens, Ga., University of Georgia Press, 1944.

MAURY, M. F., *Physical Geography of the Sea and its Meteorology*. London, 1855.

MCCLELLAN, WM. SMITH, *Smuggling in the American Colonies*, New York, 1912.

MEANS, PHILIP AINSWORTH, *The Spanish Main*. New York, Scribner, 1935.

MILLER, ERIC, "American Pioneers in Meteorology." *Monthly Weather Review*, Vol. 61, 1933.

MITCHELL, C. L., *West Indian Hurricanes and Other Tropical Cyclones of the North Atlantic Ocean*. Washington, U.S. Weather Bureau, 1924.

MOORE, WILLIS L., "I Am Thinking of Hurricanes." *American Mercury*, Sept. 1927.

MORALES-CARRIÓN, ARTURO, *Puerto Rico and the Non-Hispanic Caribbean*. Puerto Rico, University of Puerto Rico Press, 1952.

MORISON, SAMUEL E., *Maritime History of Massachusetts*. Boston, Houghton Mifflin, 1921.

——, *The Oxford History of the United States*. London, Oxford, 1928.

——, *Admiral of the Ocean Sea.* Boston, Little, Brown, 1942.

MOSELEY, MARY, *The Bahamas Handbook.* Nassau, 1926.

MUNK, WALTER H., "The Circulation of the Oceans." *Scientific American.* Vol. 193, No. 3. Sept. 1955.

MURCHIE, GUY, *Song of the Sky.* Boston, Little, Brown, 1954.

MYERS, VANCE G., "Characteristics of United States Hurricanes Pertinent to Levee Design for Lake Okeechobee, Florida." Hydrometeorological Report No. 32. Washington, D.C., 1954.

NAMIAS, JEROME, "Long Range Weather Forecasting." *Scientific American.* Vol. 193, No. 2. N.Y. Aug. 1955.

NAMIAS, J., DUNN, GORDON, and SIMPSON, R. H., "A Survey of the Hurricane Problem." U. S. Weather Bureau, Washington, D.C., 1955.

NANSEN, FRIDTJOF, *The First Crossing of Greenland.* London, Heineman, 1890.

National Hurricane Research Project, Objectives and Basic Design of the, Report No. I. Prepared by the Staff of the N.H.R.P. U.S. Weather Bureau, Washington, D.C. March, 1956.

OBER, FREDERICK A., *Camps of the Caribbees.* Boston, 1880.

——, *Our West Indian Neighbors.* New York, 1916.

ORMEROD, LEONARD, *The Curving Shore.* New York, Harpers, 1957.

ORTIZ, FERNANDO, *El Huracan.* Mexico, D. F., Fondo de Cultura Economica, 1947.

PARES, RICHARD, *A West Indian Fortune.* London, Longmans Green, 1950.

PERLEY, SIDNEY, *Historic Storms of New England.* Salem, Mass. 1891.

PETERSON, ROGER TORY, *Birds Over America.* New York, Dodd, Mead, 1948.

PIDDINGTON, HENRY, *The Sailors' Hornbook for the Law of Storms.* London, 1876.

PLACE, CHARLES A., *Charles Bulfinch, Architect and Citizen.* Boston, Houghton Mifflin, 1935.

POËY, ANDREAS, *Tables Chronologiques des Quatres Cent Cyclones.* Paris, 1863.

PRATT, FLEICHER, *The Heroic Years.* New York, Smith and Haas, 1934.

PRIESTLEY, HERBERT I., *The Luna Papers.* Deland, Fla., Florida State Historical Society, 1925.

PURVIS, JOHN C., "Notes on Hurricanes in South Carolina." Columbia, S.C., Feb. 1955.

RAGATZ, LOWELL J., *The Fall of the Planter Class in the British Caribbean,* 1763–1833. New York, Century, 1928.

RAINSFORD, MARCUS, *An Historical Account of the Black Empire of Hayti.* London, 1815.

RATTRAY, JEANETTE EDWARDS, *Ship Ashore: A Record of Maritime Disasters Off Montauk, and Eastern Long Island.* New York, 1955.

RECINOS, ADRIAN, *Popul Vuh: Las Antiguas Historias del Quiche.* Mexico, 1947.

REDFIELD, W. C., "Observations on the Hurricanes and Storms of the West Indies and the Coasts of the United States." *American Journal of Science and Arts.* No. I. Vol. XXV. New Haven, 1846.

REESE, JOE HUGH, *Florida's Great Hurricane.* Miami, Fla. 1926.

REID, W. LT. COL., *The Law of Storms,* London, 1838.

RICH, SHEBNAH, *Truro, Cape Cod.* Boston, 1884.

RICHMOND-BROWN, *Unknown Tribes, Uncharted Seas.* New York, Appleton, 1925.

RIEHL, HERBERT, *Tropical Meteorology.* New York, McGraw-Hill, 1954.

ROMANS, BERNARD, CAPT., *A Concise Natural History of East and West Florida.* Deland, Fla., Florida State Historical Society, Vol. I, N.Y.

RONCIÈRE, DE LA ST. CROIX, *Dans Les Sillages des Caravelles de Colon.* Paris, 1930.

RONDTHALER, ALICE K., *The Story of Ocracoke.* Ocracoke, N.C.

ROSENBERGER, F. C. (ed.), *Jefferson Reader.* New York, Dutton, 1953.

ROUSE, IRVING, *The West Indies: The Circum-Caribbean Tribes.* Handbook of the South American Indians, Vol. 4. BAE Bull. 143, 1948.

SCHLOEMER, ROBERT W., "Analysis and Synthesis of Hurricane Wind Patterns Over Lake Okeechobee, Florida." Hydrometeorological Report. No. 31. Washington, D. C., 1954.

SCISCO, L. D., "The Track of Ponce de Leon in 1513." Bulletin, American Geographical Society. Vol. XLV, No. 10. 1913.

SEMMES, RAPHAEL, *Memoirs of Service Afloat.* Baltimore, 1869.

SEWELL, WILLIAM G., *The Ordeal of Free Labor in the British West Indies.* New York, Harper, 1863.

SHAPLEY, HARLOW (ed.), and Others, *Climatic Change.* Cambridge, Mass., Harvard, 1953.

SIMPSON, CHARLES TORRY, *Out of Doors in Florida.* Miami, Fla. 1923.

———, *Florida Wild Life,* New York, Macmillan, 1932.

SIMPSON, R. L., and GENTRY, R. C., *Hurricanes.* National Hurricane Research Project, U.S. Weather Bureau, West Palm Beach, Fla. Washington, 1957.

SIMPSON, R. L., SEE Namias.

SPARKS, JARED, *The Life of Benjamin Franklin.* Boston, 1844.

SPROUT, HAROLD and MARGARET, *The Rise of American Naval Power.* New Jersey, Princeton University Press, 1946.

STEARNS, W. D., "Storms of the Gulf of Mexico and Their Prediction." *American Meteorological Journal,* 1894.

STEWART, JOHN A., with RICHARD GEHMAN. "What's Wrong With the Weather?" *Collier's,* Vol. 137, No. 1. Jan. 6, 1956.

STICK, DAVID, *Graveyard of the Atlantic.* Chapel Hill, N.C., University of North Carolina Press, 1952.

STONEY, SAMUEL G., *Azaleas and Old Brick.* Boston, Houghton Mifflin, 1937.

SVERDRUP, H. V., JOHNSON, M. W., FLEMING, R. H., *The Oceans.* New York, Prentice-Hall, 1946.

TANNEHILL, I. R., "Some Inundations Attending Tropical Cyclones." *Monthly Weather Review,* Vol. 55, 1927.

———, "Sea Swells in Relation to Movement and Intensity of Tropical Storms." *Monthly Weather Review,* Vol. 64, 1936.

————, *Hurricanes, Their Nature and History*. New Jersey, Princeton University Press, 1952.

————, *The Hurricane Hunters*. New York, Dodd, Mead, 1955.

TEJERA, EMILIANO, *Palabras Indijenas de La Isla de Santo Domingo*, Ciudad Trujillo, R.D., Editora del Caribe, 1951.

TERRY, T. P., *Terry's Guide to Cuba*. New York, 1929.

TERTRE, DU. R. P., *Histoire Générale de l'Establissement des Colonies Françoises dans les Ant-Isles de l'Amerique*. Paris, 1667.

THOME, JAS. A., and KIMBALL, J. H., *Emancipation in the West Indies, 1837*. New York, American Anti-Slavery Society, 1838.

THOMPSON, J. ERIC, *Rise and Fall of the Mayan Civilization*. University of Oklahoma Press, 1955.

TOZZER, ALFRED M. (ed.), *Landa's Relación de las Cosas de Yucatan*. Papers of the Peabody Museum of American Archeology and Ethnology, Cambridge, Mass. 1941.

TUCKERMAN, ALFRED, *When Rochambeau Stepped Ashore*. Newport, R.I. 1955.

ULIVARRI, SATURNINO, *Pirates y Corsarios en Cuba*. Havana, 1931.

VIÑES, BENITO, S. J., *Cyclonic Circulation and Translatory Movement of West Indian Hurricanes*. Washington, D.C. U.S. Weather Bureau, 1898.

————, *Los Hurricanes de la Antillas en Septiembre y Octubre*, 1875-76. Havana, 1877. *Practical Hints about West Indian Hurricanes* (tr. Lieut. G. L. Dyer, USN). Washington, D.C. U.S. Weather Bureau, 1885.

WARD, CHRISTOPHER, *The War of the Revolution*. New York, Macmillan, 1952.

WHITE, E. B., "The Eye of Edna." *The New Yorker*, Sept. 25, 1954.

WILKINSON, J., *The Narrative of a Blockade Runner*. New York, 1877.

WILLIAMSON, J. A., *The Ocean in English History*. London, Oxford, 1941.

————, *Hawkins of Plymouth*. London, Black, 1949.

WILLISON, GEORGE F., *Behold Virginia*. New York, Harcourt Brace, 1951.

WOOD, JANE, "He Burned the Bodies on the Florida Keys." (Unpublished ms.)

WRIGHT, LOUIS B., *The Atlantic Frontier*. N. Y., Knopf, 1947.

PERIODICALS

Caribbean, The. The Caribbean Commission, Trinidad, British West Indies.
  Hurricanes seasons of 1954, 1955, 1956.
Monthly Weather Review. The U.S. Weather Bureau, Washington, D.C.
Weatherwise, The American Meteorological Society, Boston, Mass.

NEWSPAPERS

Charlotte Observer, The. Charlotte, N.C., Oct. 1954.
East Hampton Star, The. Special Hurricane Edition, East Hampton, N.Y.
  Oct. 1954.
Hartford Times, The. Hartford, Conn. Hurricane Edition, Aug. 26, 1955.
Hartford Courant, The. Hartford, Conn. Flood Section, Sept. 1955.
Meriden Record, The. Meriden Connecticut. Aug. 24, 1955.
Miami Herald, The, and *Miami Daily News, The*. Miami, Florida.
New Bedford Standard Times, The. New Bedford, Mass. Hurricane Edition,
  Sept. 1954, Oct. 1955.
New Haven Sunday Register, The. New Haven, Conn. Sept. 4, 1955.
New York Herald Tribune, The. Sept. 1954, Oct. 1955.
Providence Journal, The. Providence, R.I. Sept. 1938, Aug. 31, 1954.
Springfield Union, The. Springfield, Mass. Aug. 20, 1955.
Taunton Daily Gazette, The. Taunton, Mass. Sept. 1938.
Toronto Telegram, The. Toronto, Canada. Oct. 1954.
Vineyard Gazette, The. Martha's Vineyard, Mass. Sept. 1938, Sept. 1954.
Wilmington Star-News, The. Wilmington, N.C. Oct. 1954.
Winsted Evening Citizen, The. Winsted, Conn. Sept. 23, 1955.

INDEX